Mathematical Modelling Skills

Titles in this Series

Mathematical Modelling Skills

Dilwyn Edwards and Michael Hamson

MACMILLAN

First published 1996 by
MACMILLAN PRESS LTD
Houndmills, Basingstoke, Hampshire RG21 6XS
and London
Companies and representatives
throughout the world

ISBN 0–333–59595–5

A catalogue record for this book is available
from the British Library.

10   9   8   7   6   5   4   3   2   1
05   04   03   02   01   00   99   98   97   96

Printed in Malaysia

Contents

Preface

The activity of solving problems by mathematical modelling is by its very nature a practical and creative process involving a number of stages, all of which demand a range of skills. Many of these skills are gradually gained through practice and experience, and any teaching course involving mathematical modelling will inevitably be centred on practical work with example models. Essential though this is, it does mean that students are left to pick up the necessary skills as and when needed, in a fairly random way. The motivation behind this book is to direct students towards building up these skills in a systematic way, through carefully constructed exercises. Experience has shown that the necessary skills are most effectively acquired by working on such exercises in addition to and *in isolation* from the main (and usually confusing) business of tackling an actual model. This book should therefore be a very useful companion to any introductory course in mathematical modelling, whether in a scientific context or business environment.

This is not a book that can be *read*; rather it is meant to be *used*. Its purpose is to provide practice and training in the skills of mathematical modelling by working through a collection of worked examples and further exercises. It is not just a collection of exercises, however; each chapter either isolates a particular skill which is relevant at some stage in the modelling process, or deals with a particular modelling concept. These skills and concepts cannot be simply learnt, they have to be used, and it is only by practice that the necessary expertise can be developed. This explains the large number of examples and exercises given. They are from a variety of subject areas and cover a wide range of difficulty, from GCSE level to first or even second year undergraduate level. Some of the problems in Chapter 9, for example, are quite advanced. Within each chapter the exercises are numbered very roughly in order of difficulty and answers are provided where appropriate. The temptation to look at the answers should be resisted until every effort has been made to solve the problem! Most of the problems are new, but a number of the topics arise from the pioneering work of many colleagues from the Open University and the former polytechnics, in the area of teaching mathematical modelling. Many of the skills are common to a number of areas so there is inevitably some overlap between the chapters.

Generally speaking it will be found convenient to take the chapters in numerical order, but readers should be warned that they are not of equal length; the idea is to move on when it is felt that an adequate level of competence has been reached. Chapter 9 is particularly long because of the importance of differential equations in modelling. By working through the examples and exercises readers will increase their confidence and strengthen their model-building skills. The effort put in will be amply repaid when real modelling problems have to be tackled.

Readers new to mathematical modelling should first read the Introduction, and all readers should bear in mind that mathematical modelling is a structured process involving a number of stages. *The complete modelling process requires the combined application of all the various skills and concepts covered in this book.* Chapters 1–4 concentrate on the development of basic modelling skills. Each of Chapters 5–11 isolates a particular modelling concept and provides exercises aimed at developing skills in the use of that concept. It is not necessary to take the chapters from 5 onwards in strict numerical order. In many places it will be found advantageous to make use of computer software for mathematical manipulations, graph-plotting and the calculation of results. Spreadsheets will be found very useful for general purposes and especially for discrete models. Software packages such as DERIVE or MATHCAD will greatly help in investigating continuous models, while packages such as MATLAB or MATHEMATICA will be useful for both discrete and continuous models. For simple models using random numbers, spreadsheets or MATHEMATICA can be used, but more complex stochastic models are best tackled using specialised discrete-event simulation software.

We have tried to eliminate typing errors and other mistakes but the large number of examples makes it unlikely that we have been totally successful. The authors would be very grateful for notification of any errors discovered by readers. Finally let us point out that by no means all of the skills of modelling have been covered here. We have not included examples of the application of the complete modelling process because such examples can be found in other books on modelling. Also modelling in practice is not usually a solitary activity but is carried out by a group working together on the problem. This demands skills of communication and organisation. The end result is finally often presented orally as well as in the form of a written report, and there are many skills involved there. Some advice on these aspects can be found in *Guide to Mathematical Modelling* published by Macmillan Press.

Introduction to Modelling

What is Mathematical Modelling?

Books dealing with mathematical methods sometimes illustrate their discussions with examples intended to show real-life applications. A hypothetical example might be 'A farmer finds that when he uses x kg of fertiliser on each m^2 of soil, his crop yield is $x^3 + 6x - 2$ kg m^{-2}.' In real life the farmer (or even the farmer's mathematician friend) would never 'find' such a thing. This is not to say that there could *not* be a formula in terms of x which predicts the crop yield when x kg of fertiliser is used. There may well be such a formula, which we call a *model*, and it could be very useful in making predictions, but it could not be just plucked out of the air. Mathematical models are patiently constructed using a well-tried process and can be based either on data (on crop yields and fertiliser in this case) or on *assumptions* (in this case about how crop yield responds to fertiliser treatment) or usually a combination of both. We can define mathematical modelling as the activity of translating a real problem into mathematics for subsequent analysis. A mathematical model will be created and its solution will usually provide information useful in dealing with the original real problem.

What are Real Problems?

Real problems can come from many different sources and at various levels of difficulty, from working out new traffic light settings to sorting out the badminton club fixtures, and from deciding the distribution of milk to home decorating and DIY. Professional mathematical modellers exist in industry and commerce working in many different areas. Elsewhere there are lots of common situations at work, home or leisure where mathematics is needed to solve a particular problem. In all cases there is some translating to be done from the problem into mathematics to form a mathematical model.

What is the Key Feature in Mathematical Modelling?

The interest lies not so much in solving mathematical equations as being able to make the most effective translation from the original problem into mathematics, so that the resulting model is of some practical use in solving the real problem. It is usually possible to get hold of computer software which will solve the equations. The main issue therefore lies in understanding the problem and its subsequent conversion into a mathematical form.

How is Modelling Carried Out?

We must not assume that the activity of formulating our problem in mathematical terms is easy; in fact it is usually much harder to do this than it is to solve the resulting equations. The difficulty is that the original problem probably will not be presented in an immediate mathematical form. Worse, it may not be fully specified, since the presenter is not a mathematician or does not actually know the full specification anyway. Thus we are concerned in understanding and perhaps modifying the original problem. We may also be concerned with what use is made of our model solution afterwards.

One of the most important points to realise is that the activity of modelling is a *process* which involves a number of clearly identifiable stages. The usual way of representing this process is by means of a modelling flow diagram similar to the one shown below, as originally

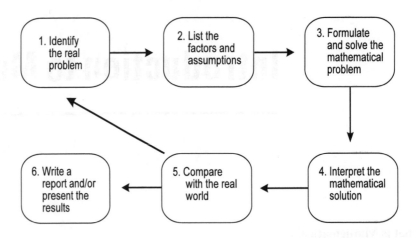

introduced by the Open University. The process is seen to be a *cycle* which may need to be traversed a number of times before the results are satisfactory. The point of the flow diagram is that it gives us a framework to refer to and acts as a channel for our thoughts and ideas.

What is the Main Objective of This Book?

The main objective is to train the reader in the skills that are required in building good mathematical models. We are not concerned primarily with explaining mathematical techniques that will then be used in analysing and solving the model, as there are plenty of textbooks already on this. The point is to concentrate first on the specification and understanding of the problem and then the resulting formulation of a model – this often turns out to be the most rewarding part of the procedure. The learning of mathematical skills and techniques is of course essential to support the modelling activity, but we must realise that 'learning to use mathematics is not the same as learning mathematics'.

Why Should This Book be Used if We Don't Want to be Professional Mathematicians?

Tackling real situations using mathematics is a challenge at all levels. Just think of a range of problems which everyone encounters from time to time: buying a car, loan repayment, household heating bills, bulk purchase, running a disco, preparing and reading timetables and routes, painting the house, measuring physical fitness, playing sport, placing a bet, foreign travel, parachuting etc. All of these activities have a quantitative element; understanding their nature and then making some decision in each case will normally need a mathematical representation or model.

Why Should This Book be Used if We *do* Want to be Professional Mathematicians?

Through tackling real problems at the starter level we can build up the confidence to take on more and more advanced situations to be met on industrial training or in the first job. Alongside modelling skills will be our development of mathematical, statistical and computing techniques necessary in solving the model. Professional mathematicians need the wide experiences gained through building models in applying their mathematics and statistics. With the help of powerful computers, mathematical models are used to help solve problems in production and distribution, design engineering, insurance services, economic forecasting and so on.

Haven't Most of the Real Industrial Problems been Solved by Now?

Computer modelling has developed in sophistication so that major issues such as weather forecasting and economic prediction are more reliable than, say twenty years ago, but there is plenty more to be done in tuning and adjusting these models to incorporate more features. This can only be done through a thorough understanding of an existing model, how it was formulated and what assumptions were made. There are many new situations arising where mathematical models are used, for instance in analysing the spread of diseases, pollution measurement, stock control, marketing a new product and many other areas.

Why is This Book Different from Other Books on Modelling?

We have concentrated on the first two boxes in the flow diagram by highlighting all the difficulties encountered and the skills needed. This is not to detract from the subsequent model solution and validation, but often the part of the modelling process found to be most difficult is that of specifying and formulating a model from an original problem. This book provides a series of exercises designed to develop the skills necessary in the various stages of the modelling process. Please see the Bibliography for examples of texts in which further modelling case studies can be found.

How to Use This Book

Each chapter either isolates a particular skill (or set of skills) relevant at some stage in the modelling process, or concentrates on showing how a particular modelling idea can be used. The aim is for you to develop your expertise with that particular skill or concept in the following way:

1. An outline of the **background** introduces the ideas and explains why they are needed and how they may be used. A brief list of the relevant mathematical skills is also given.
2. A set of **worked examples** is presented, illustrating the theme and its various applications. These should be carefully read through.
3. Further **exercises** are provided for you to test and extend your own understanding of and ability to apply the main ideas introduced in that chapter.
4. **Answers** are given to the exercises. In some cases it should be realised they are only *sample* solutions where there may well be other equally valid (or better) answers.

The main point to remember is that this is a book for *working* with, not just reading, and the effort put into the work will, we feel sure, be justly rewarded.

1 Collecting and Interpreting Data

1.1 Background

Successful mathematical modelling depends not only on learning how to formulate the model equations (this feature is concentrated on in many of the following chapters), but also in being able to 'prime' the model with some data, hopefully the correct data. Most industrial and business problems that require some quantified analysis *start* with data and *finish* with data. This might come as a surprise, but in fact any major new road project, say, will not start until local or national views have been thoroughly analysed by gathering data on traffic demand and environmental objections; a mathematical model will then be formed for the project and the model outcome will be judged by reference to cost data, length of construction time, resulting environmental hazards and so on. Thus while the modelling flow diagram in the Introduction shows the overall process, the procedure with data flow incorporated could be as shown in Fig. 1.1.

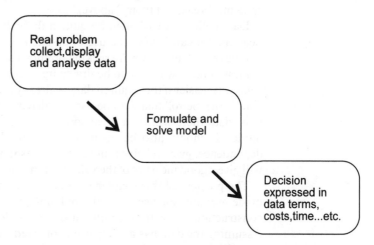

Real problem collect, display and analyse data

Formulate and solve model

Decision expressed in data terms, costs, time...etc.

Figure 1.1

The use of data in mathematical modelling is in fact very extensive and can be summarised as:

1. In the initial stage, suggesting which factors are important and indicating possible relationships between them
2. In the development stage, fixing values of parameters and constants that may occur in a model
3. In the final stage, checking model validation by comparing its predictions with real data

Within this chapter we are concerned with item 1, leaving items 2 and 3 until Chapter 12. To emphasise the initial use of data, some examples are given here:

Second-hand car   *Problem*: We need to change the car.
                       Action: Examine data on second-hand car sales.

	Model all the important facts about purchase.

Decision: Expressed in financial data terms, i.e. cost, loan repayments etc.

Supermarket checkouts *Problem*: The manager has to open some of the checkouts.

Action: Examine data on customer demand per hour per day. Examine data on staff wages.

Decision: How many checkouts to open.

Water supply *Problem*: A new housing scheme is being built.

Action: Collect data on size of all houses, existing supply pipe capacity, feasible routing for new pipes, costs of layout etc. Model layout(s).

Decision: Select layout and issue building instructions. (Remember you cannot dig all the pipes up again!)

In the case of the water supply problem, a predictive element will need to be incorporated into any suggested pipe layout so that if and when demand increases, the pipe network can cope. This predictive element is often the key reason for creating a mathematical model in the first place, and underlines why we cannot get away with simply collecting data and costing an outcome without some theoretical planning, i.e. creating a model. The model will include equations representing the water flow in this case. The behaviour of pipeline flow will need to be examined first, taking into account the effects of friction and gravity and so on. This highlights item 2 above, where data will enable the values of friction parameters, for example, to be fixed for a particular application of the model. In a quite different context, the spread of a contagious disease can be predicted using a mathematical model. Here data on the nature of a particular disease will be used to calculate relevant values for the model parameters. The effectiveness of the model can be assessed using actual data when an epidemic breaks out (item 2 above).

Data collection will often be quite a difficult operation in itself. This is because, if it is 'scientific', it can involve the use of on-site equipment that requires specialised techniques. On the other hand, if we are seeking opinions of people at large concerning some issue then a questionnaire will have to be drawn up which is unbiased and comprehensive. The task is somewhat easier if the required data is already available from a library source. At any rate the data is the 'petrol' that is to be used in 'driving' the model along. Clearly, with incorrect or poor data there will be a breakdown, notwithstanding some well-constructed theoretical model. It should also be mentioned that model sensitivity can be investigated for data dependence: given reliable input data, the response of the model to small changes in the data will give a good measure of the validity of the model itself.

The purpose of this chapter is to discuss some of the issues arising when data has been made available for use in model building. We are not concerned here with questionnaire construction or with scientific instrumentation, important though these matters are. Assuming the data has already been collected, the display and interpretation are important tasks in their own right. Sometimes a mathematical 'fit' to the data is immediately carried out; methods for achieving this are given in Chapter 12. Statistical analyses can be used to assess the significance of detected relationships within the data, but here we are interested in *initial appraisal* for clarity, credibility, trends, possible meaningful deductions and so on. *This is an important skill for the intending modeller.* This may be seen as a simple job, but it is well to remember that there is daily bombardment in the media by charts, tables and graphs with supposedly reliable statistical deduction often biased to reflect some interest group (say party political). Some relevant questions to ask concerning presented data are:

- Is it displayed objectively?
- Is it correctly scaled?
- Are all variables labelled and units of measurement given?
- Are the data sources given?
- Do we use a bar or pie chart, or a line graph?

- Is there some predictive element expected from the display?
- Are the variables absolute data values or relative to some base?

The data analysis process is essentially a two-stage process: the first is the display of data and the second is the *deduction* of some feature(s) from the display which show a trend or pattern that can form the basis of a subsequent mathematical model. The data will be mostly 'raw', since we want to highlight the initial job of data examination. The smoothing of data and fitting of a mathematical function to the data is a secondary consideration for the moment. Displaying the data, or parts of it, and examining the resulting graphs, is a basic skill for mathematical modellers and comes logically before all the other skills. It is at this stage that computer software packages such as spreadsheets and word processors are especially relevant. Modellers need to gain mastery of these information technology skills at the outset. Other software tools are also needed later in developing and processing models.

In examining and graphing data, very often we are looking at an input/output situation where the *input* variable is *time* (usually represented by the horizontal axis) and the *output* variable is some *contextual measurement* (displayed on the vertical axis). The context can be physical, biological, economic, behavioural, political and so on.

The worked examples below show the application of some of the above considerations.

1.2 Worked Examples

1.1 The population of England and Wales is recorded (in millions) from the censuses since the year 1801 as follows:

Year	1801	1811	1821	1831	1841	1851	1861	1871	1881	1891	1901	1911	1921	1931	1951	1961	1971	1981
Population	8.9	10.2	12.0	13.9	15.9	17.9	20.1	22.7	26.0	29.0	32.5	36.1	37.9	40.0	43.8	46.1	48.8	49.2

Set up a suitable display of this data and comment on the behaviour.

Solution The bar chart (Fig. 1.2) clearly indicates the population growth over the 180 year period. The trend shows rapid increase with evidence of a tailing off since about 1960. As the population may be thought of as a continuous variable, a line graph (Fig. 1.3) is also given here for the same data. Note the absence of the census for the wartime year of 1941.

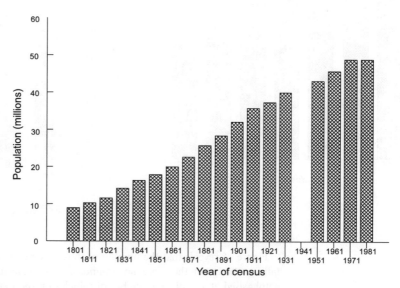

Figure 1.2

This flattening of the curve is a common phenomenon, especially in the life sciences, and can be modelled using a logistic curve (see Chapters 6 and 12). The physical explanation in the context of population growth lies in growth-limiting factors such as social and economic factors in the case of human populations (often seen in developed, first-world countries).

3

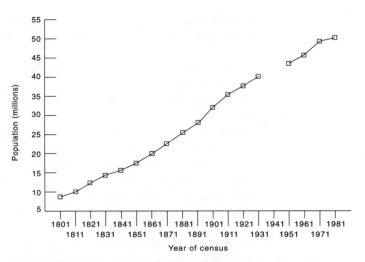

Figure 1.3

1.2 Data on UK traffic accidents concerning fatalities and injuries is available as follows:

Year	Killed	Seriously injured	Slightly injured	Total
1986	5382	68 752	247 317	321 451
1987	5125	64 293	242 055	311 473
1988	5052	63 491	253 762	322 305
1989	5373	63 158	273 061	341 592
1990	5217	60 441	275 483	341 141
1991	4568	51 605	255 096	311 269
1992	4229	49 245	257 199	310 673

Display this data in a suitable fashion and draw some tentative conclusions about the apparent trends.

Solution The graphs shown in Figs. 1.4 and 1.5 pick out some of the important features indicated by the data. The number of fatalities is seen to be falling as is the number of seriously injured. Part of the reason for this could be greater pressure from advertising for more care on the roads. Note that the data does not divide the total killed into drivers and pedestrians.

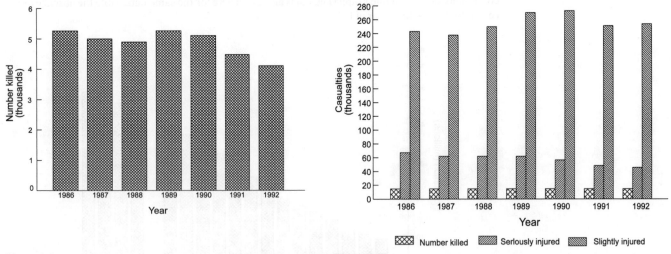

Figure 1.4   **Figure 1.5**

Figure 1.5 reveals that the number of those deemed to be 'slightly injured' does not show the same falling trend, but there are no grounds for complacency here; as road care becomes ever more emphasised at school, the number of vehicles on the roads in the UK continues to rise which gives greater potential for accidents.

1.3 Data on the activities of school leavers is available from the European Union. This enables some comparison to be made between various EU countries concerning training and college initiatives against employment. The age point is 16 years, when most young people finish compulsory secondary education. Averaged data over recent years (early 1980s) gives:

Country	Full-time academic education (%)	Full-time vocational education (%)	Apprenticeships (%)	Working or unemployed
Belgium	56	36	4	4
Germany	21	19	51	9
Luxembourg	31	31	23	15
France	27	40	14	19
Italy	21	51	24	4
Netherlands	26	29	9	26
Ireland	56	10	5	29
Denmark	24	13	31	32
UK	32	10	14	44

Solution The data reflects policy within each country regarding post-compulsory education. Also, the exact meaning of terminology will be different for the categories listed. We do not have a 'time series' situation for graphical portrayal either, so comparisons will be carried out using pie charts, especially as the data is given in percentage terms. We note first the difference between Belgium (Fig. 1.6) and the UK (Fig. 1.7).

A stacked bar chart (Fig. 1.8) is useful for displaying all the countries' data. The differences in attitudes to training of young people can easily be seen. Again with most data sets there will be ambiguities in meaning: there are overlaps here between 'work' and 'apprenticeship' which can lead to confusion. For some cases, putting people into 'vocational education' may be deliberate policy to avoid entry in the unemployment column.

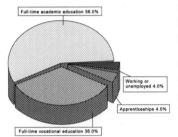

Figure 1.6 Belgium.

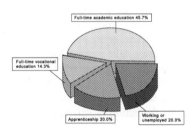

Figure 1.7 United Kingdom.

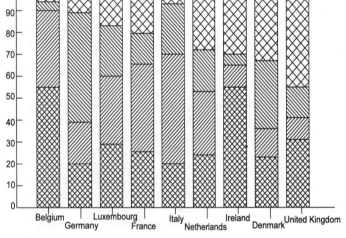

Figure 1.8   ▨ F/T Acad.educ. ▨ F/T Voc.educ. ▨ Apprentice ▨ Work/unemployed

1.4   Sporting achievement is always interesting as performances improve and records are broken. In athletics, the question is never far from the headlines as both men and women strive to run faster, throw

Women's 200 m gold medallists

Year	Name	Country	Time (s)	Speed (m.p.h.)
1948	F. Blankers-Koen	Netherlands	24.4	18.3
1952	M. Jackson	Australia	23.7	18.8
1956	B. Cuthbert	Australia	23.4	19.1
1960	W. Rudolph	USA	24.0	18.6
1964	E. McGuire	USA	23.0	19.4
1968	I. Szewinska	Poland	22.5	19.8
1972	R. Stecher	East Germany	22.40	19.9
1976	B. Eckert	East Germany	22.37	20.0
1980	B. Wockel	East Germany	22.03	20.3
1984	V. Brisco-Hooks	USA	21.81	20.5
1988	F. Griffith-Joyner	USA	21.34	20.9

further etc. One line of discussion, apart from whether there is some limit on human performance, concerns a certain rivalry between the sexes: can women actually catch up with men in the future and run just as fast? From the available records it is interesting to note that when the world mile record fell below four minutes (Roger Bannister in 1954), the women's time for the mile had just broken *five* minutes! The runner (Diane Leather) would have finished 320 m behind Bannister. Today (1994) it is thought the distance would be cut to 180 m. The data given here is for the men's and women's 200 m Olympic Games winning times since the event began.

Men's 200 m gold medallists

Year	Name	Country	Time (s)	Speed (m.p.h.)
1900	W. Tewksbury	USA	22.2	20.1
1904	A. Hahn	USA	21.6	20.7
1908	R. Kerr	Canada	22.6	19.8
1912	R. Craig	USA	21.7	20.6
1920	A. Woodring	USA	22.0	20.3
1924	J. Scholz	USA	21.6	20.7
1928	P. Williams	Canada	21.8	20.5
1932	E. Tolan	USA	21.2	21.1
1936	J. Owens	USA	20.7	21.6
1948	M. Patten	USA	21.1	21.2
1952	A. Stansfield	USA	20.7	21.6
1956	R. Marrow	USA	20.6	21.7
1960	L. Berruti	Italy	20.5	21.8
1964	H. Carr	USA	20.3	22.0
1968	T. Smith	USA	19.83	22.5
1972	V. Borzov	USSR	20.00	22.3
1976	D. Quarrie	Jamaica	20.23	22.1
1980	P. Mennea	Italy	20.19	22.1
1984	C. Lewis	USA	19.80	22.5
1988	J. DeLoach	USA	19.75	22.6

Compare men's and women's speeds over the 100 year period.

Solution   Figure 1.9 reveals some interesting trends. The times recorded by men are quicker than for women, which does not surprise us. In fact, examination of the women's times seems to indicate that the 1988 winner would not have won the men's event after 1928, since which date equipment and track conditions have improved as well as fitness and preparation levels. However, take a closer look at the *progress* of both sexes over the period. This gives a different story: the steepness of the graph representing the women's times is greater than that for the men, indicating better improvement rate. If we take this to continue into the next century, then the two graphs can be extrapolated, showing that equality will be obtained by about the year 2024. Do you think this deduction is reasonable? Can similar trends be seen in other athletics events?

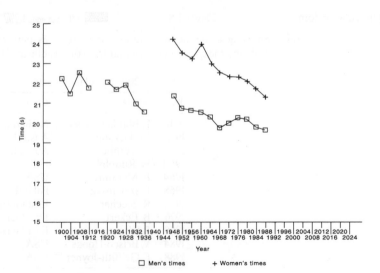

Figure 1.9 Olympic Games 200 m gold medal.

The manner in which it is suggested that extrapolation can be carried out could be invalid with the above. We are assuming that improvement for both men and women will continue at their same almost constant rates so that the projections are *linearly extended* over the next 30 years.

1.5   There is often confusion in media reporting, between the behaviour of the *rate of change* of some price, profit or cost and the behaviour of the variable itself. The fact that professional commentators can appear muddled about this is rather worrying. Rates of change are discussed in Chapter 8, but consider here the example of a report on house prices in Britain which appeared in a national newspaper. The information was presented in graphical form similar to that shown in Fig. 1.10. The writer informed the readers that 'prices peaked nationally around the beginning of 1989 before falling'. Notice however that the y-axis denotes the percentage year-on-year *price change*. Where y is positive prices are still rising and the graph for y first becomes negative near the *end* of 1989 ($t \approx 36$). At this point prices begin to fall, so this is actually the point of maximum prices. The reporter has confused the rate of increase with the actual house price.

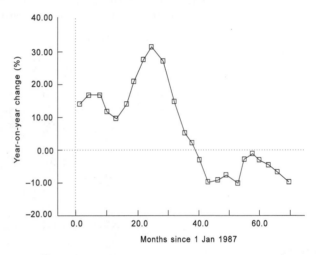

Figure 1.10   House price changes.

1.6   Traffic accidents associated with drinking and driving have long been a cause of concern. Strenuous attempts through new laws and public pressure have been made to try to persuade people not to combine driving with alcoholic drinking. Data on drink-driving convictions in England and Scotland show how the situation has been influenced by the legislation:

Totals of convictions (nearest thousand)

	1978	1979	1980	1981	1982	1983	1984	1985	1986
England	102	105	110	98	97	98	82	76	69
Scotland	15	16	16	14	12	10	8	6	4

This data is shown by a bar chart in Fig. 1.11. What conclusions can be drawn?

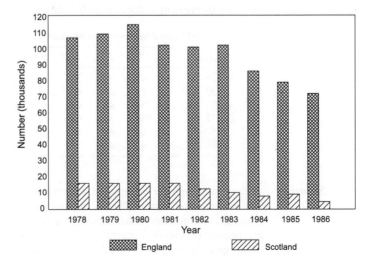

Figure 1.11   Drink-driving convictions: totals convicted.

This graph indicates a lot more convictions in England than Scotland. It also shows the decline in both countries throughout the 1980s as the campaign against drinking and driving gained momentum. What the graph does *not* indicate of course is that Scotland is much more law-abiding in this respect than England. A truer comparison is provided by re-casting the data as 'convictions per 100 000 people':

	1978	1979	1980	1981	1982	1983	1984	1985	1986
England	205	213	220	198	196	199	165	150	136
Scotland	240	260	267	220	190	157	132	100	70

Again a bar chart can be used to show the pattern (Fig. 1.12). This display contrasts sharply with that shown in Fig. 1.11. We can see that the problem was much more serious in Scotland than England over the period 1978 to 1981. After that the pressure to stop driving after drinking takes effect in both countries, but shows a particularly sharp decline in Scotland, so that the conviction rate falls well below that for England by 1986. The reasons for this may include local habits concerning the licensing laws for public houses and possibly greater concentration on this sort of crime by the police in Scotland.

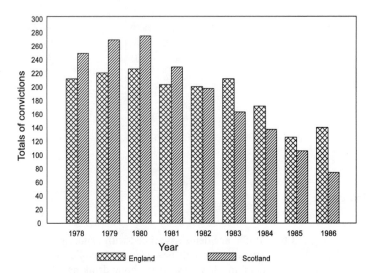

Figure 1.12 Drink-driving convictions: convictions per 100 000 people.

1.7 Smoking habits have changed somewhat over the years thanks to the intensive campaign mounted by health bodies and by the government. The effect of all these efforts is mixed, however, as would appear from the following data taken from surveys conducted on cigarette smoking throughout the UK. Of particular interest is the comparison between men and women over the period with regard to changes in smoking habits. The data for women is given as an exercise below, but the table supplied here gives data for men over the period 1974 to 1992. We should notice that the age demarcations are unequal, to indicate periods of adult maturity more typical for expected changing smoking habits. Also the data does not indicate the degree of smoking, i.e. whether we have heavy or infrequent smokers. The percentages given should be interpreted to mean that 'regular' smokers are counted. What interpretations can be deduced from this data?

Percentage of men who are smokers

Age	1974	1976	1978	1980	1982	1984	1986	1988	1990	1992
16–19	43	39	35	32	31	29	30	28	28	29
20–24	55	47	45	44	41	40	41	37	38	39
25–34	56	48	48	47	40	40	37	37	36	34
35–49	55	50	48	45	40	39	37	37	34	32
50–59	54	49	48	47	42	39	35	33	28	28
60 and over	47	40	38	36	33	30	29	26	24	21

Solution A composite graph can be displayed to contrast the behaviour of the age groups. This is shown in Fig. 1.13. The predominant feature is the fall in percentage admitting to be smokers over the 18 year time span. Another clear indicator is that the drop in smoking seems to have 'levelled off' for most males, with the exception of the over 60s. There is evidence that the smoking levels have bottomed out to a rough 'one in three' apart from older men who begin to realise the folly of damaging their health terminally.

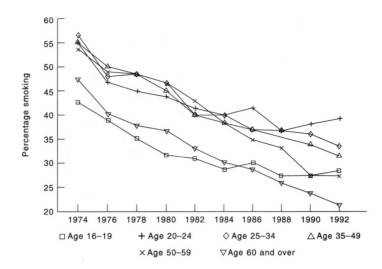

Figure 1.13 Male smoking habits (1974–92).

Considering the vast amount of pressure put out by health groups on the dangers of smoking, it is disappointing that so many men still smoke cigarettes.

1.8   With the growth of sports centres around the country, there has been the opportunity for many more people to participate in games and sports with the objective of keeping fit as well as becoming more proficient in certain activities through coaching. Data collected on the sporting activities in general refers to the two years 1987 and 1990. This shows the sporting claims of different age groups to recent participation in a variety of common activities broadly all concerned with keeping fit and healthy.

The table gives the percentages of people claiming to have taken part in the activity listed *at least once in the four-week period* just before the survey was conducted.

Activity	Year	Age						
		16–19	*20–24*	*25–29*	*30–44*	*45–59*	*60–69*	*over 70*
Walking	1987	42	40	41	43	40	37	20
	1990	45	42	45	43	44	42	25
Swimming (indoor)	1987	20	18	18	16	6	4	1
	1990	22	19	19	17	9	5	1
Keep fit/yoga	1987	14	13	14	10	7	5	3
	1990	19	20	17	14	9	6	4
Cycling	1987	21	10	10	11	7	5	2
	1990	24	11	11	11	8	6	3
Weight training	1987	16	12	9	5	1	0	0
	1990	16	12	9	5	2	0	0
Badminton	1987	12	6	4	5	2	0	0
	1990	12	6	4	4	2	0	0
Football	1987	21	13	9	4	1	0	0
	1990	20	13	10	4	1	0	0
None of the	1987	14	23	26	29	44	53	74
activities	1990	13	19	22	27	37	46	69

Pick out some of the salient features from this data.

Solution   Over the four years 1987–90 there has been some small increase in the participation of 'walking' and 'swimming'. There is also overlap between the various activities in so far as people take part in more than one event. The data from the last two rows show percentages of people not taking part in any of the events listed. As one might expect, there is a fall in the non-participatory percentage. Changes over the four years are generally small; we would preferably have required data from further back before the advent of sports centres. Examining the data for swimming, there is a little evidence of increase as shown in Fig. 1.14. Further graphs (Fig. 1.15 and Fig. 1.16) compare the prevalence of sports between the 16–19 group and the 30–44 group for 1990. We can see the decline in football playing and the participation interest switching more to keep-fit activities as opposed to competitive games.

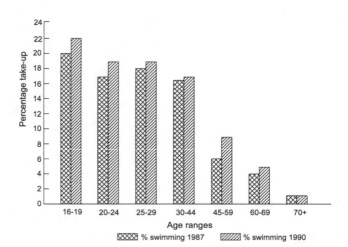

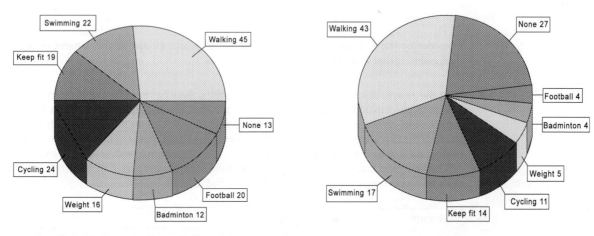

Figure 1.14 Indoor swimming (1987–90) by age.

Figure 1.15 Activity 16–19 (1990).

Figure 1.16 Activity 30–44 (1990).

1.9 The resourcing of schools is always under discussion and the various political parties in Britain are never slow to call for change, especially when not currently in government. One of the most used statistics as a basis for criticism is the ratio of pupils to teachers. Consider the historic data here, which refers to primary schools in England and Wales. The data is quoted for every ten years since 1860; the pupil and teacher totals are given in thousands.

Year	Pupil total	Teacher total	Ratio
1860	774	7.6	101.8
1870	1231	14.4	85.5
1880	2864	44.6	64.2
1890	3750	77.0	48.7
1900	4754	119.0	40.0
1910	5382	164	32.8
1920	5206	167	31.2
1930	4930	169	29.2
1940	—	—	
1950	4005	134	29.9
1960	4133	144	28.7
1970	5023	188	26.7
1980	4371	195	22.4
1990	3920	180	21.8

Solution The pattern of school numbers is interesting in itself. In the early days primary schooling was not compulsory; various Acts of Parliament altered this so that in the 20th century primary school numbers reflect the population data. What is meant by a primary school may need clarification; also whether the large body of private schools are included. In most cases the primary age range is from five

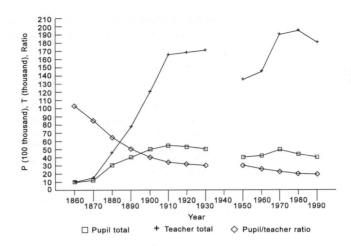

Figure 1.17 Pupil and teacher numbers and pupil/teacher ratio (1860–1990).

to eleven years and private schools are included. The pupil/teacher ratio is the most interesting feature and is seen to be falling consistently as facilities are expanded and the roles and duties of teaching staff are expanded. Figure 1.17 shows the situation quite succinctly, where all three data sets have been graphed to show the trends. Notice how the pupil total rose monotonically for the period up to the First World War. This then falls sharply until 1950 due to the effects of both World Wars, before rising again until the 1970s, when falling birth rates have an effect on primary pupil totals. With regard to the teacher totals, it can be seen that these rise steeply as the education service develops and the numbers and training of teachers expand. Note how latterly the teacher numbers stabilise in step with pupil totals, as governments do not want to overproduce primary teachers. The pupil/teacher ratio begins at a horrendous value close to 100 and more or less consistently falls to the present day level in which the 'class of thirty' seems to be comfortably beaten. However, teacher numbers will include head teachers, those on special assignments, special needs etc., which accounts for the 1990 ratio of around 20 pupils per teacher.

1.10 The continual increase in the number of cars and commercial vehicles wishing to make use of the limited UK road space presents an almost unsolvable problem. The clamour for more and better roads will not alleviate the congestion as the number of vehicles rises. What are the figures for the number of vehicles and how have these evolved with time? The data below sets out the scene since 1905, where the numbers of vehicles are given in thousands. Comment on the data provided.

	1905	1910	1915	1920	1925	1930	1935	1940	1945	1950	1955	1960	1965	1970	1975	1980	1985	1988
Private cars	16	53	139	187	580	1056	1477	1423	1487	2258	3526	5526	8917	11 515	13 747	14 772	16 454	18 432
Commercial	16	54	129	176	323	449	520	525	572	1032	1211	1491	1699	1 694	1 887	2 146	2 410	2 730

Solution A bar chart has been presented to show the trend (Fig. 1.18) over the 90 year period. Projections are what interest everyone from motor manufacturers, private citizens and government. A curve fit of this data (see Chapter 12) could be used for a *mathematical* projection which will only be valid if current social conditions hold. The amount of available road for all these vehicles to drive on is also relevant. In

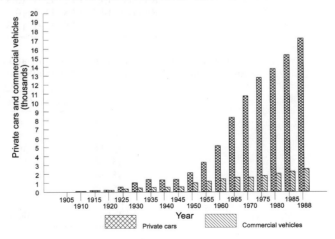

Figure 1.18 Growth in road transport (1905–88).

Fig. 1.18 we see an almost exponential rate of growth followed by an apparent tail-off after 1970. Should the Department of the Environment continue to build more roads?

1.3 Exercises

In the following exercises, some data is provided mainly in tabular form for a wide range of contexts. The objective in each case is to display the data by graphs from which the essential features can be drawn out and commented upon. A brief discussion of apparent trends and behaviour is what is required. Possible reasons for the behaviour should be considered where appropriate – these will be contextual and may depend on local knowledge. Sometimes in newspapers or magazines the data provided is not strictly in tabular form, but presented in some idiosyncratic manner to convey a message or perhaps a timetable. Some exercises are intended to highlight the interpretative skills necessary for the understanding and use of the information.

1.1 The population of Ireland over the past 170 years is given in the table. Population figures are in thousands and refer to both parts of Ireland combined.

Year	1821	1831	1841	1851	1861	1871	1881	1891	1901	1911	1926	1937	1951	1961	1966	1971	1981
Population	6802	7767	8175	6552	5799	5412	5175	4705	4459	4390	4229	4250	4332	4243	4369	4514	4986

1.2 A similar exercise to that of Worked Example 1.5 concerns the annual inflation rate in Britain. Examine the graph shown in Fig. 1.19 and comment on the behaviour of shop prices after 1990.

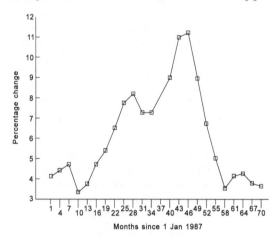

Figure 1.19 Annual inflation rate.

1.3 Listening to the radio remains popular despite the ever-greater choice of TV broadcasting. The various radio stations compete for listeners and to some extent try to appeal to different sections of the public. Data in the following table refers to listening figures in the early morning and the survey that gathered the data was looking for regular listeners to the particular station. The figures quoted give the percentage of those surveyed who claimed to be regular listeners of BBC Radio 1 and 2 and ILR (independent local radio).

	1981	1982	1983	1984	1985	1986	1987	1988	1989	1990
Radio 1	15.5	15.5	15.0	13.9	13.0	12.7	12.0	11.8	11.8	11.7
Radio 2	14.2	13.8	11.7	10.2	9.1	9.0	8.9	8.7	8.5	7.9
ILR	11.0	13.9	12.0	11.3	10.9	11.8	12.6	12.7	13.4	14.2

To help explain the behaviour, the listening audience may be stratified by age. This is borne out in the following table. Here, from those who show allegiance to a particular radio station, the percentages of the

Age range (yrs)	Radio 1	Radio 2	ILR
4–15	6	1	6
16–24	30	1	17
25–34	36	3	24
35–44	17	8	20
45–54	7	18	14
55–64	2	31	10
65+	2	38	9
Total	100%	100%	100%

listeners in various age ranges are given for one particular year. A further relevant piece of information could be the start of breakfast television in 1983.

1.4 Pollution is a major source of concern to environmentalists nowadays. One particular investigation still ongoing is into the effects of radioactive pollution from the nuclear power station disaster at Chernobyl in 1986. This had an effect on the ecology of north-west England; in particular, pollution of the Lake District was accentuated by rainfall carrying radioactive substances onto the grassland fells and also into the lakes. Ecologists are examining the levels of caesium-137, this radionuclide (with a half-life of about 30 years) being the most significant deposit. The reactor exploded on 26 April 1986 and the gaseous plume passed over NW England during the first week of May. Levels of caesium-137 were measured in the lakes and the data from the small Crummock Lake are given in the table. (Note the unevenness of the time data, including two readings taken on the same day.)

Observation	Date	Day count	$^{137}Cs\ (mBq\ l^{-1})$
1	14 Jul 1986	69	98
2	7 Aug 1986	93	80
3	7 Aug 1986	93	77
4	25 Sep 1986	142	106
5	3 Nov 1986	181	74
6	18 Nov 1986	196	31
7	5 Dec 1986	213	42
8	5 Dec 1986	213	51
9	2 Mar 1987	300	26
10	9 Apr 1987	338	11
11	20 Jun 1987	410	12
12	24 Aug 1987	475	16

1.5 Data for the total size of the population of England and Wales was examined in Worked Example 1.1. The figures can be of further interest when broken down into age categories. This will show the manner in which the population is changing, and this is important fof planners of all the social services, such as education, health and old age provision. Data going back to 1841 is shown in the table. The age categories are in 10 year bands over the 10 year census period, so those people recorded in a certain group at one census will have moved forward into the next group for the next census. The population totals are in thousands.

Age	1841	1851	1861	1871	1881	1891	1901	1911	1921	1931	1951	1961	1971	1981
0–9	4011	4440	5046	5778	6669	6948	7203	7551	6841	6313	6880	6860	7949	6117
10–19	3319	3670	4038	4606	5347	6175	6589	6837	7163	6642	5516	6926	6941	7866
20–29	2833	3137	3398	3785	4376	4996	5945	6255	6111	6851	6206	5723	6922	6838
30–39	2052	2365	2611	2901	3287	3810	4578	5490	5546	5858	6403	6227	5657	6747
40–49	1527	1768	2065	2283	2551	2885	3424	4159	5007	5217	6537	6266	6071	5481
50–59	1026	1235	1420	1663	1829	2045	2382	2880	3645	4449	5248	6149	5873	5862
60–69	700	809	934	1064	1231	1345	1519	1827	2268	2928	3973	4437	5240	4959
70+	446	503	555	633	687	801	888	1073	1306	1693	2996	3518	4095	4848

1.6 Transport data was considered in Worked Example 1.10, where the number of cars registered in Britain was examined. The amount of road space available for them can be examined from the following table. The source for this data (and a number of other data sets used here) is *British Social Trends since 1900* edited by A.H. Halsey. What is listed here is the total of classified road length in the UK (in miles), taken every two years since 1960.

Year	1960	1962	1964	1966	1968	1970	1972	1974	1976	1978	1980	1982	1984	1986	1988	1990	1992
Road Length	194 180	196 135	199 743	202 064	203 969	207 891	211 072	214 442	216 812	218 925	220 935	223 716	225 982	227 527	230 161	232 425	235 158

As well as graphing the data and deducing simple trends, the question arises as to whether the roads are matching the cars, i.e. is there now a lot less space on the roads than was the case 30 years ago? Compare the data here with that shown in the Worked Example 1.10.

1.7 As a contrast with the growth of road transport, consider the situation with the railways. The data set here gives the length (in kilometres) of railway line open for use in the UK from 1830 to 1988.

Year	1830	1840	1850	1860	1870	1880	1890	1900	1910	1920	1930	1940	1950	1960	1970	1980	1990
Railway (km)	157	2 390	9 797	14 603	21 000	25 060	27 827	30 079	32 184	32 707	32 632	32 094	31 336	29 562	18 969	17 645	16 550

1.8 A well-known shipping company operates ferry services in and around the islands of Scotland. Examine the following data concerning its affairs over the period 1988–92 and decide whether the business is in a healthy state.

	1988	1989	1990	1991	1992
Total passengers	5355	5835	6157	6394	6214
Cars	1120	1231	1273	1309	1296
Commercial vehicles	100	108	111	111	111
Revenue subsidy per passenger (£)	1.22	1.08	0.93	0.91	0.97
Operating costs per passenger (£)	4.31	4.27	4.59	4.74	5.22
Revenue subsidy as % of turnover	25.8	23.3	20.0	18.3	18.3
Revenue earned per employee (£000)	22.7	25.1	28.3	31.2	31.6

1.9 Buying a second-hand car is always a tricky business, with lots of often conflicting advice on values. Each month the *Motor Trade Guide to Used Car Prices* gives information for every model regarding the likely second-hand price. Three valuations are usually quoted, First Class, Good Average and Below Average. There is also a Trade-In price, this being the amount the dealer will pay for the customer's car in part exchange for the purchased vehicle. Issues of interest are whether second-hand cars hold their value, which can be dependent on the particular model as well as the amount of wear. Consider the following two data sets at either end of the market. Do not forget that the 'Price new' quoted refers to the price *at the time of purchase*, while the second-hand prices are what you will have to pay *now* to buy the car. Inflation may be taken as fixed at about 3% over the periods given. Two sets of data are given for each year due to the registration letter changing every August.

BMW 318i 4 door saloon automatic

Year	Price new	First class	Good average	Below average	Trade-in
91 H	16 460	12 000	11 325	8 895	10 635
91 J	16 460	13 315	12 625	10 050	11 880
92 J	16 620	14 260	13 495	10 820	12 730
92 K	17 100	15 115	14 350	11 615	13 585
93 K	17 395	15 565	14 790	11 985	14 020
93 L	16 995	16 605	15 765	12 740	14 940
94 L	16 995	—	—	—	—

Reliant Robin LX 3 door hatchback

Year	Price new	First class	Good average	Below average	Trade-in
91 H	6 150	4 035	3 545	2 430	3 310
91 J	6 832	4 380	3 900	2 705	3 655
92 J	6 579	4 715	4 220	2 965	3 995
92 K	6 316	4 970	4 475	3 140	4 240
93 K	6 316	5 220	4 735	3 320	4 495
93 L	6 720	5 475	4 990	3 505	4 755
94 L	6 720	—	—	—	—

People claim that the greatest loss in value of a new car occurs in the first year of its life. This suggests some sort of exponential decay model. Does the data support this view? Note in passing the different running costs for the two models: the urban petrol consumption estimated for the BMW is 25 m.p.g. whereas for the Reliant it is 51 m.p.g.

1.10 Travel costs are scrutinised for the best bargain, and how much you pay can depend not only on the mode of transport, but also on how far in advance the booking is made. Consider the following data taken for a journey from London to Edinburgh, city centre to city centre. All the fares are 'singles' and were applicable some time in 1992. You have to decide what 'measure' to use in order to rank the five cases.

Mode of travel	Total cost of journey (£)	Total time needed
Plane	116.40	3 h 35 min
Rail	57.90	6 h 41 min
Car	28.69	9 h 25 min
Coach company 1	30.40	9 h 52 min
Coach company 2	31.40	9 h 57 min

1.11 Understanding what can be obtained from data may not always be straightforward. Consider the following taken from the 'progress' down the track of a 100 m male sprinter:

Elapsed time (s)	Distance (m)	Velocity (m s^{-1})
0	0	0
1	2.5	5.3
2	9.5	6.8
3	19.0	7.7
4	27.5	8.4
5	37.5	8.95
6	45.0	9.4
7	52.0	9.5
8	60.0	9.6
9	70.5	9.6
10	78.0	9.6
11	87.0	9.6
12	94.5	9.55
12.6	100.0	9.5

Can the velocity data be obtained from the distance/time data? What about the acceleration of the athlete? Is it possible to get an 'equation of motion'? (M. Stewart Townend, *Mathematics in Sport*, Ellis-Horwood, Chichester, 1984.)

1.12 Pollution control is a very contentious issue since one person's profit could be another one's law to prevent excessive pollution. Air pollution affects everyone and emissions from motor vehicle exhausts in particular are sources of considerable pollution. Lead-free petrol is now common within the UK, though by no means all vehicles can make use of this type of petrol. Consumption of petrol has increased over the years with the increase in the numbers of vehicles on the roads. Consider and analyse the following data for petrol consumption in 'millions of tonnes'. The data for lead emission is estimated from the petrol quality and the units are thousands of tonnes.

	1975	1976	1977	1978	1979	1980	1981	1982	1983	1984	1985	1986
Petrol consumption	16.12	16.88	17.34	18.35	18.68	19.15	18.72	19.25	19.57	20.22	20.40	21.47
Lead emission	7.4	7.6	7.4	7.3	7.3	7.5	6.7	6.8	6.9	7.2	6.5	2.9

1.13 Another set of data that indicates air pollution is given here. It refers to quantities of sulphur dioxide and smoke in the atmosphere. Data is given in terms of a 'base' measure of 100 in 1981/82, where 100 is equivalent to 50 μg m^{-3} in the case of sulphur dioxide, and for smoke 100 means 23 μg m^{-3}.

Year	Sulphur dioxide	Smoke
1975/76	135	140
1976/77	135	145
1977/78	118	113
1978/79	126	113
1979/80	114	109
1980/81	96	83
1981/82	100	100
1982/83	81	74
1983/84	79	78
1984/85	76	67
1985/86	73	67

1.14 Which is the most successful football team? Among professional English League football supporters this is an unanswerable question. Famous clubs have their ups and downs; also a 'measure' is needed to total an overall score to represent success. Consider those teams with continuous membership of the First Division (as it was then called) over the ten year span 1978–88. The table gives the position in the final league table of each season.

	'79	'80	'81	'82	'83	'84	'85	'86	'87	'88
Arsenal	7	4	3	5	10	6	7	7	4	6
Coventry City	10	15	16	14	19	19	18	17	10	10
Everton	4	19	15	8	7	7	1	2	1	4
Liverpool	1	1	5	1	1	1	2	1	2	1
Manchester United	9	2	8	3	3	4	4	4	11	2
Nottingham Forest	2	5	7	12	5	3	9	8	8	3
Southampton	14	8	6	7	12	2	5	14	12	12
Tottenham Hotspur	11	14	10	4	4	8	3	10	3	13

1.15 Comparisons across the European Community (now Union) are important, particularly with grant aid at stake. The population figures compared with country size are useful to begin with. The table here gives the figures for the 12 EC countries (in 1991), using area of land (km^2) and population in 1991 in thousands.

Country	Area (km^2)	Population (000s)
Belgium	30 500	10 004.5
Denmark	43 100	5 154.1
Germany	356 900	79 364.5
Greece	132 000	10 200.0
Spain	504 800	39 024.9
France	544 000	57 055.4
Ireland	70 300	3 523.8
Italy	301 300	57 661.3
Luxembourg	2 600	387.1
Netherlands	41 200	15 069.6
Portugal	92 400	9 852.3
United Kingdom	244 100	57 410.7

Evaluate and compare the population densities.

1.16 Motor vehicle comparisons across the EC countries are also interesting. Is it easier to drive around in France compared with Ireland, say? Are driving standards consistent throughout the EC – or are you more likely to hit someone in the UK compared with Germany? Consider the following data for the 12 countries. The data below gives the number of private cars registered (in thousands), the length of drivable roadways (in thousands of km) and the number of recorded personal injuries, including death. The data refers to the year 1990.

Country	Private cars	Total road length	Total traffic injuries
Belgium	3 864	—	88 160
Denmark	1 590	70 904	11 287
Germany	30 685	500 995	456 064
Greece	1 736	40 642	29 128
Spain	11 996	158 801	162 424
France	23 550	808 098	236 149
Ireland	796	92 329	9 907
Italy	26 267	—	228 645
Luxembourg	183	5 169	1 849
Netherlands	5 509	104 590	53 408
Portugal	2 552	9 817	69 528
United Kingdom	21 485	382 115	352 902

Note that Belgium and Italy do not publish a figure for the total road length. Use this data to consider questions about the relative traffic density and road safety among the EC countries.

1.17 With regard to Worked Example 1.10, further data is available for the number of registered motor vehicles after 1988:

Year	1989	1990	1991
Private cars (thousands)	19 248	19 742	19 737

Incorporate these figures into the graph shown earlier, and comment.

1.18 The Department of Transport produces figures projecting the number of vehicles and also the use they make of the roads in Britain. Clearly the use of vehicles is of more importance to road traffic planners than the number of registered vehicles, some of which may be driven very little. The data values are scaled to a base of 100 for 1992.

	1982	1987	1992	1995	2000	2005	2010	2015	2020	2025
Car density: lower estimate	68	85	100	106	116	126	136	145	154	164
upper estimate	68	85	100	110	126	142	158	172	186	199
Car numbers: lower estimate	75	90	100	106	115	124	131	138	145	152
upper estimate	75	90	100	109	122	134	144	153	162	169

Examine the data and consider the implications for road planning in the next century.

1.19 British female smoking habits over the last 20 years are represented in the table below. The data shown indicates the percentage in each age group who are regular smokers. Interpretation of this data can be compared with that for men which was considered in Worked Example 1.7.

Ages	1974	1976	1978	1980	1982	1984	1986	1988	1990	1992
16–19	39	34	33	32	30	32	30	28	32	25
20–24	48	45	43	40	40	36	38	37	39	37
25–34	49	43	32	44	37	36	35	35	34	34
35–49	48	45	43	43	38	36	34	35	33	30
50–59	47	46	42	44	40	39	35	34	29	39
60+	25	24	24	24	23	23	22	21	20	19

1.20 Cinema attendances have shown something of a recovery, according to market research. Consider the following data where the response is that for 'at least one cinema visit in the year'. The figures given are percentages.

Age group	1984	1986	1988	1990	1992
7–14	73	87	84	85	90
15–24	59	82	81	87	88
25–34	49	65	64	79	70
35–44	45	60	61	70	70
45 and over	13	25	34	41	39
All age groups	38	53	56	64	61

Comment on the data.

1.4 Sources of Data

Annual Abstract of Statistics, Central Statistical Office, HMSO.
Eurostat Review 1976–85.
General Household Statistics, Office of Population, Censuses and Surveys, HMSO.
A.H. Halsey, *British Social Trends since 1900*, Macmillan, Basingstoke, 1988.
R.M. Harrison (ed.), *Understanding our Environment: an Introduction to Environmental Chemistry and Pollution*, Cambridge University Press, Cambridge, 1992.
Manpower Services Commission, *Outlook on Training*, 1990.
B.R. Mitchell, *International Historical Statistics: Europe 1750–1988*, Macmillan, Basingstoke, 1992.
National Road Traffic Forecasts (UK), HMSO.
New Motor Vehicle Registrations (monthly from Department of Transport).
'Packets Project': *The Fast Track* (US Mathematics Project).

2 Setting up Models

2.1 Background

The purpose of modelling is to solve real practical problems, and this means that we must understand from the outset exactly what problem we are trying to solve. Successful mathematical modelling depends on getting things right from the start, and, as in most other scientific endeavours, we are more likely to succeed if we adopt a methodical approach. In most cases it is found useful to complete the following steps:

1. Clarify the problem.
2. List the factors.
3. List the assumptions.
4. Formulate a precise problem statement.

Clarifying the Problem

Essentially, a problem will be proposed, often by a non-mathematician, or indeed a non-scientist, and a particular answer requested from the model outcome, the answer often to be interpreted in non-mathematical terms.

The exact nature of the problem must be understood clearly before a start is made.

A specific objective can then be identified. As mathematical modellers we must resist getting stuck into the mathematical formulation before this step has been achieved. Misunderstandings will be very costly if there is a failure to carry out a preliminary investigation first and the wrong problem is modelled and 'solved'.

Establishing the true nature of the problem involves asking a number of questions. No matter how simple the situation appears, it will be worthwhile to ask questions of the problem provider to establish what is needed from the subsequent model:

- Who is intending to use the model – how much sophistication and complexity are needed?
- Is there an underlying physical/scientific behaviour to be taken into account?
- Is there data available or does it have to be collected or looked up?
- What underlying assumptions and simplifications about the problem can reasonably be made?
- When is the model 'solution' required – what time limits have been set?
- In what form is a solution wanted – written report, short oral presentation?
- Are there conflicting outcomes at stake, perhaps concerning the cost of implementing two different courses of action? (If so whose side are you on – who is paying whom?)

This last remark is quite important, as the essence of mathematical modelling in the real world is often to help answer *conflicts* between opposite viewpoints. For example, in the Post Office, when a large queue of customers forms and the cry goes up 'Why don't they open more service counters?', there is a conflict between the Post Office manager, who cannot afford to employ an abundance of staff due to wage budget limits, and the customer, who reasonably wants a fast service and will go elsewhere if patience is tried too far!

As mathematical modellers we must be clear what *we* can achieve before we launch into the above questions. What do we need to establish before starting on a model? We must appreciate both the scope and the limitations of modelling, and that we may have some powerful computing tools at our disposal with which a mathematical solution can be found. What must be established in discussion with the problem provider is exactly what we *can* deliver. This will involve pinning down specific objectives and removing vague or irrelevant features from the context, at least until a first model has been completed and explained to the provider.

Our wider objectives are to produce a model, probably using algebra and other mathematical tools, which is sufficiently general that it can be reused for other similar situations. Do not forget, however, that problem providers are usually less interested in general mathematical models than in particular answers to *their* problem, and the capability of the model in dealing with questions of the 'what if' type.

Listing the Factors   Every problem involves a number of different 'factors' which may have a bearing on the solution. At the early stage of model-building we need a *list* of these factors. In mathematical modelling we tend to concentrate mainly on *quantifiable* factors, i.e. those which can be given numerical values (in terms of suitable units). Quantifiable factors can normally be classified as **variables, parameters** or **constants**, and each of these can be **continuous, discrete** or **random**. Brief explanations of these categories are as follows:

- *Continuous*: takes all real values over an interval, e.g. time, velocity, length, cost (accepting values correct to 2 decimal places in £ sterling), area, etc. (Note that these quantities are measurements in some particular unit.)
- *Discrete*: takes on certain isolated values only. Very often these will be whole numbers (integers), e.g. the number of people, tickets, matches played etc., in which case there are no units of measurement.
- *Random*: unpredictable in advance, but governed by some underlying statistical model. For example, buses timed to arrive theoretically every 5 min but with actual random inter-arrival times with a *mean* of 5 min. The model can either be based on data (histogram) or assumed to be a particular theoretical form.
- *Constants*: quantities whose values we cannot change. These can be mathematical constants, such as π, or physical constants, such as acceleration due to gravity or the speed of light.
- *Parameters*: quantities which are constant for a particular application of a model, but can have different values for another application of the same model. For example, fixed costs in a simple business model, the dimensions of a room, price of a ticket, density of a fluid, mean inter-arrival time of a bus service.
- *Input variables*: quantities which determine subsequent evaluations within the model, such as rainfall rate into a collecting butt, the number of people attending a disco, the number of months elapsed before you sell your car etc. Note that an input variable is expected to be known, or given or assumed, or can be considered to have an arbitrary value.
- *Output variables*: quantities which are *consequences* of given values of input variables and parameters and cannot be given arbitrary values. These represent the *outcome* from a model, such as the profit made on a business deal, the level in a reservoir as a result of user demand and evaporation, the time taken for a certain number of people to evacuate a room.

(Note that some overlap occurs in this categorisation, since inputs/outputs can be continuous, discrete or random.)

In order to make the mathematical work easier, all the factors need to have suitable algebraic symbols assigned to them and some which represent measurements will need units (information concerning common units is given at the end of this chapter). To set up the list of factors we use the following headings:

Description	Type	Symbol	Units
For example: Speed	Input variable	V	$\mathrm{m\,s^{-1}}$

Listing Assumptions   While the factors provide the building blocks of the model, it is the assumptions which provide the glue with which to combine the factors together into a working model. How easy or difficult the model is to use and how successful it turns out to be depend very largely on what assumptions we make. The most common and important types of assumption that have to be made are:

(a) Assumptions about whether or not to include certain factors.
(b) Assumptions about the relative magnitudes of the effects of various factors.
(c) Assumptions about the forms of relationship between factors.

Generally speaking, and especially when developing a new model for the first time, we try to choose assumptions which keep the model as simple as possible. Assumptions of types (a) and (b) help to keep the list of factors from being longer than strictly necessary. Assumptions of type (c) could be said to represent the *heart* of the model. It is these that make possible further development of the model, as discussed in Chapter 3. Beware of *implicit* assumptions which you may have made without realising. Try to make sure that all assumptions are clearly listed.

Problem Statement   We will have already discussed our problem under the heading 'Clarifying the Problem' above. In most problems we can identify the following ingredients:

(a) Something is known or given.
(b) Something is to be found, estimated or decided.
(c) There is some condition to be satisfied or objective to achieve.

As a result of our considerations we should now be able to crystallise our thoughts into a precise *problem statement*, expressed in terms of the factors that we have listed under the heading 'Listing the Factors'. This statement will have the general form:

Given {inputs, parameters, constants} *find* {outputs} *such that* {condition is satisfied or objective achieved}.

This may look like an over-simplification, but in fact the vast majority of problems can be condensed into this precise form and it helps enormously in creating a model appropriate to the problem. Note that the *same* problem can have *different* problem statements, depending on what we consider to be *given* and what we want the model to *find*.

Summary   1. Clarify what is to be accomplished.
2. Draw up a list of all the factors to be used in building the model. For each factor, make a note of its type, give it a symbol and write down its units of measurement.
3. Make a list of all the assumptions to be made in constructing the model.
4. Formulate a precise problem statement of the form *Given* . . . *find* . . . .

2.2 Worked Examples

Ten examples are presented here. The context of each problem is explained and, where appropriate, a possible conflict of interest in the outcome is stated. A series of questions (Q) are posed that need to be answered before model formulation can commence. Factors (F) affecting the outcome are then listed, together with any assumptions made (A), and the problem statement (P) is given in words and in symbols. Some 'What if' questions are suggested in each case, perhaps leading to extensions of the model. Example 'answers' are provided if the resulting model is very simple.

2.1 Club Raffle   Context: a social club organises a raffle to be drawn at a suitable event. The outcome will contrast a possible large profit for the club *versus* attractive prizes for people who buy tickets.

Q: • Will all the tickets be sold at the same fixed price?
    • How many prizes will there be?

- What value will the prizes have?
- Are there any overhead costs that must be covered?
- If there is to be some flexibility in block purchase of tickets, what scheme is to operate?

F: We need to account for the price of tickets, the number sold, the cost of the prizes and a small overhead cost for the purchase of books of raffle tickets. The factor list can now be drawn up:

Description	Type	Symbol	Units
Price of a ticket	parameter	p	pence
Number of tickets sold	input variable	n	—
Cost of 1st prize	input variable	C_1	£
Cost of 2nd prize (etc.)	input variable	C_2	£
Total cost of prizes	input variable	C	£
Overhead costs	constant	O	£
Profit to organisers	output variable	P	£

A: Assume that all tickets are sold at the same price.

P: How many tickets must be sold before a profit is made? In terms of the above symbols this statement becomes: *Given p, C_1, $C_2 \ldots$, C, O find n* so that $P > 0$.

Solution $C = C_1 + C_2 + \cdots$ and $P = np/100 - (C + O)$. So in order for a profit to be made ($P > 0$), we need $n \geqslant 100(C + O)/p$.

What if:
(i) The ticket price is increased?
(ii) Some tickets are sold in bulk at a lower individual price?

2.2 Evacuation

Context: the amount of time required to evacuate a building or an aircraft when there is an emergency needs to be known by the local safety officer. Sufficient exits and passageways must be provided and this may contrast with the objective of a promoter who wants to carry as many people as can possibly be fitted in.

Q:
- What is the important statistic required?
- Can useful results be given for evacuating one room (or one section of an aircraft)?
- Are intermediate results needed, such as how many people are evacuated after 2 min, 5 min, ... etc.?
- What is the 'configuration' of the people before the alarm is raised?
- What data is available about maximum capacities?
- What are the architectural constraints to rapid exit, i.e. blockages, queues?

F: Confine attention to a single room for a first model and examine how a single chain of people will form up and exit the room. Factors included will be the number of people in the room, the speed of exit, the crowding of people as they leave and a time delay before the first person exits the room.

Description	Type	Symbol	Units
Number of people to be evacuated	parameter	N	—
Time elapsed after alarm raised	input variable	t	min
Number evacuated at time t	output variable	n	—
Total time to evacuate everyone	output variable	T	min
Spacing between exiting people	parameter	d	m
Speed of chain	parameter	v	$\mathrm{m\,s^{-1}}$
Initial delay before first person can exit	constant	t_0	min

A: Assume that the chain of people files out in an orderly manner so that both d and v (in the above factor list) are constant. Assume there are no constrictions within the room preventing an orderly file forming.

P: How many people will have exited in t min and how long will it take for everyone to evacuate (the most important statistic)? In symbols: *Given N, v, d, t_0 and t find n and T.*

Solution $n = 1 + 60v(t - t_0)/d$ and $T = t_0 + (N - 1)d/(60v)$

What if:

(i) Two or more exiting chains of people have to merge to continue their evacuation along a narrow corridor?

(ii) There are several exit points as in aircraft evacuation?

2.3 Order of Play

Context: you are called upon to organise the playing order for the tennis club's annual 'American' doubles tournament in which every pair is to play every other pair.

This is a slightly different sort of problem involving logistics. A simple pot-luck playing order may compare badly with players' requirements to have equally spaced matches for all participants.

Q: • How many pairs have entered?
     • How many tennis courts are available?
     • How long is each match to last (in games played)?
     • How many total hours can the event last?
     • Are there any constraints concerning rest time between matches?

F: Decide to make each match the same time length as far as is possible by making a match a fixed number of games long. Include this in the factor list, together with the number of pairs entering, the total time available for the tournament and so on.

Description	Type	Symbol	Units
Number of pairs entered	input variable	N	—
Total time available	parameter	T	hours
Time for a match	input variable	t_m	min
Number of courts	parameter	n	—
Time gap between matches	parameter	t_g	min
Total number of matches	output variable	M	—

A: Pairs do not worry about taking a rest between their matches.
    Each match takes the same time to complete.

P: *Given* that there are two courts and eight pairs, *find*

(a) how long it will take to complete the event and
(b) the order of matches.

Solution $M = {}^N C_2; \quad T = (t_m \times M/2)/60$

Any order will do as there are no restrictions. This does not inform on the *play order*, which needs careful planning even when there are only two courts. (Why?)

What if:

(i) There is a rule that no pair will play two matches in succession – can an order of play be worked out?
(ii) A pair suddenly withdraws?
(iii) The number of courts available is increased?

2.4 Potatoes

Context: is it better to buy large potatoes rather than small ones from the point of view of preparation time and loss of potato material due to peeling?

Q: • Are both sorts of potato from the same variety?
     • Does the subsequent cooking usage matter in deciding size of potato?
     • Is the price independent of the size of potato?
     • Will the peeling be carried out in the same way for all potatoes?
     • Is peeling small potatoes as easy as peeling large ones?
     • What is the overall objective here?

F: The factors listed include the weight and size of the potatoes, the thickness of the peel and the time taken in peeling. Potatoes are bought by weight, so the number you have must be calculated from the relative weights of the potatoes. The size of potato will matter and also how many you need for dinner and how long it takes to prepare a pot full. Not all the factors listed here are independent of one another.

Description	Type	Symbol	Units
Weight of bag of potatoes purchased	input parameter	W	kg
Weight of small potato	input parameter	w_s	g
Weight of large potato	input parameter	w_l	g
Number of small potatoes	output variable	n_s	—
Number of large potatoes	output variable	n_l	—
Diameter of a small potato	input parameter	d_s	cm
Diameter of a large potato	input parameter	d_l	cm
Time taken to peel a small potato	input parameter	T	s
Amount of small potatoes used for dinner	output variable	A_s	kg
Amount of large potatoes used for dinner	output variable	A_l	kg
Number of people for dinner	input variable	N	—
Time taken to fill the pot with small potatoes	output variable	t_s	min
Time taken to fill the pot with large potatoes	output variable	t_l	min

A: Assume that there is a typical size that defines large and small potatoes and that a given weight is bought of each for a trial to take place. Assume that the potato peeler used will be the same for all potatoes so that the peel thickness is constant. Assume that all potatoes can be taken as spherical in shape and that the densities of the potatoes are equivalent.

P: *Given* the number of people for dinner and that the guests have no special preference regarding small or large potatoes, *find* (a) how long it will take to prepare the pot before cooking and (b) how much of the original bag of potatoes will have been used. (There are two separate issues to be addressed here.)

What if:
(i)   Cooking time must be taken into account?
(ii) The peel thickness is different for the two sizes of potato?

2.5 Second-hand Car

Context: when is the best time to trade in a second-hand car and in return buy another?

Q: • What hire purchase options are available?
    • Over how many years will repayments be made?
    • What will the depreciation rate be in value of the car?
    • What is the main problem: lowest monthly repayment or advice on when it is best to resell the vehicle because of its depreciation?
    • Is the building up of replacement funds to be taken into account?

F: The depreciation of the vehicle can be based on data from the *Car Buyer's Guide*. Typical data on loan repayments can be supplied. The factor list must include all the quantities necessary for a financial plan to be drawn up.

Description	Type	Symbol	Units
Time length of loan	parameter	T	years
Total amount of loan	input variable	A	£
Interest rate charged	parameter	r	%
Amount owed after n years	output variable	P_n	£
Depreciation rate of vehicle	parameter	R	%
Value of vehicle at n years	output variable	V	£
Monthly saving amount	input variable	M	£
Annual interest rate on savings	input variable	R	%

A: Assume that inflationary effects can be ignored in a first model. Assume also that no unexpected events take place to upset the calculations (i.e. car crash, change in personal circumstances).

P: *Given* the outlay on a second-hand car, *find* (a) how much must be invested each month so that a replacement vehicle can be purchased in the future and (b) the optimum time to trade in the vehicle again and set up another purchase.

2.6 Drink Cans   Context: the ubiquitous cola can contains 330 ml, since this is reckoned to be an appropriate quantity for consumption at one meal. Why is the shape of the can normally as it is? What would be the outcome if the *minimum* amount of metal were used to construct the cylindrical can?

Q: This is related to the well-known problem of minimum container material for a given volume, but on examining a cola tin we notice that the metal top is of a different quality from the rest. The can is tapered at the top so that the standard metal top of given size can be fixed in. The cost of the metal top will be higher than the cost of metal for the rest of the can. What are the problem variables and what items are fixed beforehand?

F: Most of the factors listed will be to do with the geometry of the can. The cost factor concerning the rigid top piece will always be present and so does not form part of the problem.

Description	Type	Symbol	Units
Volume of the can	constant	V	ml
Base radius of the can	input variable	r	cm
Height of cylindrical part of can	input variable	h	cm
Radius of fixed top piece	constant	R	cm
Height of tapered part of can	input variable	x	cm
Surface area of metal	output variable	S	cm^2

A: Assume that the can is cylindrical and that the tapered part has the fixed top piece sitting on top. Assume the quantity S does not include the top piece, so this is the quantity to be minimised. The variables will therefore be r, h and x.

P: *Given* the volume of fluid to be contained, *find* the minimum amount of metal necessary to make a cylindrical can, *such that* there is a fixed top piece of given size that must always fit on.

What if:
(i) The mathematical solution is impractical for design?
(ii) There must be a certain minimum height value so that the can is easily held in the hand?

2.7 Bus Shelter   Context: a bus stop position has to be placed along a road in a new estate. There will be a covered shelter provided. Where should the stop be placed so that the maximum number of people will be encouraged to use the service? The bus company wants people to use the service, but cannot lay on buses 'on demand'.

Q: • Does it matter whether the road is straight?
     • Why not put up several bus stops along the road?
     • Is there any reason for the bus company not to put the stop half-way along the road?
     • Does the *shelter* have any significance on the decision?
     • Does the frequency of service matter in making the decision?
     • Are there alternative sources of transport nearby?

F: The factors to be listed can include details about the road and its houses, the bus company timetable, cost of bus shelters and so on.

Description	Type	Symbol	Units
Length of the road	input variable	L	m
Number of houses	input variable	N	—
Number of people per house	input parameter	p	—
Distance of shelter from one end of the road	input variable	x	m
Spacing of houses along road	input parameter	s	m
Distance walked by people to the bus shelter	output variable	d	m
Capacity of typical bus	input parameter	C	—
Frequency of bus arrivals	input parameter	T	min

A: Assume that only one bus shelter will be erected. Assume that crossing the road to reach the bus stop does not significantly affect the distance walked by customers. Suppose that the bus capacity and timetable are not important factors.

P: *Given* a certain road length and density of housing, *find* where the bus stop should be placed *so that* the distance walked to reach it is minimised.

This is quite a restricted problem statement; a more difficult situation arises when some of the 'what if' features are included.

What if:
(i)   Two bus stops are introduced?
(ii) The bus company wants to plan for rush-hour demand and shelter size?
(iii) Crossing the road does matter and can only be affected at some pedestrian crossing?

2.8 Cable Winding

Context: industrial cable such as that used for telecommunications is initially wound around a large holder. It will be laid out linearly underground alongside other utilities such as gas and water pipes. How much cable can be stored on a holder of given size? Here there is no special controversy to be weighed; the problem is to be able to analyse how cable can be wrapped around the holder core in the most efficient manner. Similar situations occur in any 'roll' problem, from kitchen rolls to carpets, although here we have a winding situation as well as a roll situation.

Q: Will the cable be rolled on to the holder in a neat manner? Is there just one type of cable involved?

F: Factors to be listed will include the dimensions of the holder, and the thickness and length of cable.

Description	Type	Symbol	Units
Inner diameter of holder	input parameter	d_1	m
Outer diameter of holder	input parameter	d_2	m
Length of stem of holder	input parameter	l	m
Thickness of cable	input variable	x	cm
Length of wound cable in single wind	output variable	y	m
Distance between two adjacent lateral cable winds	output variable	s	cm
Total length of stored cable in holder	output variable	L	m

A: Assume that the cable is wrapped neatly to provide a compact wind. Assume also that the cable is of circular cross-section and so fits into the packing as it is wound on.

P: *Given* the dimensions of a large wooden holder and the thickness of a cable, *find* the length of cable that can be compactly wound onto the holder *such that* the fit is as tight and neat as possible.

This is a well-defined problem, albeit somewhat difficult. What if the scene is changed to winding cotton onto a bobbin?

2.9 Lifts

Context: there never seems to be a lift waiting for use in a tall university building. When one is available at last, there are always some people who only want to go as far as the first or second floor, whereas you are anxious to reach the top floor for an important mathematics class. All the lifts currently operate on the basis of stopping at any time at any floor. You initiate an enquiry to make at least some of the lifts go non-stop to a high floor.

Q: ● Are all the floors equally in demand?
    ● What alternative method is available to reach the upper floors?
    ● Would the non-stop lift be non-stop down as well as up?
    ● Can a change of setting be easily carried out by the lift company?

F: There is a *random* element in this problem, since at any typical time, a sample of waiting people will contain a mixture of customers for all floors. A *probability distribution* is needed to reflect the demand for every floor, and the outcome will have to be *simulated* to obtain a true comparison between the current situation and the proposed alternative, where at least one lift is fast.

A: Assume that there is a large group waiting for the lifts on the ground floor. Collect data on the customer demand and assume that the floor required by the customers can be represented as a probability distribution in histogram form. Assume that the time spent stationary at some higher floor is constant while people get out. To produce a *first* model outcome, assume that no-one gets on at an intermediate floor and the lifts come straight down when empty. Assume for simplicity that there are only two lifts, one slow and one fast.

Description	Type	Symbol	Units
Number of floors in the building	input parameter	N	—
Number of lifts	input parameter	L	—
Capacity of a lift	input parameter	C	—
Time taken for lift to travel one floor	constant	t_1	s
Time taken for lift to travel n floors	constant	t_n	s
Time spent at each floor by a lift	constant	T	s
Number of people waiting at the ground floor for a lift	input variable	P	—
Floor to which a fast lift will travel	input variable	m	—

P: *Given* that there are two lifts, one slow and one fast, and *given* a certain demand by customers to reach higher floors, *find* by simulation methods whether *all* the customers can reach their destinations quicker compared with the situation when both lifts call at all floors.

What if:
(i)   The fast service is available downwards as well as up?
(ii) The floor to which a lift is fast is varied between several lifts?

2.10 Student Loans

Context: most students have to borrow money to survive at college now that maintenance grants have been cut. Leaflets provide information to a student on the terms of the loan. The amount that can be borrowed is kept low and the repayment interest is also low since the scheme is intended to be cheaper to finance than an alternative from a High Street bank.

Q: ● How much can be borrowed for a three-year course?
    ● When and how is the loan paid off?
    ● How many years' worth of loan are permitted?

(These questions and many others are answered by the Student Loans Company Ltd, 100 Bothwell St, Glasgow G2 7JD, but for mathematical modellers there is interest in setting up the general model.)

F: Factors listed will include the amount of the loan, the number of successive years required, repayment terms and so on. The loan leaflet states that the scheme allows for a period of five years for normal repayment, starting in the April after completion of the course. Currently (September 1994), the daily interest rate is stated to be 0.006 235 902% and the APR is 2.3%. Can this be checked?

Description	Type	Symbol	Units
Amount of the loan per year	input variable	P	£
Number of years a loan is taken	input variable	n	—
Date of start of repayments	constant	—	—
Time period for repayment	input parameter	T	months
Interest rate of scheme per annum	input parameter	r	%
Total amount paid back	output variable	A	£

P: *Given P, n, T and r find A.*

What if:
(i)   Repayments are calculated over a longer time period?
(ii) You get behind with the repayments?
(iii) You are unemployed after graduation and the debt builds up?

2.3 Exercises

2.1 For each of the following, draw up a list of questions that need to be dealt with before modelling can commence. Imagine you are the mathematical modeller writing to a company technical manager for more details, or perhaps you are just trying to rationalise a household DIY decision.

(a) A new television is required. Would it be better policy to rent a TV, or should complete purchase be arranged?
(b) Deep freeze purchase: will it be cost effective over a long period of time?
(c) Postman's route: which is the way to go along some designated

street network so that deliveries can be completed in the shortest time?

(d) Travel to work by train: which is the most cost effective way to travel, bearing in mind possible season ticket purchase?
(e) Free-fall parachute drop: when should the parachute be opened so that a soft safe landing is ensured?
(f) Forestry management: trees are planted and later cut and sold for timber; what is the best replanting policy to maintain a steady state?
(g) Car park layout: optimise layout required to maximise the number of users.
(h) College disco: examine the profitability of running a disco, bearing in mind the costs of setting up the event against the expected revenue generated by ticket sales.
(i) Warehouse siting: a new supermarket chain sets up in several towns and needs a service depot within easy reach of all the shops. Where should the depot be sited?
(j) Reservoir siting: water supply needs to be radically increased in certain parts of a country, due to drought. What are the problems in respect of supply of water, demand, loss from the reservoir and so on?

2.2 For each of the following everyday situations make a list of relevant factors:

(a) Taking a photograph
(b) Making wine
(c) Mixing concrete
(d) Planning a dinner party
(e) Choosing a holiday
(f) Buying a car

2.3 For each of the following (i) clarify the question, (ii) make a list of factors, identify their type and suggest suitable units, and (iii) formulate a precise problem statement.

(a) How many cars can get through a traffic junction on a green light?
(b) What is the best angle at which to throw a javelin?
(c) How often should a lawn be mown?
(d) How far apart should trees be planted?
(e) How far apart should lampposts be placed along a street?
(f) What is the best size for bicycle wheels?
(g) How long should a traffic light be on red?

2.4 Formulate each of the following questions in terms of things that can be *measured*. What data would you collect and how? What assumptions would you make in attempting to derive an answer?

(a) How many cars will be on the roads of the UK in the year 2020?
(b) How much violence do young children see on TV?
(c) Are men stronger than women?
(d) What is the average wage in this country at present?
(e) Is there a connection between poverty and crime?

2.5 Estimate each of the following and in each case make a list of the assumptions that you made in arriving at your estimate.

(a) The average age of the next 10 cars you see.
(b) The total leaf area of a tree.
(c) The amount of money you will spend during the next year.

2.6 For each of the following draw up lists of factors and assumptions and formulate precise problem statements in terms of the factors.

(a) *Interior decorating*
Context: we want to minimise the cost of decorating a room *balanced against* quality of wallpaper used and time taken.
(b) *Maximum motorway speed*
Context: in heavy traffic on a motorway, the authorities need to place warning signs for drivers. These warnings can either state the maximum safe speed or minimum closing distance (marked by painted 'chevrons' on the road surface). Which type of warning is best and what exactly should the warning say?
(c) *Crossing the road*
Context: the local authorities are debating whether to install a pelican crossing system outside the university on a busy road.
(d) *Windscreen wiper*
Context: the rear windows of most vehicles have a single wiper blade. What is the best design for the operation of the blade?

2.4 Units

The recommended scientific system of units is the SI system. This has seven basic units with accepted symbols as follows.

Quantity	Unit	Symbol
Length	metre	m
Mass	kilogram	kg
Time	second	s
Electric current	ampere	A
Temperature	kelvin	K
Luminous intensity	candela	cd
Amount of substance	mole	mol

Take care to use the correct symbols; a time of ten seconds, for example, can be abbreviated to 10 s (*not* 10 sec or 10 secs) and stick to lower or upper case letters as appropriate.

There are other commonly used units which are combinations of the above and have been given their own names and symbols.

Quantity	Unit	Symbol
Force	newton	$N (kg\,m\,s^{-2})$
Energy	joule	$J (kg\,m^2\,s^{-2})$
Power	watt	$W (J\,s^{-1}$ or $kg\,m^2\,s^{-3})$
Frequency	hertz	$Hz (s^{-1})$
Pressure	pascal	$Pa (N\,m^{-2}$ or $kg\,m^{-1}\,s^{-2})$

Note the use of positive and negative indices where a combination of units is involved and that a negative index is preferred to '/'. There are also some non-SI units which are in common use by scientists and engineers of which the main ones are given below.

Quantity	Unit	Symbol
Area	hectare	$ha (= 10^4\,m^2)$
Volume	litre	$l (= 10^{-3}\,m^3)$
Temperature	degree Celsius	$°C (0\,°C \approx 273\,K)$
Mass	tonne	$t (= 10^3\,kg)$
Energy	kilowatt hour	$kW\,h (= 3.6 \times 10^6\,J)$
Energy	calorie	$cal (= 4.1868\,J)$
Pressure	bar	$bar (= 10^5\,Pa)$

For large or small multiples of the basic SI units we use prefixes based on powers of 10 whose names and symbols are given below.

Factor	Prefix	Symbol
10^{12}	tera	T
10^{9}	giga	G
10^{6}	mega	M
10^{3}	kilo	k
10^{-2}	centi	c
10^{-3}	milli	m
10^{-6}	micro	μ
10^{-9}	nano	n

To convert between SI units and the old British Imperial units use the following conversion factors.

Starting from $\longrightarrow$	Multiply by $\longrightarrow$	To get
inch	2.54	cm
foot	0.304 8	m
mile	1.609 344	km
square foot (ft^2)	0.092 903 04	m^2
cubic foot (ft^3)	0.028 316 85	m^3
UK gallon (gal)	$4.546\ 09 \times 10^{-3}$	m^3
pound mass (lb)	0.453 592 37	kg
pound force (lbf)	4.448 22	N
ton (2240 lb)	1016.047	kg
mile per hour (m.p.h.)	0.447 04	$m\,s^{-1}$
pound per square inch (p.s.i.)	$6.894\ 757 \times 10^3$	Pa
British Thermal Unit (Btu)	$1.055\ 06 \times 10^3$	J
therm	105.506	MJ
horsepower (hp)	745.7	W
degree (° angle)	0.017 453 3	rad
revolution per min (r.p.m.)	0.104 720	$rad\,s^{-1}$
pressure in mm Hg	133.322	$N\,m^{-2}$
pressure in std. atmos.	1.013 25	bar
To get $\longleftarrow$	Divide by $\longleftarrow$	From

3 Developing Models

3.1 Background

In Chapter 2, having represented our variables by symbols we then made assumptions about how our variables behaved, or were related to each other. An essential part of the modelling process is to **translate** such verbal statements into precise mathematical relationships between the symbols. These mathematical statements then become amenable to manipulation by mathematical techniques.

Verbal statements are sometimes vague and there may be a selection of possible equivalent mathematical statements. For example, the verbal statement 'as x goes up, y goes up' can be modelled mathematically in many ways. The simplest model is obtained by assuming that y is directly proportional to x. The equivalent mathematical statement is then $y \propto x$, or as an equation, $y = kx$ where k is the constant of proportionality. By choosing this particular mathematical statement we are making a very clear assumption, which may well be criticised. A graph of y against x showing a straight line through the origin would be the ultimate justification.

The next simplest model is the linear form $y = ax + b$ in which we are saying that y increases by 'a' units for every unit increase in x and that $y = b$ when $x = 0$. This also includes the case where y *decreases* as x increases. In that case the parameter a is negative (the gradient of the straight line graph). Another simple way of modelling the statement 'y decreases as x increases' is by inverse proportion, i.e. $y \propto 1/x$ or $y = k/x$. This makes y decrease more steeply with x than is the case in the linear model. One way of testing the validity of this assumption would be to check whether xy remains nearly constant. Another way is to see if the plot of $\ln y$ against $\ln x$ is a straight line of slope -1. A well-known example from physics is Boyle's Law, which expresses the connection between the volume (V), pressure (P) and temperature (T) of a fixed mass of gas. The equation is $PV = RT$, where R is a constant. From this it can be seen that if T is kept constant then $V \propto 1/P$ and $P \propto 1/V$, while if V is kept constant then $T \propto P$, for example.

More general models can be created using the form $y = kx^a$, which gives convex curves for values of the parameter $a > 1$ and concave curves for $a < 1$. In biology, the relationship between the sizes of various parts of an organism can often be represented by such non-linear models. When there are several variables and y is assumed to be proportional to each of them, i.e. $y \propto x_1$ and $y \propto x_2$ and $y \propto x_3$ for example, then these combine into the single model $y = kx_1x_2x_3$. (Note the multiplication here.) In Boyle's Law for example, T is proportional to both P and V, i.e. $T \propto PV$.

As was the case in the above examples, mathematical translations of verbal statements are often **equations**. Sometimes they can also be **inequalities**, such as $x < 5$. When a number of inequalities apply simultaneously, the easiest way of studying the implications is by plotting graphs and looking for regions where all the inequalities are satisfied.

Not all verbal statements are as vague as 'when x goes up, y goes up'. Sometimes the verbal statement is perfectly clear and precise, but just happens to be expressed in words. Once we have translated it into symbols, however, it becomes amenable to all the tools of mathematical analysis. After the translation has been carried out there may also be some algebraic manipulation required to change the equation into a more useful form. If it seems difficult to carry out the translation using symbols, it may be found helpful to try an example with numbers first. Some exercises in the basic skills of algebraic manipulation are given at the end of this chapter, in addition to exercises in mathematical translation.

Note that the values of constants and parameters appearing in an equation have usually to be found by fitting the model to data (see Chapter 12). Note, also, that it matters what units of measurement are used for the variables. Suppose for example that a model predicts the daily growth rate (r) of grass (in g m^{-2} day^{-1}) to be $r = 0.05x - 0.000\,039x^2$ when the grass bio-density is $x\,(\text{g m}^{-2})$. If we are dealing with x values between 100 and 1000 it might be more convenient to measure x in units of 100 g m^{-2} day^{-1}. In effect, this would be like changing to a new variable $y = x/100$, with y lying between 1 and 10, and the model could be rewritten

$$r = 0.05(100y) - 0.000\,039(100y)^2 = 5y - 0.39y^2.$$

Generally speaking, if a variable z ranges from 0 to $z_{\max}$ it may be convenient to change to a new variable $w = z/z_{\max}$ which will go from 0 to 1. This is especially useful when we want to plot several graphs together using the same axes.

Summary   As part of the modelling process we need to:

- Represent variables by mathematical **symbols**
- Make **assumptions** about how the variables are related
- **Translate** the assumptions into mathematical equations or inequalities.

When choosing symbols we usually use single letters and, as often as possible, the first letter of the name of the variable, such as t for time. It is also traditional to use Greek letters, such as α, β, θ and ϕ, for angles.

When making assumptions, we choose the simplest versions which seem likely to reflect the behaviour of the real variables. If we later realise that we have made an over-simplification, then a revised model will be necessary.

When making the translation the following simple forms may be useful to remember. More complex forms can often be broken down into combinations of these.

Verbal statement	Mathematical equivalent
Sum/total	$+$
Difference between/change in	$-$
Less than	$<$
Greater than	$>$
At least	$\geqslant$
Not more than	$\leqslant$
Ratio	$/$
y proportional to x	$y = kx$
y inversely proportional to x	$y = k/x$
y is x% of z	$y = (x/100)z$
y is x% more than z	$y = (1 + x/100)z$
Rate of change of y with time, t	dy/dt

Note that some care is needed with the words 'difference' and 'ratio'. The difference between A and B may mean $A - B$ or it may mean the *size* of the difference between them, i.e. $A - B$ when $A > B$, but $B - A$ when $A < B$. These two can be combined into the single expression $|A - B|$. Similarly 'the ratio of A to B' could be interpreted as A/B or B/A.

Note also that 'an increase of x' translates to '$+x$', while 'an increase of z%' translates to 'multiply by $(1 + z/100)$'. Similarly, 'a decrease of w%' is equivalent to 'multiply by $(1 - w/100)$'.

3.2 Worked Examples

3.1   Translate the following statements into symbols.

(a) Profit is the difference between Sales and Costs, and Profitability is the Profit expressed as a percentage of the Costs.

(b) X is less than 3 times the difference between Y and Z.

(c) The difference between A and B is at least one more than the sum of the squares of C and D.

Solution   (a) Using obvious symbols, $P = S - C$ and Profitability is $(P/C) \times 100\%$

(b) $X < 3|Y - Z|$

(c) $|A - B| \geqslant 1 + C^2 + D^2$

3.2   An item is priced at £P and a shop sells Q of these items every week. The shop manager estimates that for every £1 reduction in price, N more items would be sold every week. According to this assumption, what will be (a) the number sold per week and (b) the weekly revenue when the price is £X?

Solution   For each £1 reduction we sell N more items. Therefore, for a reduction of $P - X$ we sell $N(P - X)$ more items. It follows that (a) the number sold when the price is X is $Q + N(P - X)$, and (b) the corresponding revenue is $[Q + N(P - X)]X$.

3.3   A bath takes 3 minutes to fill and 4 minutes to empty. How long does it take to fill the bath with the plug out? What is the answer if it takes F minutes to fill and E minutes to empty?

Solution   In one minute the taps supply one third of a bath-full while one quarter of a bath-full goes down the drain. The net result is that in one minute we get $1/3 - 1/4 = 1/12$ of a bath-full, so it will take 12 minutes to fill the bath.

In the general case, the equivalent calculation is $1/F - 1/E$ in one minute, so the number of minutes it takes to fill the bath is $1/(1/F - 1/E) = FE/(E - F)$ *provided* that $E > F$!

3.4   If n_1 workers take t_1 days to complete a certain job:

(a) How long will it take n_2 workers to do the same job?

(b) How many workers are needed to complete the job in t_2 days?

Solution   The 'work content' of the job is $n_1 t_1$ worker-days. With n_2 workers it will therefore take t_2 days, where $n_2 t_2 = n_1 t_1$ from which we find that the answer to part (a) is $t_2 = n_1 t_1 / n_2$.

From the same equation, by rearrangement, we find that the answer to (b) is $n_2 = n_1 t_1 / t_2$, *except* that this may not come out to be an integer, which n_2 has to be! We obviously want the nearest integer above, so that if, for example, $n_1 t_1 / t_2$ comes out to be 4.3, we will take $n_2 = 5$ workers. The standard function INT takes the integer part of a real number, for example INT[4.3] = 4. We can get the answer we want by writing $n_2 = 1 + \text{INT}[n_1 t_1 / t_2]$. This will work except when $n_1 t_1 / t_2$ happens to be an integer, in which case it gives us one too many.

3.5   Suppose you are faced with choosing between two queues at a supermarket checkout. In Queue 1 there are m_1 customers, all with n_1 items in their baskets, while in Queue 2 there are m_2 customers, all with n_2 items. If it takes t seconds to process each item and p seconds for each person to pay, write down the condition for Queue 1 to be the better queue to join.

Solution   The time it takes one customer in Queue 1 to pay for his or her items is $p + n_1 t$. The total time it will take for all the customers in Queue 1 to progress through the checkout is therefore $m_1(p + n_1 t)$. There is a similar expression for Queue 2, so the condition for you to reach the front of the queue faster in Queue 1 is

$$m_1(p + n_1 t) < m_2(p + n_2 t)$$

3.6   An ice cream seller at a summer fair estimates that the number of ice creams sold in a day will be:

(a) Proportional to the number of people attending the fair.

(b) Proportional to the temperature in excess of 10 °C.

(c) Inversely proportional to the selling price of the ice creams.

Combine these assumptions into a model for predicting the number of ice creams sold.

Solution   Let $N =$ the number of ice creams sold

        $n =$ the number of people attending

        $T =$ the temperature (°C)

        $p =$ the price of one ice cream.

The above assumptions can then be represented by $N \propto n$, $N \propto (T - 10)$ and $N \propto 1/p$. To combine these into one model we **multiply** the proportionalities. This finally produces the model $N = kn(T - 10)/p$, or $N = \text{INT}[kn(T - 10)/p]$, since N has to be an integer.

Note:

(i)   The model gives $N = 0$ when $n = 0$, as required, and $N = 0$ when $T = 10$ in accordance with assumption (b).

(ii) The model is valid for $T \geqslant 10$ only.

3.7   A mass M_m of cold milk at temperature T_m is added to a mass M_c of hot coffee at temperature T_c. What is the temperature of the coffee immediately afterwards?

Solution   The principle we use here is the conservation of energy. The amount of heat energy contained by a body of mass M at temperature T is McT, where c is the specific heat capacity of the material from which the body is made. If we assume the same value of c for both milk and coffee, then before mixing, the energies of the milk and coffee are $M_m c T_m$ and $M_c c T_c$ respectively. Afterwards, if the mixture has a temperature T its energy is $(M_m + M_c)cT$. Equating this to the sum of the separate energies before mixing, we get

$$(M_m + M_c)cT = M_m c T_m + M_c c T_c$$

so

$$T = (M_m T_m + M_c T_c)/(M_m + M_c)$$

is the required answer.

3.8   A retailer sells an amount D of a certain item every year and his maximum stock level is Q_M. At certain times he places an order with the manufacturer for Q_M more items. These are delivered just in time to avoid running out of stock, bringing his stock level up to Q_M again. Each delivery costs C_O in administration, transport and other charges and takes L days (lead time) to arrive. Stock holding costs are C_H per item per year. Write down expressions for:

(a) The number of deliveries per year.

(b) The time T (days) between deliveries.

(c) The stock level $Q(t)$ at time t (days) after the last delivery.

(d) The time of placing the next order.

(e) The reorder point (the stock level at the time when the next order is made).

(f) The total annual cost C_{TOT} (stockholding plus reordering).

Solution   (a) If there are n deliveries per year then $nQ_M = D$ so $n = D/Q_M$.

(b) If there are n deliveries per year then the time between them is $T = 1/n = Q_M/D$ (years) $= 365Q_M/D$ (days).

(c) $Q(t) = Q_M - tQ_M/T$ gives $Q(0) = Q_M$ and $Q(T) = 0$ as required, so the required model is $Q(t) = Q_M - tD/365$.

(d) The next order must be placed at time $t = T - L = 365Q_M/D - L$ (days).

(e) The stock level at the time of reordering is $Q(T - L) = Q_M - (365Q_M/D - L)D/365 = LD/365$.

(f) $C_{TOT} =$ stockholding costs $+$ ordering costs

           $= C_H \times$ average stock level $+ C_0 \times$ number of orders per year

           $= C_H Q_M/2 + C_O D/Q_M$.

3.9   Rival supermarkets enter into a price war over the price of cat food. Supermarket A drops its price and as a result the daily sales volume of supermarket B is changed by an amount proportional to:

(i)   The difference between B's price and A's price.

(ii) The difference between B's price and the recommended retail price.

(iii) The difference between A's price and the recommended retail price.

Construct a model for the new sales volume of supermarket B.

Solution Let:

$$V = \text{daily sales volume of B before the price war}$$
$$x \,(\text{pence}) = \text{the new price per tin at A}$$
$$y \,(\text{pence}) = \text{the new price per tin at B}$$
$$p \,(\text{pence}) = \text{the normal recommended price per tin}$$

We can write down the new sales volume of B, say V_{NEW}, as

$$V_{\text{NEW}} = V - k_1(y - x) - k_2(y - p) - k_3(p - x)$$

The ks are proportionality constants: k_1, for example, is the change in daily sales at B resulting from each penny difference between the prices at A and B. Note that the model is **additive** with respect to the proportionalites, unlike Example 3.6. It can be useful to examine special cases; for example, if $y = x$ the model gives

$$V_{\text{NEW}} = V - k_2(x - p) - k_3(p - x)$$
$$= V - (k_2 - k_3)(x - p)$$

What matters now is the relative importance of (ii) and (iii). It is likely that (ii) is more important than (iii), so $k_3 < k_2$ which means that if A's price is reduced further below the recommended retail price then we get a net **increase** from V to V_{NEW}, as we would expect.

3.10 An increase in the level of tax on cigarettes will bring in *extra* tax revenue, but on the other hand it could lead to a reduction in the number of cigarettes sold, which could mean *less* revenue. Suppose we make the following assumptions:

(a) At present, N packets of cigarettes are sold every day and there is a tax t on each packet.
(b) The reduction in the number of cigarettes smoked is proportional to the increase in price.

If the tax is increased by x pence per packet, what is the limit on the value of x if the increase is to be worthwhile from the point of view of the Chancellor of the Exchequer? What is the answer if assumption (b) is replaced by:

(c) There is a constant percentage decrease in cigarette smoking for each penny rise in the price of a packet?

Which model is likely to be more realistic?

Solution Using assumptions (a) and (b), before the tax rise we have N packets sold every day with a tax t on each. After the rise the tax on each packet changes to $t + x$ and the number of packets sold every day changes to $N - kx$, where k is some constant. (We are assuming that the price rise is all tax.) The difference in tax revenue every day is therefore

$$(N - kx)(t + x) - Nt = x[N - k(t + x)]$$

which will be positive if $N > k(t + x)$. This is equivalent to the condition $x < N/k - t$.

Using assumption (c) instead of (b), let $r\%$ be the percentage reduction. Note that this does *not* mean that if the tax is increased by, say, 10 pence, the reduction will be $10r\%$. The correct expression for the number of packets sold when the tax is increased by x pence is $(1 - r/100)^x N$. The effects of the two assumptions (b) and (c) are compared in Fig. 3.1.

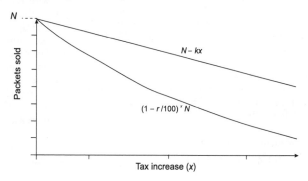

Figure 3.1

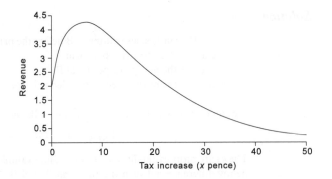

Figure 3.2

After the tax rise we now have $(1 - r/100)^x N$ packets sold daily with tax $(t + x)$ on each so the net difference in the daily tax revenue is $(1 - r/100)^x N(t + x) - Nt = [(1 - r/100)^x(t + x) - t]$. This will be > 0 if $(1 - r/100)^x(t + x) > t$. The graph of the function $(1 - r/100)^x(t + x)$ is shown in Fig. 3.2 for the case $r = 10$, $t = 2$. It seems to indicate that x could go up to about 25 before the net revenue drops.

The graphs in Fig. 3.1 indicate that for a certain level of increase x the assumption (b) predicts that the number of packets sold will become zero. This is probably less realistic than the gradual diminution predicted by model (c).

3.3 Exercises

3.1 Translate the following statements into symbols:

(a) Y is 5 units greater than X.
(b) The difference between Y and X is 2.
(c) The ratio of Y to X is 2.
(d) The difference between A and B is three times the ratio of C to D.
(e) Y is 5% of X.
(f) Y is 5% greater than X.
(g) Y is 5% less than X.
(h) Y is less than 5% of X.
(i) Y differs from X by at least 10.
(j) Y is always at least 50% greater than X.
(k) W is proportional to the square of the difference between X and Y.
(l) W is inversely proportional to the square root of the difference between U and the sum of V and X.
(m) Variable y added to variable x gives an amount which is 20% greater than variable z.
(n) X is not more than ninety per cent of the size of Y.
(o) The sum of a and b is proportional to the difference between the squares of x and y.
(p) The product of a and b is inversely proportional to the square of the difference between x and y.

3.2 Which is the bigger price reduction, (a) a 30% cut or (b) a 20% cut followed by a 10% cut?

3.3 A child says, 'Think of a number, double it, add ten, divide by two, take away the number you first thought of and the answer is five'. Put this into symbols and so explain how the trick works.

3.4 Translate the following into *symbols*: Albert weighs more than Beverley and Beverley weighs more than twice Caroline's weight. Albert and Caroline together weigh more than Beverley, and Caroline is 35 kg lighter than Albert.

3.5 Translate the following into *words*:
(a) $\sqrt{(ab)} = |x - y^2|$ (b) $q \propto 1/(x^2 + y^2)$

3.6 How many words are there in a book of P pages if each page has L lines and each line has W words?

3.7 How long will your money last if you have £N now, spend £S every week and you have an income of £Q ($< S$) per week?

3.8 Express the following statements using symbols.

(a) The intensity of illumination decreases with the square of the distance from a lamp.
(b) The frequency of vibration of a mass suspended by a vertical spring attached to a fixed point is inversely proportional to the square root of the mass.
(c) The mass of a planet is proportional to its density and to the cube of its radius.
(d) The gravitational force between two masses (M_1 and M_2) is directly proportional to their masses and inversely proportional to the square of the distance (x) between them.

3.9 Express the following as simply as possible using equations:

(a) The more money (M) you have, the more you spend (S).
(b) The time (T) of a journey decreases if you increase your speed (V).
(c) If a fixed amount of prize money is shared equally between x members of a team how does each person's share (S) vary with x?
(d) As the price (P) of an item increases, the demand (D) decreases.
(e) The time (T) it takes to dig a hole of a given size decreases with the number (N) of men who are doing the digging.
(f) The more you practise (P) the less time (T) it takes you to swim one length of a pool.
(g) The number (N) of shopping trips made to a shopping centre by people living a distance x from the centre (i) decreases as x increases and (ii) increases as the size (S) of the centre increases.

3.10 An item in a shop sale is marked 'X% off'. If the sale price is £S what was the original price?

3.11 How much paint (in litres) is needed to paint a wall x metres high and y metres wide containing a window of height h and width w if one litre of paint covers A m^2? How many cans are needed if one can contains L litres of paint?

3.12 A car goes from A to B, which is a distance of x_{AB} miles, in t_{AB} minutes, then from B to C, a distance of x_{BC} miles, in t_{BC} minutes. What was the average speed in m.p.h. for the whole journey?

3.13 If cars pass a certain point at an average rate of M cars per minute, what is the average time between cars in seconds?

3.14 If interest is paid at $x\%$ per annum how long will it take an investment to double itself?

3.15 A car does m miles per gallon of petrol at a speed of s m.p.h. How fast is it using up petrol (in gallons per hour)? If its petrol consumption is L litres per 100 km, what is the connection between L and m?

3.16 A motorist travels from A to B at a constant speed S_1 (m.p.h.) and does the return journey from B to A at a constant speed S_2 (m.p.h.). What is the average speed in m s^{-1} for the whole journey?

3.17 Observations show that the distance moved by a fish for one beat of its tail is nearly always the same fraction of its body length. Convert this statement into a relation between tail beat rate T (beats per second), length L and speed V.

3.18 Divide £M between two people:

(a) so that one gets x times the other,
(b) so that one gets £x more than the other.

3.19 Given the following statement: 'For every five miles per hour of speed over fifty a car does one mile less per gallon of petrol', write down a formula for the miles per gallon when the speed is s (m.p.h.) if you get 40 m.p.g. when the speed is 50 m.p.h.

3.20 The cost of electricity includes a standing quarterly charge and a charge for each unit used. The electricity supply company is considering reducing the standing charge by £s and increasing the cost per unit by c (pence) so that the amount to be paid for the first 1000 units remains the same. What is the connection between s and c?

3.21 Using the notation of Worked Example 3.8, translate the information given in each of (a) and (b) below into symbols by writing down appropriate values or expressions for C_O, C_H, D and C_{TOT}.

(a) A newspaper publisher uses 8000 rolls of paper each year at a cost of £600 per roll. The cost of holding stocks of these rolls is 10% per annum of the value of the stock held. Each order of fresh supplies involves an additional cost of £100.
(b) A manufacturer uses 50 000 kg of a certain chemical every year. Stockholding costs are 8% of the value of the stock, per year. The chemical costs £10 per kg and transport and delivery costs consist of £160 per delivery plus £0.50 per kg of chemical delivered.

3.22 You are organising a meeting and the room costs £C to hire and you want to spend £F per person on food and drink. If n people come

(a) What is the total cost?
(b) How much should you charge per ticket to break even?
(c) If the price per ticket is £P, how many people do you need to come to break even?

3.23 A ferry has a total deck space of area A. It takes on board cars (which take up an amount C of deck space each) and lorries (which take up an amount L of deck space each). Each car pays £p for the crossing and each lorry pays £q. The manager wants to know how many cars (x) and how many lorries (y) to take on so as to obtain the maximum revenue.

(a) What are the variables and what are the parameters?
(b) Write down an expression for the revenue R.
(c) Write down a restriction on the values of x and y due to the limited deck space.
(d) List the assumptions that have been made.

3.24 Suppose you are organising a party and have up to £100 to spend on food and drink. At least 40% of it is to be spent on food and at least £30 on drink. Translate this information into conditions on the amounts £d and £f to be spent on drink and food respectively.

3.25 Translate the following assumptions into a simple model.

(a) The more fossil fuel is burned (B) in a factory the more pollution (P) is released into a river.
(b) The more pollution there is in the river the fewer fish (F) can live in the river.
(c) The fewer fish there are in the river the more society awareness (A) grows.
(d) The more society awareness there is, the less fossil fuel is burned.

3.26 In a population, let L_x represent the proportion of females who live from birth to age x. Let M_x represent the number of female babies produced by females of age x. Express in words the *meaning* of $\sum_{x=0}^{\infty} L_x M_x$.

3.27 A fruit stall sells eating apples. The stall-holder wants to sell all of her stock by 5:00 p.m. Starting at 9:00 a.m., she keeps a fixed price p_0 (pence kg^{-1}) for four hours, reduces the original price by 10% for the next two hours and then halves the previous price for the remaining two hours. Construct a model for $p(t)$, the price at time t hours after 9:00 a.m.

3.28 Suppose farmers grow their crops at various distances from a city centre where the crop is eventually sold. Let Y be the number of kg of crop yielded by one m^2 of land, P = profit per kg of crop, and T = cost of transporting one kg of crop a distance of 1 km. Write down a model for the net revenue of a farmer who owns A m^2 of land at a distance D from the city centre.

3.29 At 1 a.m. the depth of water in a reservoir is 5 m. It starts to rain at 2 a.m., slowly at first but gradually increasing to a peak of 1 cm h^{-1} at 3 a.m. It then gradually subsides until at 5 a.m. the rainfall rate is 4 mm h^{-1}. It then continues to rain at a decreasing rate until it stops altogether at 9 a.m. Obtain equations defining a model for the rainfall rate, $r(t)$ (cm h^{-1}) at time t hours after midnight.

3.30 If n_1 workers take t_1 days to complete x_1 units:

(a) How long will it take n_2 workers to complete x_2 units?
(b) How many units will n_2 workers complete in t_2 days?
(c) How many workers are needed to complete x_2 units in t_2 days?

3.31 Students on an Open University course receive marks out of 100% for each of four 'Tutor-marked assignments'. The 'Substitution Rule' says that any student can have his or her worst mark (W) replaced by his/her average mark (M).
  Write down a mathematical expression for the new improved average mark in terms of W and M.

3.32 Two workers A and B are not equally productive. When they work together a certain job takes them d days. If A worked alone she could finish the same job in x days. How long would B take to do the same job by herself?

3.33 Suppose a swimmer can swim at a constant speed U relative to the water for a time T, but then becomes totally exhausted. A river flows at a speed V and the swimmer goes a distance x then turns round and swims back so that he arrives at his starting point just as he reaches the point of exhaustion. What is the relationship between x, U, V and T? Does it matter whether he swims upstream or downstream first? What is the corresponding answer if he swims at an angle θ to the bank? Check that your second answer reduces to your first when $\theta = 0$.

3.34 Two students A and B are standing at points a distance d apart on a straight road. They record the times at which two cars (1 and 2) pass the points where they are standing. If these times are denoted by t_{A1}, t_{A2}, t_{B1} and t_{B2} write down expressions for (a) the speeds of the two cars and (b) the distance between the two cars when car 2 passes B.

3.35 A goat is tethered to a post at the centre of a circular field of radius R. If the length of its tether is L:

(a) Write down an expression for the proportion (P) of the total field area which the goat is able to graze and sketch the graph of P as a function of the fraction $f = L/R$.
(b) What is the answer if the field is a square of side $2R$?
(c) What is the answer if the field is the surface of a sphere of radius R?

3.36 The brightness (b) of a planet as seen from Earth varies directly as the albedo (a), directly as the phase (p), directly as the square of the planet's radius (r), inversely as the square of the planet's distance (s) from the Sun, and inversely as the square of the planet's distance (e) from the Earth. (The albedo is the percentage of sunlight reflected and the phase is the percentage of the planet's disc lit by the Sun.)

Write down a model for b in terms of the other variables, incorporating all the above assumptions.

On one particular night the ratio of the brightness of Venus to that of Jupiter was estimated by observation to be about 6.9 to 1. Given the following extra information, use the model to estimate the ratio of the radii of Venus and Jupiter.

	a	p	s	e
Jupiter	0.52	1.0	5.28	6.23
Venus	0.49	0.82	0.72	1.28

(s and e are measured relative to the mean Earth–Sun distance.)

3.37 A newly created volcanic island is gradually colonised by species arriving from the mainland. Let N_i represent the number of species on the island i years after the eruption. Assume the number of new species arriving every year is:

(a) Proportional to the area (A) of the island.
(b) Proportional to the difference between the number of species on the island and the number of species (N_S) on the mainland.
(c) Inversely proportional to the number of species already on the island.
(d) Inversely proportional to the square of the distance (d) from the mainland to the island.

Using these assumptions write down an equation connecting N_{i+1} and N_i.

3.38 An increase in the level of tax on cigarettes will bring in *extra* tax revenue but on the other hand it could lead to some smokers giving up smoking altogether which could mean *less* revenue. Suppose an extra tax of x pence on a packet of cigarettes (which has price p at present) causes a proportion $g(x)$ of smokers to give up. Sketch a graph of a possible model for $g(x)$ as a function of x. Assuming that other smokers continue as before, write down a condition on x if the tax rise is to be worthwhile from the point of view of the Chancellor of the Exchequer.

3.39 Suppose a drainage basin is divided into areas numbered $1, 2 \dots N$ such that the runoff from area number x reaches the basin outlet x hours after the rain has fallen. Let A_x be the ground area (m^2) of area number x and let c_x be the fraction of rainfall that is converted into runoff in that area. Suppose it starts to rain at time 0 and continues for three hours with $r_n =$ rainfall (m s^{-1}) in hour n (assumed uniform over the whole catchment area). Assuming $N > 3$, write down a model for $Q_i =$ the total quantity of water (m^3) reaching the outlet in hour i.

3.40 The combined ages of Mary and Ann are 44 years and Mary is twice as old as Ann was when Mary was half as old as Ann will be when Ann is three times as old as Mary was when Mary was three times as old as Ann was. How old is Mary? [*Hint*: Translate into equations.]

The remaining exercises are for practice in manipulating expressions.

3.41 Rearrange each of the following equations to express x in terms of the other variables:

(a) $a + x = cx + b$ (b) $a + 1/x = b$
(c) $1/\sqrt{x} - a = b$ (d) $\sqrt{(x + a)} = b$
(e) $(a + x^2)/(b + x^2) = c$ (f) $\sin(ax + b) = c$

3.42 If $\ln y = -1.2x + 2.2$, express y in terms of x.

3.43 Which of the following expressions are equivalent?

(a) $(V_1 + V_2)(V_3 + V_1)$
(b) $V_1 V_2 (V_1 + V_2 + V_3 + 1)$
(c) $V_1^2 + V_2 V_3 + V_1(V_2 + V_3)$
(d) $V_1^2 + V_1 V_2 V_3 + V_1 V_3 + V_3^2 V_1$
(e) $V_1^2 V_2 + V_1 V_2 V_3 + V_1 V_2^2 + V_1 V_2$

3.44 Which of the following equations are equivalent?

(a) $x/y - y/x = u^2 - v^2$
(b) $(x - y)/(u - v) = (u + v)xy/(x + y)$
(c) $u/v - v/u = x^2 - y^2$
(d) $(x - y)/xy = (u^2 - v^2)/(x + y)$
(e) $u^2 - v^2 = uv(x^2 - y^2)$
(f) $x^2 - y^2 = xy(u^2 - v^2)$

3.45 If $(p + a/v^2)(v - b) = RT$ express

(a) a in terms of the other variables
(b) b in terms of the other variables
(c) p in terms of the other variables

3.46 Rearrange

$$\frac{2}{D - d} + \frac{2}{D + d} = \frac{1}{f}$$

to give d in terms of D and f.

3.47 If $F_1 = A/(1 + L_1/L_2)$ and $F_2 = A/(1 + L_2/L_1)$, show that $F_1 + F_2 = A$ and $F_1 L_1 = F_2 L_2$.

3.48 If $r = s(1 + m/2s)^2$ show that $\sqrt{(1 - 2m/r)} = (2s - m)/(2s + m)$.

3.49 If $x = 0.5(u + 1/u)$ and $y = 0.5(u - 1/u)$, show that $\sqrt{(x^2 - 1)} + \sqrt{(y^2 + 1)} = x + y$.

3.50 If $y = x + x^{-1}$, express $x^4 + x^{-4}$ in terms of y.

3.4 Answers to Exercises

3.1
(a) $Y = X + 5$
(b) $|Y - X| = 2$
(c) $Y/X = 2$
(d) $|A - B| = 3C/D$
(e) $Y = 0.05X$
(f) $Y = 1.05X$
(g) $Y = 0.95X$
(h) $Y < 0.05X$
(i) $|Y - X| \geqslant 10$
(j) $Y \geqslant 1.5X$
(k) $W \propto (X - Y)^2$
(l) $W \propto 1/\sqrt{(U - V - X)}$
(m) $y + x = 1.2z$
(n) $X \leqslant 0.9Y$
(o) $A + B \propto |X^2 - Y^2|$
(p) $AB \propto 1/(X - Y)^2$

3.2 (a) ((b) is equivalent to a 28% cut)

3.3 $(2x + 10)/2 - x = 5$

3.4 $a > b, b > 2c, a + c > b, c = a - 35$

3.5
(a) The square root of the product of a and b is equal to the magnitude of the difference between x and the square of y.
(b) q is inversely proportional to the sum of the squares of x and y.

3.6 PLW

3.7 $N/(S - Q)$ weeks

3.8
(a) $I \propto 1/x^2$
(b) $f \propto 1/\sqrt{m}$
(c) $M \propto \rho r^3$
(d) $F \propto M_1 M_2/x^2$

3.9
(a) $S = kM$
(b) $T = k/V$
(c) $S = k/x$
(d) $D = k/P$
(e) $T = k/N$
(f) $T = k/P$ or (more realistically) $T - L = k/P$ for some limit L
(g) $N = kS/x$ or kS/x^2

3.10 £$S/(1 - X/100)$

3.11 $(xy - hw)/A, 1 + \text{INT}[(xy - hw)/AL]$

3.12 $60(x_{AB} + x_{BC})/(t_{AB} + t_{BC})$

3.13 $60/M$ s

3.14 $\ln 2/\ln(1 + x/100)$ years

3.15 s/m gal h^{-1}, $L = 282.5/m$

3.16 $0.894/(1/S_1 + 1/S_2)$ m s^{-1}

3.17 $V = kTL$

3.18
(a) $M/(x + 1), xM/(x + 1)$
(b) $(M - x)/2, (M + x)/2$

3.19 $m = 50 - 0.2s$ m.p.g.

3.20 $s = 10c$

3.21
(a) $D = 8000, C_O = 100, C_H = 60,$
$C_{TOT} = 30Q_M + 8 \times 10^5/Q_M$
(b) $D = 50\,000, C_O = 160 + 0.5Q_M,$
$C_H = 8, C_{TOT} = 25\,000 + 4Q_M + 8 \times 10^6/Q_M$

3.22 (a) £$(nF + C)$, (b) £$(F + C/n)$, (c) $C/(P - F)$

3.23
(a) variables: x, y; parameters: p, q, L, A, C
(b) $xp + yq$
(c) $xC + yL \leqslant A$
(d) Unlimited cars and lorries available. All available space usable.

3.24 $d + f \leqslant 100, f/(f + d) \geqslant 0.4, d \geqslant 30$

3.25
(a) $P = k_1 B$
(b) $F = F_0 - k_2 P$
(c) $A = k_3/F$
(d) $B = k_4/A$

3.26 $\sum_{x=0}^{\infty} L_x M_x$ = average number of females produced by one female in her lifetime.

3.27 $p(t) = \begin{cases} p_0 & 0 \leqslant t \leqslant 4 \\ 0.9p_0 & 4 < t \leqslant 6 \\ 0.45p_0 & 6 < t \leqslant 8 \end{cases}$

3.28 $AY/(P - TD)$

3.29 $r(t) = \begin{cases} 0 & 0 \leqslant t \leqslant 2 \\ t - 2 & 2 \leqslant t \leqslant 3 \\ 1.9 - 0.3t & 3 \leqslant t \leqslant 5 \\ 0.9 - 0.1t & 5 \leqslant t \leqslant 9 \end{cases}$

3.30
(a) $n_1 t_1 x_2/n_2 x_1$
(b) $1 + \text{INT}[n_2 x_1 t_2/n_1 t_1]$
(c) $1 + \text{INT}[n_1 t_1 x_2/x_1 t_1]$

3.31 $(5M - W)/4$

3.32 $xd/(x - d)$

3.33 $x = T(U^2 - V^2)/2U, x = T(U^2 - V^2)/2\sqrt{\{U^2 - V^2 \sin^2 \theta\}}$

3.34
(a) $d/(t_{A1} - t_{B1}), d/(t_{A2} - t_{B2})$
(b) $d(t_{B2} - t_{B1})/(t_{A1} - t_{B1})$

3.35
(a) $P = f^2$
(b) $P = \begin{cases} \pi f^2/4 & 0 < f < 1 \\ \sqrt{(f^2 - 1)} + f^2(\pi/4 - \cos^{-1}f^{-1}) & 1 < f < \sqrt{2} \\ 1 & f > \sqrt{2} \end{cases}$
(c) $P = (1 - \cos f)/2$

3.36 $b = kapr^2/s^2e^2$, 0.084

3.37 $N_{i+1} = N_i + kA(N_S - N_i)/(d^2 N_i)$

3.38 $x[1 - g(x)]/g(x) > p$

3.39 $Q_1 = c_1 A_1 r_1$, $Q_2 = c_1 A_1 r_2 + c_2 A_2 r_1$

       $Q_i = \sum_{x=i-2}^{x=i} c_x A_x r_x$, $3 \leqslant i \leqslant N$

       $Q_{N+1} = C_N A_N r_2 + c_{N-1} A_{N-1} r_3$, $Q_{N+2} = c_N A_N r_3$

3.40   27.5 years

3.41   (a) $x = (a - b)/(c - 1)$ (b) $x = 1/(b - a)$

       (c) $x = 1/(a + b)^2$ (d) $x = b^2 - a$

       (e) $x = \sqrt{[(bc - a)/(1 - c)]}$

       (f) $x = \sin^{-1}\{(c - b)/a\}$

3.42 $y = \exp(2.2 - 1.2x)$ or $9.025\exp(-1.2x)$

3.43   (a) = (c),   (b) = (e)

3.44   (a) = (f) = (b) = (d),   (c) = (e)

3.45   (a) $a = v^2\{RT/(v - b) - p\}$

       (b) $b = v - RT/(p + a/v^2)$

       (c) $p = RT/(v - b) - a/v^2$

3.46 $d = \sqrt{(D^2 - 4Df)}$

3.50 $y^4 - 4y^2 + 2$

4 Checking Models

4.1 Background

The crucial test of a model is how well it fits the real situation. Is it good enough for the purpose? Checking a model against data is considered in Chapter 12. Here we discuss simple checks that can be made during the process of building the model. These checks help to determine whether the model is sensible, appropriate and adequate, without being unnecessarily complicated. There will also be more checking to do at a later stage in the modelling process, in the validating and likely revising of the model.

It is generally found useful to ask the following questions about any model:

1. Is it logically **consistent**?
2. Does it have the right kind of **behaviour**?
3. Does it give roughly the right **answers**?
4. Is it as **simple** as it could be?

Consistency

We can check whether a model is consistent with the *assumptions* and also whether it is *logically* consistent (containing no contradictions) and *dimensionally* consistent. Consistency with the assumptions is mainly a question of how the variables behave when one of them is changed. Logical consistency is usually fairly easy to check. Dimensional consistency involves checking that all the terms in an equation have the same physical dimensions. Almost all physical quantities can be expressed in terms of the three fundamental dimensions mass (M), length (L) and time (T). These ideas are discussed in more detail on page 41.

Behaviour

We need to examine the model's predictions (a) qualitatively and (b) quantitatively. The *qualitative* examination usually involves investigating how the model predicts that one variable will change as a result of changes in other variables. Much of this can be carried out by remembering simple facts such as 'as x increases $1/x$ decreases' and 'exponentials increase or decrease faster than polynomials'. A fraction like a/b increases when a increases and decreases when b increases (assuming both a and b are positive). It sometimes helps to do some algebraic simplification first. For example, if a, b and c are positive parameters what happens to the expression $F = ax/(bx + c)$ as x increases? On dividing through by x we can rewrite F as $a/(b + c/x)$. Now as x increases, c/x decreases, so the denominator decreases and F itself increases.

Other general questions to ask about a model are what happens at extreme values of the variables (i.e. very small or very large values)? Are there any special values when something interesting happens, e.g. a variable reaches a local maximum or minimum value or becomes zero or infinite? Is there a square root term which can become negative? Are the numerical ranges of some variables restricted in some way because of their contextual meaning? The model's *quantitative* behaviour can be investigated to some extent by rough estimates, but a more careful examination requires comparison with data.

Rough answers

At the stage of developing a model it can be very worthwhile to work out rough estimates for (a) the numerical values of parameters, variables etc. which will form parts of the model and/

or (b) the numerical values which will be produced as outputs from the model. Sometimes good data is available from which these estimates can be worked out, but at other times we have to use our judgement and make up our own estimates. The idea is to avoid detailed calculations by using simple common sense combined with some practical skill to produce estimates which are 'roughly' right.

In doing 'rough arithmetic' it may be found useful to remember the following simple facts:

- If x is small, x^2 is very small
- If x is large, x^2 is very large
- If x is small, $1/x$ is large, and $1/x^2$ even larger
- If x is large, $1/x$ is small, and $1/x^2$ even smaller
- Dividing by small quantities gives large answers
- Dividing by large quantities gives small answers
- Multiplying by small quantities gives small answers

The following strategies may also be found useful:

- Neglect small quantities added to (or subtracted from) large quantities
- Round to a nearby square before taking a square root
- When x is small drop large positive powers of x
- Drop values which make only a small contribution to the answer

It is helpful to think in 'powers of ten'. Models and equations will often involve several terms of differing sizes and **scientific notation** gives us a way of writing down numbers of any size in a compact form:

$$a \times 10^b$$

where a (the mantissa) is a number between 1 and 10 and b (the exponent) is an integer (positive or negative). For example, $25\,300 = 2.53 \times 10^4$, $0.000\,000\,253 = 2.53 \times 10^{-7}$. This is sometimes referred to as 'floating point notation' and may appear on your calculator as (for example) 2.53E-7. You can enter numbers into your calculator in this form using the **EXP** button. Closely related is the 'order' notation, by which we describe a quantity as being of the order of 10 when the exponent $b = 1$ and of the order of 10^2 when $b = 2$ etc. A capital O is used to stand for 'of the order of', so, for example, if a variable x is known to have a value measured in tens rather than hundreds we write $x \sim O(10)$. Examples are $36 \sim O(10)$, $360 \sim O(10^2)$ and $0.36 \sim O(10^{-1})$.

In calculating rough answers it is a good policy to work out upper and lower limits. Suppose we want an estimate of the number N of people who can fit into one room. If $a \times b$ are the floor dimensions (m) and we allow each person one m^2 of floor space then we get $N \approx ab$. This may be a low estimate, and an upper limit could be obtained by allowing each person only 0.1 m^2, giving $N \approx 10ab$.

Simplicity   The best models are those which give adequate answers while at the same time being as simple as possible. To help achieve this it can be useful to compare the relative importance of the various components making up the model. Are all the variables really necessary? For example, in models in mechanics it can often be debatable whether it is worth including frictional forces or air resistance. In any particular equation we can investigate whether all the terms are of roughly equal importance. Two practical ways of doing this are:

(a) Compare the orders of magnitude of the various terms in the model and decide whether to drop the smallest terms.
(b) Investigate the effects of the various terms in the model on the *answer* which we want the model to predict. If we need the answer to be accurate to 1% then we may decide that a term which affects the answer by only 0.1% is not needed.

Technique (b) is sometimes referred to as sensitivity analysis and can be carried out by numerical experimentation or mathematically by using partial derivatives (see Chapter 8).

Series expansions such as Maclaurin series can be useful in simplifying expressions for small values of the variables. For example, if $y = 1/(1 + x) = 1 - x + x^2 - x^3 + \cdots$, then for small x we could use $y = 1 - x$ (referred to as a **first-order approximation**). Similarly, if $y = \cos x$, a second-order approximation for y when x is small is $y = 1 - x^2/2$ (obtained from the Maclaurin series for $\cos x$).

The effect of a small change in one of the parameters or variables can sometimes be surprisingly large, as in the following example. A railway line is exactly 1 mile long and one night a vandal cuts the line and inserts an extra foot of metal. The line is constrained at its two ends so it is now forced to bend into an arc. How high above the ground is it at the midpoint? To obtain a rough answer we can imagine the line to form two straight lines meeting at the highest point, rather than an arc. We then have a right-angled triangle of height h with the two other sides of lengths 0.5 miles and (0.5 miles + 0.5 ft). Pythagoras' Theorem then gives

$$h = \sqrt{(2640.5)^2 - (2640)^2} \approx 50 \text{ ft}$$

Note that measuring the gradients of straight lines is often a sensitive procedure. Small changes in the values of gradients can lead to surprisingly large ranges in the subsequent answers produced by a model.

4.2 Dimensions

In physical science all quantities can be expressed in terms of the fundamental quantities mass, length and time, denoted by the symbols M, L and T. We can write this relationship for a general quantity Q as $[Q] = M^a L^b T^c$ where the square brackets [ ] denote 'the dimensions of' and a, b and c are rational numbers. For example, speed v is distance divided by time so we write $[v] = L/T = LT^{-1}$ and in this case $a = 0$, $b = 1$ and $c = -1$.

Knowing the dimensions of a quantity also gives an indication of the units in which it could be measured. For example, speed can be measured in m s^{-1}, and acceleration, which is the rate of change of speed = (speed change)/time, has dimensions $(LT^{-1})/T = LT^{-2}$ and can be measured in units of m s^{-2}. Note, however, that the dimensions of a quantity are independent of the *system* of units used.

Any sensible equation must be dimensionally consistent, i.e. [left-hand side] = [right-hand side]. For example, suppose a model predicts that the rate at which water will flow out through a hole in a tank is given by $Q = A\sqrt{(hg)}$, where A is the area of the hole, h is the depth of water in the tank and g is the acceleration due to gravity. Q gives the volume of water flowing out every second so $[Q] = L^3T^{-1}$. We have $[A] = L^2$, $[h] = L$ and $[g] = LT^{-2}$ so $[A\sqrt{(hg)}] = L^2\sqrt{L(LT^{-2})} = L^3T^{-1}$ and the equation is at least dimensionally consistent. This does not of course prove that the model is correct; in fact a much better model is $Q = A\sqrt{(2hg)}$. (Being a pure number, the 2 does not alter the dimensions.) Sometimes however, modelling errors *can* be revealed using dimensional checks.

Any parameters and constants appearing in our equations can be dimensionless (i.e. pure numbers) or can have dimensions. For example, the rate of heat transfer across the interface between two bodies at different temperatures can be modelled by $h \times$ (area of interface) $\times$ (temperature difference), where h is a parameter. The dimensions of energy are ML^2T^{-2} (as can be seen from 'kinetic energy $= mv^2/2$', for example). So the rate of heat transfer has dimensions ML^2T^{-3}. For the equation to be dimensionally consistent the parameter h must have dimensions MT^{-3}. The units for h, however, will not be just kg s^{-3} because the temperature difference is measured in kelvins, so h will be measured in kg s^{-3} K^{-1} (or equivalently W m^{-2} K^{-1}).

A combination of quantities such that the total dimensions come to zero is called a **dimensionless group** and is a useful concept in modelling physical systems. Simple examples are ratios of quantities with the same dimensions; for example, the ratio of inertial and viscous forces in fluid flow gives a very important dimensionless group called the **Reynolds number,** which determines the type of flow. Note that if we have an equation containing e^y or

$\ln(y)$ then y must be dimensionless, and we cannot work out, for example, $\sin(0.5 \text{ metres})$. Similarly, if expressions involving e^{kt} or $\sin kt$ or $\cos kt$ appear in our model, where t stands for time, the parameter k must have dimensions T^{-1} so that kt is a dimensionless number.

Geometrically similar (isometric) shapes in two or three dimensions have their linear dimensions in constant proportion. That is, if one shape has a particular length which is k times the corresponding length in a similar shape, all other lengths are also k times as long. The areas of the two shapes, however, will be proportional to the *square* of corresponding lengths, i.e. in the ratio of k^2 to 1. In three dimensions, if we take a particular shape and magnify it so that a certain length L within it changes, then its surface area $S \propto L^2$ and its volume $V \propto L^3$, from which we can also deduce that $S \propto V^{2/3}$. The third relation is important in biology because it implies that as the volume of an animal increases, its surface area does not increase in the same proportion, but in proportion to the two-thirds power of its volume. For a cube we have $S = 6V^{2/3}$ and for other shapes we will have $S = kV^{2/3}$, with different values of k. The value of k measures how compact the shape is, the most compact being the sphere, for which $k \approx 4.836$ (the smallest possible k).

Dimensions of Some Common Physical Quantities

Quantity	Dimensions	SI units
Velocity	LT^{-1}	m s^{-1}
Acceleration	LT^{-2}	m s^{-2}
Force	MLT^{-2}	N or kg m s^{-2}
Pressure	$ML^{-1}T^{-2}$	$\text{Pa or N m}^{-2} \text{ or kg m}^{-1} \text{ s}^{-2}$
Energy	$ML^{-2}T^{-2}$	$\text{J or kg m}^{-2} \text{ s}^{-2}$
Power	$ML^{-2}T^{-3}$	W or J s^{-1}
Volume flow rate	L^3T^{-1}	$\text{m}^3 \text{ s}^{-1}$
Mass flow rate	MT^{-1}	kg s^{-1}

4.3 Worked Examples

4.1 A variable w is related to two other variables x and y in such a way that w is proportional to x and also proportional to y. Which of the following correctly expresses the relationship?

(a) $w = a(x + y)$ (b) $w = ax + by$ (c) $w = axy$

Solution   The correct answer is (c), as can be seen by the fact that according to the original statement, w will be doubled (for example) if either x or y is doubled. This does not happen with (a) or (b).

4.2 A variable y depends on two other variables w and z. The following facts are known:

(i) when w increases, y decreases
(ii) when z increases, y increases
(iii) when w and z are both zero, y is also zero

Which of the following models are consistent with facts (i), (ii) and (iii)?

(a) $y = aw + bz$ (b) $y = bz - aw + c$ (c) $y = cz/w$
(d) $y = cwz$ (e) $y = az - bw$

(a, b and c are positive constants.)

Solution   Only (e) fits all the facts because (a) and (d) both contradict (i) and (b) and (c) both contradict (iii).

4.3 A model predicts a quantity F from the equation $F = ax/(c - bx)$ where a, b and c are positive parameters and x is a variable taking values between 0 and c/b. What happens to F as

(a) *a* increases?
(b) *b* increases?
(c) *c* increases?
(d) *x* increases?

Solution (a) As *a* increases the numerator increases and *F* consequently increases.
(b) As *b* increases the numerator decreases and *F* consequently increases.
(c) As *c* increases the numerator increases and *F* consequently decreases.
(d) As *x* increases the numerator decreases and *F* consequently increases, becoming very large when *x* is near to *c/b*.

4.4 If V is a volume, M is a mass, ρ is a density, x is a length, A is an area and k is a dimensionless constant, which of the following equations are dimensionally consistent?

(a) $M = \rho A x$ (b) $V = A/x + M/\rho$ (c) $A = V/x + M/\rho$
(d) $x = KV/A$ (e) $A/V = k/x + \rho A/M$ (f) $A/x = k/V + M/\rho$

Solution (a) $[\rho A x] = (ML^{-3})(L^2)(L) = M$, which agrees with the LHS.
(b) $[V] = L^3$, $[A/x] = (L^2)/(L) = L$ so there is inconsistency here.
(c) $[A] = L^2$, $[V/x] = (L^3)/(L) = L^2$ but $[M/\rho] = M/(ML^{-3}) = L^3$ so the equation is inconsistent.
(d) $[x] = L^2$, $[kV/A] = (L^3)/(L^2) = L$, so the equation is consistent.
(e) $[A/V] = (L^2)/(L^3) = L^{-1}$, $[k/x] = L^{-1}$ and $[\rho A/M] = (ML^{-3})(L^2)/M = L^{-1}$, so this equation is consistent.
(f) $[A/x] = L^2/L = L$ but $[k/V] = (L^3)^{-1}$ so this equation is inconsistent.

4.5 Without using a calculator, what is roughly the value of $\sqrt{(37.15)}/[100 + (0.015)^2]$?

Solution We can round 37.15 to 36 so the square root gives 6 and the 0.015^2 is negligible compared with 100. We therefore get the rough answer $6/100 = 0.06$.

4.6 In agriculture, if the planting density N (= number of plants in one m² of ground) is increased beyond a certain point the plants suffer from competition and a common result is that each individual plant grows to a smaller size than it would if it had unlimited space. It is found in practice that a plot of log W against log N, where W is the individual plant weight, produces an approximately straight line graph with gradient $-3/2$. Use a simple model to explain this. Derive a model for the *total* weight of crop which could be expected from a given plot of land, as a function of the planting density.

Solution *Variables*

Description	Type	Symbol	Units
Planting density	variable	N	m^{-2}
Weight of a fully grown plant	variable	W	kg
Total weight of crop from field	variable	W_{tot}	kg
Maximum possible weight of plant	parameter	W_{max}	kg
Total area of field	parameter	A_{tot}	m^2
Critical planting density	parameter	N_{crit}	m^{-2}

Problem statement: Given A_{tot}, W_{max}, N_{crit} and N find W_{tot}

Suppose each plant grows until it occupies an area A of ground and then stops growing because of the overcrowding. The amount of area A available to each plant is inversely proportional to the number of plants, so $A \propto 1/N$.

The weight W of an individual plant $\propto$ volume $\propto L^3$ where L is a typical length for the plant. The area of ground it occupies is $A \propto L^2$ We therefore have $L^2 \propto A \propto 1/N$, so that $L \propto N^{-1/2}$ and $W \propto L^3 \propto (N^{-1/2})^3 \propto N^{-3/2}$, which is what we wanted to explain.

When the planting density N is low, each individual plant will have enough space to be able to reach its maximum weight W_{max}. If N is increased beyond a certain critical density N_{crit}, the overcrowding effect will apply and we will have $W \propto N^{-3/2}$. A simple model for W is therefore

$$W = W_{max} \qquad 0 \leqslant N \leqslant N_{crit}$$
$$= kN^{-3/2} \qquad N > N_{crit}$$

For agreement at $N = N_{crit}$ the constant k must equal $W_{max}N_{crit}^{3/2}$. We can also relate N_{crit} and W_{max} because at the critical density the total area of land used up by the plants is $N_{crit}A_{max}$ where A_{max} is proportional to $W_{max}^{2/3}$. There will therefore be some constant b such that $N_{crit} = bA_{tot}W_{max}^{-2/3}$.

If A_{tot} is the total area of the field then the total weight, W_{tot} of crop at harvesting should be $N \times W \times A_{tot}$ which leads to the model

$$W_{tot} = NW_{max}A_{tot} \qquad\qquad 0 \leqslant N \leqslant N_{crit}$$
$$= N^{-1/2}W_{max}N_{crit}^{3/2}A_{tot} \qquad N > N_{crit}$$

The dimensions of N and N_{crit} are L^{-2} and W_{tot} and W_{max} have dimensions M, so checking dimensions we have:

$$[NW_{max}A_{tot}] = L^{-2}ML^2 = M \quad \text{for} \quad N \leqslant N_{crit}$$

and

$$[N^{-1/2}W_{max}N_{crit}^{3/2}A_{tot}] = (L^{-2})^{-1/2}M(L^{-2})^{3/2}L^2 = LML^{-3}L^2 = M \quad \text{for} \quad N > N_{crit}$$

See Fig. 4.1.

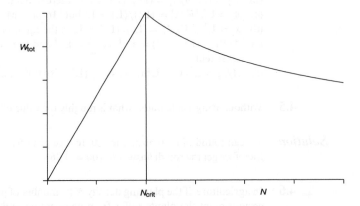

Figure 4.1

4.7 Assume that the volume flow rate Q through a cylindrical pipe is:

(i)   proportional to the pressure difference P
(ii)   inversely proportional to the length l of the pipe
(iii) inversely proportional to the viscosity μ of the fluid
(iv) proportional to some power (a) of the radius r of the pipe

Find an appropriate value for the constant a.

Solution   First note that (dynamic) viscosity is defined in terms of the force between two surfaces on either side of a layer of fluid. This force (F) is assumed to be:

(a) proportional to the area A of the surfaces
(b) inversely proportional to the thickness x of the layer of fluid
(c) proportional to the viscosity μ of the fluid
(d) proportional to the relative velocity v between the two surfaces

We can combine all these assumptions into one equation: $F = \mu Av/x$. Checking dimensions, we have $[F] = [\mu]L^2(LT^{-1})/L$ or $[MLT^{-2}] = [\mu]L^2(LT^{-1})/L$ so that $[\mu] = ML^{-1}T^{-1}$.

The assumptions (i)–(iv) imply a relationship of the form $Q = kPr^a/\mu l$. Considering dimensions, we have $[Q] = L^3T^{-1}$, $[P] = (MLT^{-2})/L^2 = ML^{-1}T^{-2}$. Substituting in the equation, we get $L^3T^{-1} = [k](ML^{-1}T^{-2})L^a/(ML^{-1}T^{-1}L)$, simplifying to $L^3 = [k]L^{a-1}$ We can satisfy this with a dimensionless constant k if we take $a = 4$ giving the model $Q = kPa^4/\mu l$.

4.8 A model predicts a quantity F from four other quantities a, b, c and d through the equation $F = a^2b + c/d$. If $a \approx 1$, $b \approx 5$, $c \approx 10$ and $d \approx 2$, find what percentage difference in the value of F is caused by a 1% change in each of a, b, c and d.

Solution Altering only one of the parameters at a time, and taking values 1% more and 1% less than the given values, we can calculate two values of F in each case as follows:

$$a \in [0.99, 1.01] \Rightarrow F \in [9.9005, 10.1005] \Rightarrow \text{up to } 1.005\% \text{ change in } F$$
$$b \in [4.95, 5.05] \Rightarrow F \in [9.95, 10.05] \Rightarrow \text{up to } 0.5\% \text{ change in } F$$
$$c \in [9.9, 10.1] \Rightarrow F \in [9.95, 10.05] \Rightarrow \text{up to } 0.5\% \text{ change in } F$$
$$d \in [1.98, 2.02] \Rightarrow F \in [9.9505, 10.0505] \Rightarrow \text{up to } 0.5\% \text{ change in } F$$

4.9 A model is required to predict the depth d to which a ball of diameter D will sink in water if the specific gravity of the material from which the ball is made is s. It is suggested that for given values of D and s the required value of d can be found by solving the equation $sD^3 = d^2(3D - 2d)$ Check the model.

Solution Mathematical or physical checks are not intended here. We can check dimensional consistency and behaviour as follows.

Dimensions
The specific gravity s is the ratio of the density of the ball to the density of water, so s is a dimensionless number. The variables d and D are lengths, so both sides of the equation have dimension L^3. This proves dimensional consistency, but does not of course mean that the model is necessarily correct.

Behaviour
We can imagine the following three special cases:

(i)   When $s = 1$ the ball will be completely submerged, so $d = D$.
(ii)   When $s = 0.5$ the ball will float half-submerged, so $d = 0.5D$.
(iii) When $s = 0$ the ball is so light that it floats on the surface, so $d = 0$.

We can also put forward the following two statements about the behaviour of the model:

(a) As s increases d should increase.
(b) As D increases d should increase.

In fact, we can produce a stronger version of (b) by saying that d should be proportional to D. This makes it relevant to deal with the ratio $x = d/D$, which also simplifies the model to $s = x^2(3 - 2x)$. Our general problem is: given s find x. This cannot be done directly, so we continue to work with the cubic equation as it stands. In terms of s and x our three special cases are

(i)   When $s = 1, x = 1$
(ii)   When $s = 0.5, x = 0.5$
(iii) When $s = 0, x = 0$

Substituting these values into the equation makes it balance in all three cases (although we note that for a given value of s the equation can produce up to three values of x). The truth of statement (a) is most easily seen by referring to the graph of s against x shown in Fig. 4.2. Finding x for a given value of s is equivalent to finding where the horizontal line at that value of s crosses the graph. Our model applies only for $0 < x < 1$ and it is clear that raising the value of s raises the value of x.

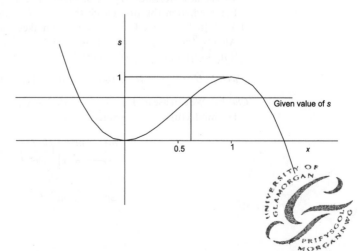

Figure 4.2

4.10 At time $t = 0$ a bullet of mass m is fired vertically into the air with speed U. A model is required to predict (a) the highest point it reaches and (b) the time it takes to reach the highest point. Three simple models based on a uniform vertical acceleration $-g$ due to gravity can be derived by:

(i)   Ignoring air resistance
(ii) Assuming the force due to air resistance $= k_1 \times (\text{speed})$
(iii) Assuming the force due to air resistance $= k_2 \times (\text{speed})^2$ where k_1 and k_2 are parameters

Model (i) predicts that the greatest height reached above the initial point is $H = U^2/(2g)$ at time $T = U/g$.

Model (ii) gives the predictions

(a) $H = mU/k_1 - (m^2g/k_1^2) \ln[1 + k_1 U/(mg)]$
(b) $T = (m/k_1) \ln[1 + k_1 U/(mg)]$

Model (iii) gives the predictions

(a) $H = (0.5m/k_2) \ln[1 + k_2 U^2/(mg)]$
(b) $T = \sqrt{[m/(k_2 g)]} \tan^{-1}\{U\sqrt{[k_2/(mg)]}\}$

(A) Check these models for consistency.
(B) How big are the differences between the predictions made by these models?
(C) How sensitive are the answers to the values assumed for the parameters?

Solution (A) We can check the following:

1. Dimensions.
2. All the models should give $H = 0$ and $T = 0$ when $U = 0$.
3. The predictions of Model (ii) should agree with those of Model (i) when $k_1 \to 0$.
4. The predictions of Model (iii) should agree with those of Model (i) when $k_2 \to 0$.
5. The value of H predicted by Model (ii) should be $< U^2/(2g)$.
6. The value of H predicted by Model (iii) should be $< U^2/(2g)$.

Check 1. Dimensions: Model (i) gives (a) $H = U^2/(2g)$ and $[U^2/(2g)] = (LT^{-1})^2/(LT^{-2}) = L$ as required; also (b) $T = U/g$ is dimensionally correct because $[U/g] = (LT^{-1})/(LT^{-2}) = T$.

For Model (ii); first note that $k_1 v$ is a force, so $[k_1 v] = MLT^{-2}$ from which $[k_1]LT^{-1} = MLT^{-2}$ and so $[k_1] = MT^{-1}$.

For prediction (a), first check that $k_1 U/(mg)$ is dimensionless. We have $[k_1 U/(mg)] = (MT^{-1})(LT^{-1})/\{M(LT^{-2})\} = 1$, so it makes sense to have $\ln\{1 + k_1 U/(mg)\}$.

We can now work out $[H] = [mU/k_1 - (m^2g/k_1^2) \ln\{1 + k_1 U/(mg)\}] = [(MLT^{-1}/(MT^{-1})) - M^2(LT^{-2})/(MT^{-1})^2] = L$ as required.

It is also easy to check the dimensions of prediction (b), since $[(m/k_1) \ln\{1 + k_1 U/(mg)\}] = [m/k_1] = M/(MT^{-1}) = T$.

For Model (iii), first note that $k_2 v^2$ is a force so $[k_2 v^2] = MLT^{-2}$, from which $[k_2](LT^{-1})^2 = MLT^{-2}$ and so $[k_2] = ML^{-1}$.

For prediction (a); first check that $k_2 U^2/(mg)$ is dimensionless.
We have $[k_2 U^2/(mg)] = (ML^{-1})(LT^{-1})^2/\{M(LT^{-2})\} = 1$ so it makes sense to have $\ln\{1 + k_2 U^2/(mg)\}$.

We can now work out $[H] = [(0.5m/k_2) \ln\{1 + k_2 U^2/(mg)\}] = [m/k_2]M/(ML^{-1}) = L$ as required.

For prediction (b), first check that $U\sqrt{\{k_2/(mg)\}}$ is dimensionless. We have $[U\sqrt{\{k_2/(mg)\}}] = (LT^{-1})\{(ML^{-1})/M(LT^{-2})\}^{1/2} = 1$, so it makes sense to have $\tan^{-1}[U\sqrt{\{k_2/(mg)\}}]$.

Also, $[\sqrt{(m/(k_2 g))}] = \{M/((ML^{-1})(LT^{-2}))\}^{1/2} = T$. It follows that $[\sqrt{(m/(k_2 g))}] \tan^{-1}[U\sqrt{\{k_2/(mg)\}}] = [\sqrt{(m/(k_2 g))}] = T$.

Check 2. $U = 0$ gives $H = 0$ and $T = 0$ in all cases because $\ln(1) = 0$ and $\tan^{-1}(0) = 0$.

Check 3. We can use $\ln(1 + x) = x - x^2/2 + x^3/3 - \cdots$ and $\tan^{-1} x = x - x^3/3 + \cdots$.
For Model (ii) when k_1 is small we have

$$H = \frac{mU}{k_1} - \frac{m^2g}{k_1^2}\left[\left(\frac{k_1 U}{mg}\right) - \frac{1}{2}\left(\frac{k_1 U}{mg}\right)^2 + \frac{1}{3}\left(\frac{k_1 U}{mg}\right)^3 - \cdots\right]$$

$$= \frac{U^2}{2g} - \frac{1}{3}\left(\frac{k_1 U^3}{mg^2}\right) + \cdots$$

and

$$T = \frac{m}{k_1} \left[\left(\frac{k_1 U}{mg} \right) - \frac{1}{2} \left(\frac{k_1 U}{mg} \right)^2 + \cdots \right]$$

$$= \frac{U}{g} - \frac{1}{2} \left(\frac{k_1 U^2}{mg^2} \right) + \cdots$$

and for Model (iii) when k_2 is small,

$$H = 0.5 \frac{m}{k_2} \left[\left(\frac{k_2 U^2}{mg} \right) - \frac{1}{2} \left(\frac{k_2 U^2}{mg} \right)^2 + \cdots \right]$$

$$= \frac{U^2}{2g} - \frac{1}{4} \left(\frac{k_2 U^4}{mg^2} \right) + \cdots$$

and

$$T = \sqrt{\frac{m}{gk_2}} \left[U \sqrt{\frac{k_2}{mg}} - \frac{1}{3} U^3 \left(\frac{k_2}{mg} \right)^{3/2} + \cdots \right]$$

$$= \frac{U}{g} - \frac{1}{3} \left(\frac{k_2 U^3}{mg^2} \right) + \cdots$$

From these results we note the following:

(i)   In all cases, when the k parameter becomes zero we get back to the results of Model (i).
(ii) In all cases the prediction differs from that of Model (i) by an amount which is *negative*.

These conclusions confirm Checks 3, 4, 5 and 6.

(B) To obtain a fair comparison between the two models with air resistance we need to balance the k_1 and k_2 values. We could take values such that the force due to air resistance at the initial moment (when it is greatest) has the same value in both models. In other words, we assume that $k_1 U = k_2 U^2$. The differences from the zero-resistance model then become

Model (ii): $-k_1 U^3/(3mg^2)$ for H, $-k_1 U^2/(2mg^2)$ for T
Model (iii): $-k_1 U^3/(4mg^2)$ for H, $-k_1 U^2/(3mg^2)$ for T

So in these circumstances, Model (iii) is closer to Model (i). For small k values, the differences in the predictions of Models (ii) and (iii) are in the ratio 4:3 for H and 3:2 for T. Models (ii) and (iii) differ from each other's predictions by approximately $k_1 U^3/(12mg)^2$ for H and $k_1 U^2/(6mg^2)$ for T.

(C) Taking sample values $m = 10\,\text{g} = 0.01\,\text{kg}$, $U = 200\,\text{m s}^{-1}$, $k_1 = 10^{-6}\,\text{kg s}^{-1}$ and $k_2 = 5 \times 10^{-9}$ kg m^{-1} the models give the following predictions (to 5 significant figures).

Model	H (m)	T (s)
(i)	2038.7	20.387
(ii)	2036.1	20.367
(iii)	2036.7	20.374

Increasing k_1 by 10% we get

Model	H (m)	T (s)
(ii)	2036.5	20.372
(iii)	2035.8	20.365

Note that in Model (ii) H is worked out by subtracting two large numbers, which can be numerically unreliable.

4.4 Exercises

4.1 A variable w is related to three other variables x, y and z in such a way that w is inversely proportional to x and also proportional to the sum of y and z.

Which of the following correctly expresses the relationship?

(a) $w = ay/x + bz/x$ (b) $w = ay/x + az/x$
(c) $w = a(y + z) + b/x$ (d) $w = a(y + z)/x + b/x$

4.2 A variable y depends on two other variables w and z. The following facts are known:

(i)   when w increases, y increases
(ii)   when z increases, y decreases
(iii)   when z is very small, y is very large

Which of the following models are consistent with facts (i), (ii) and (iii)?

(a) $y = a/w + bz$ (b) $y = a/(z + bw)$
(c) $y = a/z + bw$ (d) $y = aw - bz$

(a and b are positive constants.)

4.3 A model predicts a quantity F from the equation $F = (ax - b)/(cx + d)$ where a, b, c and d are all positive parameters and x is a variable taking values $> b/a$.

What happens to F as:

(a) a increases?
(b) b increases?
(c) c increases?
(d) d increases?
(e) x increases?

4.4 Do the following expressions increase (I) or decrease (D)

(a) as a increases
(b) as b increases
(c) as c increases?

(A) $\dfrac{a}{1 + b/c}$ (B) $\dfrac{b}{c} - a + \dfrac{b}{a}$ (C) $\dfrac{abc}{a + bc^2}$

(Assume a, b and c are all positive.)

4.5 Which of the following models correspond to which graphs in Fig. 4.3? (Assume that a and b are positive parameters.)

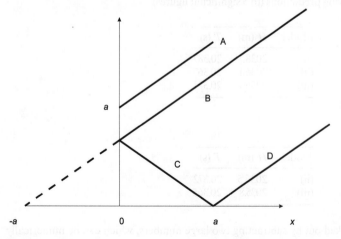

Figure 4.3

(a) $y = b(a - x)$ (b) $y = a + bx$
(c) $y = b(x + a)$ (d) $y = b(x - a)$

4.6 Which of the following expressions:

(i)   are very large for small positive x?
(ii)   are increasing for all x?
(iii)   become very small at very large x?
(iv)   are unbounded for large x?

(a) $x + 1/x$ (b) $1/(1 + x)$
(c) $x/(1 + x^2)$ (d) $1 - e^{-x}$
(e) $1 + e^x$ (f) xe^{-x}
(g) $x \log x$

4.7 Investigate the effects of changing the values of the parameters a, b and c in each of the following expressions:

(a) $a + be^{-cx}$ (b) $c + axe^{-bx}$

4.8 A model gives the period of oscillation of a simple pendulum of length l as $T = 2\pi\sqrt{(l/g)}$, where g is the acceleration due to gravity. Check that this is dimensionally correct.

4.9 If x and L are lengths and t and T are times, which of the following expressions make sense dimensionally?

(a) $\sin(x)\cos(t)$ (b) $\sin(x/L)\cos(t/T)$
(c) $\ln(1 + x/t)$ (d) $\ln(1 + t/T)$
(e) $\exp(xt/LT)$ (f) $\sin(x + t)$
(g) $\exp\{(x + L)t/T\}$ (h) $\sin(x/L + t/T)$

4.10 A student is trying to remember the form of Bernoulli's equation, which relates the pressure p and speed of flow u at a depth z below the surface of a fluid of density ρ, but cannot decide which of the following four is the correct version. Use dimensional checks to select the correct form.

(a) $p + \rho z + u^2/2 = $ constant   (b) $p + gz + u^2/2 = $ constant
(c) $p + \rho gz + \rho u^2/2 = $ constant   (d) $p + \rho gz + u^2/2 = $ constant

4.11 If A is area, x, y and z are lengths, t is time and u is speed, which of the following equations are dimensionally consistent?

(a) $A = xy + yz$ (b) $u = x/t + y/t$
(c) $At = xyz/u$ (d) $A/t = xu$
(e) $A = ut + xy$ (f) $x = Au + y$
(g) $A = xy + xyt$ (h) $y = A/x$

4.12 A model gives the pressure p at a depth h below the surface of a fluid of density ρ as $p = p_0 + \rho gh$, where p_0 is the pressure at the surface and g is the acceleration due to gravity. Check that this is dimensionally correct.

4.13 A model predicts the height $h(t)$ of water in a cylindrical tank at time t to be $h = (\sqrt{h_0} - a\sqrt{(g/2)}t/\pi r^2)^2$, where $h_0 = $ height of water above the outlet at time $t = 0$, $r = $ radius of cross-section of tank, $a = $ area of cross-section of the outlet pipe and $g = $ acceleration due to gravity. Check that this model is dimensionally consistent.

For what range of t values does it apply?

4.14 A particle of mass m is projected vertically upwards from the ground with speed U at time $t = 0$. If the force due to air resistance is modelled by kv^2, where v is the speed at any instant, then the particle is predicted to return to the ground at time

$$T = \sqrt{\frac{m}{kg}} \left\{ \tan^{-1} U \sqrt{\frac{k}{mg}} + \ln\left(U\sqrt{\frac{k}{mg}} + \sqrt{1 + \frac{kU^2}{mg}} \right) \right\}$$

with speed $V = U \Big/ \sqrt{1 + \dfrac{kU^2}{mg}}$.

Check that these predictions (i) are dimensionally correct, and (ii) agree with the zero air resistance model when $k = 0$.
  Obtain approximate expressions for
(a) the reduction in V and (b) the reduction in T due to air resistance. How sensitive are the predictions to the values of U, m, k and g?

4.15 *Without* using your calculator, write down approximate answers for:

(a) $\sqrt{\{(100.08)(99.3)\}}$
(b) $(101/9.98 + 6/(143)^2)^3$
(c) $(3 + 1/177)\sqrt{(4.008)}/\sqrt{(145)}$
(d) $\sqrt{\{(4.001)(2.998)\}}/\sqrt{\{3 + 1/(210)^2\}}$
(e) $\{101/[100 + \sqrt{(1 + e^{-4})}]\}^5$
(f) $\{14\,016.5 + 5908 + \sin(1.438)\}^2$

4.16 A cube of steel weighs 40 tonnes. How big is it?

4.17 Estimate the number of rolls of wallpaper which you would need to cover a wall 16 ft long by 90 in high if one roll is 11 yards long and 20.5 in wide.

4.18 How big is a 50 000 tonne ship?

4.19 How much skin area does a 6 ft tall person have?

4.20 Estimate the number of table tennis balls which would fill the room you are in at present. (Give upper and lower limits.)

4.21 Estimate the amount of glass in the building you are in at present.

4.22 Estimate the number of times an average human breathes in a lifetime.

4.23 Forty people are attending a lecture when the fire alarm rings. How long will it take them all to evacuate the lecture room?

4.24 Given the following (approximate) data:

(a) Radius of Earth ≈ 4000 miles
(b) Earth's surface is about 3/4 water, 1/4 land
(c) Eventually 70% of all land could be made fertile
(d) A plot of fertile land 100 ft $\times$ 100 ft will support one person
(e) Earth's population in 1900 was 1.6×10^9 and in 1950 was 2.4×10^9

estimate the maximum number of people the Earth can support.
  How soon will we reach this figure?

4.25 If a is about 10 000 and b is about 10, take the expression below

$$\frac{\sqrt{\dfrac{1}{a} + b^2}}{\left(\sqrt{a} + \dfrac{1}{b^3} \right)}$$

and:

(a) *Estimate* its value.
(b) Identify the largest and smallest terms.
(c) Replace it by a simpler approximate expression.

4.26 Replace the expression $(e^{(x^3 + 1/x)} + x^2)\sqrt{x^2 + 1/x}$ by a simpler form:

(a) for small values of x
(b) for large values of x

4.27 Replace the expression $e^{-x}/(1 - x)$ by a simpler form:

(a) for small values of x
(b) for large values of x

4.28 Replace the expression

$$\frac{y}{\dfrac{x}{y} + x^2 y + x^3 y^3 + \dfrac{y^2}{x}}$$

by a simpler form:

(a) when x is small
(b) when y is small

4.29 Replace the expression $1 + a\sin(\Omega t) + a^2\Omega^2 \cos(\Omega t)$ by a simpler form:

(a) when t is small
(b) when a is small
(c) when Ω is small

4.30 For small values of θ, $\sin \theta$ is roughly equal to θ when θ is measured in radians. How large can θ be and still allow this approximation to be correct to within 10%?

4.31 The function $\sinh x$ is defined by $\sinh x = 0.5(e^x - e^{-x})$. As x increases, e^x increases while e^{-x} decreases, so we can expect that for sufficiently large x, $\sinh x$ can be approximated by $0.5e^x$. How large does x have to be for this to be accurate to less than 5%?

4.32 A rule of thumb gives $72/r$ (years) as the time it takes a sum of money to double itself when the interest rate is $r\%$ p.a. How accurate is this rule over the range 5% to 15%?

4.33 When the Earth is modelled as a sphere (of diameter 12.72×10^3 km) it is obvious that if the walls of a tall building are vertical, they cannot be parallel. Suppose that a tower block is 400 m tall and that the ground floor has an area of 2500 m^2. Roughly how much extra area is there on the top floor?

4.34 In the following exercises the parameters a, b and c have the values $a = 0.1$, $b = 0.01$ and $c = 0.001$, and the variable x can be assumed to lie in the interval $[1, 10]$.

(a) Identify the smallest and largest terms in each of the following expressions:

(i) $x/b + a/x + c$
(ii) $ax/b + bx^2 + ab$
(iii) $a/x + bx^3/a + c/(ax^2)$

(b) Simplify the following expressions by dropping the smallest term in each:

(i) $x^2 - 2cx + a$

(ii) $ac + bx^2 + a/x$

(iii) $b \sin x + a\sqrt{x}$

(c) Simplify the following by dropping all terms of order 10^{-n} with $n > 2$.

(i) $bx^3(1 - b^3x + cx - x^2c^2)$

(ii) $(b^3 + 2c/x + a^2)/(c^3x + b)$

(iii) $\sqrt{(cx)} + c\sin x + be^{-x}$

(d) Simplify the following as far as possible by retaining only the largest terms:

(i) $\dfrac{a}{x^2} + 10\dfrac{b}{x} + cx$

(ii) $\dfrac{x^2 + ax}{b + cx + \dfrac{x^2}{c}}$

(iii) $\dfrac{(ax + c\sin^2 x)(b^3x + a)}{(bx + c)}$

4.35 For each of the following variables write down dimensions using the M, L, T notation and also give appropriate units using SI units for measured quantities and £ for costs:

(a) force (= mass × acceleration)
(b) energy (= force × distance)
(c) power (= rate of energy output)
(d) density of material (= mass per unit volume)
(e) cost per unit area of office space
(f) rate of change of temperature in a room
(g) mass flow rate in a pipe (= mass of fluid flowing past a point in each unit of time)
(h) air pressure in a tyre

4.36 The force F due to air resistance on a body moving with speed v can be modelled as $F = kAf(v)$, where A is the area of the body at right angles to the motion and $f(v)$ is some function of v. What are the dimensions and units of the constant k in the following cases?

(a) When $f(v) = v$ (small bodies, low speeds)
(b) When $f(v) = v^2$ (large bodies, high speeds)

4.37 The Reynolds number for fluid flow is given by $Re = \rho ul/\mu$ where ρ and μ are the density and viscosity of the fluid, u is the speed of flow and l is a typical length involved in the flow (for example the diameter of a pipe). Verify that Re is dimensionless.

4.38 When a fluid flows through a pipe the pressure difference P between the ends of the pipe can be assumed to be:

(i) proportional to the length l of the pipe
(ii) proportional to the square of u, the fluid speed
(iii) inversely proportional to the diameter d of the pipe
(iv) inversely proportional to the acceleration g due to gravity

(a) Write down an expression for P in terms of l, u, d and g and involving a constant k.
(b) What are the dimensions of k?
(c) In what units could k be measured?

4.39 What is the weight in lb of a pint of mercury (density = $13\,546\,\mathrm{kg\,m^{-3}}$)?

4.40 If a car does 40 miles per gallon of petrol in Britain what does it do in France in litres per km?

4.41 The speed of light is about 186 000 miles per second. What is this in kilometres per minute?

4.42 A car accelerates from rest to M m.p.h. in T seconds. What is its acceleration in $\mathrm{m\,s^{-2}}$?

4.43 How much wine is left in a bottle after pouring g glasses each holding $x\,\mathrm{cm^3}$ of wine if the full bottle contained L litres of wine?

4.44 How many days does it take to sail around the world at a constant speed of s m.p.h. if R is the radius of the Earth in kilometres?

4.45 A cyclist passes N lampposts in M minutes. What is her average speed in $\mathrm{m\,s^{-1}}$ if the lampposts are spaced F feet apart?

4.46 The energy stored in an elastic spring is given by the model $E = 0.5ke^2$ where e is the extension of the spring and k is its stiffness. What are the dimensions of k and in what units could it be measured?

If one end of the spring is attached to a fixed point and a mass m is attached to the bottom end, the period T of vertical oscillations depends on k and m. If $T \propto k^a m^b$ what are appropriate values for a and b?

Use your answer to predict what happens to T if m is increased. Is this what you would expect?

4.47 The rate of heat loss by radiation from a surface of area A and temperature T is given by $\sigma A(T^4 - T_0^4)$, where T_0 is the ambient temperature. What are the dimensions of the constant σ and in what units could it be measured?

4.48 The power output, P, of a wind generator depends on its efficiency α (a percentage), the density ρ of the air, the radius r of the vanes and the speed w of the wind. If P is predicted by a model of the form $P = \alpha\rho r^a w^b$ what are appropriate values for a and b?

4.49 If a planet's diameter is d times the Earth's diameter and its average density is s times that of the Earth, how does the planet's mass compare with the Earth's mass?

4.50 In the model $S = kV^{2/3}$ relating surface area and volume, what are:

(a) the smallest possible value of k for circular cylinders?
(b) the value of k for human beings? (Make up a model!)

4.5 Answers to Exercises

4.1 (b)

4.2 (c) only

4.3 (a) increases (b) decreases (c) decreases (d) decreases
(e) increases

4.4 (a) I, D, I (b) D, I, I (c) I, D, D

4.5 (a) C (b) A (c) B (d) D

4.6 (i) (a)
(ii) (d), (e)

(iii) (h), (c), (f)
(iv) (a), (e), (g)

4.9 (b), (d), (e), (g), (h)

4.10 (c)

4.11 (a), (b), (c), (d), (h)

4.13 $0 \leqslant t \leqslant (\pi r^2/a)\sqrt{(2h_0/g)}$

4.14 (a) $kU^3/(2mg)$ (b) $kU^3/(2mg^2)$

4.15 (a) 100 (b) 1000 (c) 0.5 (d) 2 (e) 1 (f) 4×10^8

4.16 1.72 m

4.17 3

4.18 Assuming (for example) a $5 \times 1 \times 1$ shape, about $22\,\text{m} \times 22\,\text{m} \times 103\,\text{m}$

4.19 About 26 ft^2

4.22 5×10^8

4.23 About 90 s

4.24 About 98 billion by about 2400

4.25 (a) 0.1 (b) smallest: $1/a$, largest: b^2 and $\sqrt{a}$ (c) $b/\sqrt{a}$

4.26 (a) $e^{(1/x)}\sqrt{x}$ (b) $x\exp(x^3)$

4.27 (a) $1 + x^2/2$ (b) 0

4.28 (a) x/y (b) y^2/x

4.29 (a) $1 + a^2\Omega^2 + a\Omega t$ (b) $1 + a\sin(\Omega t)$ (c) $1 + a\Omega t$

4.30 $0.786r$

4.31 $x > 1.472$

4.32 Up to 3.3% accurate

4.33 About 0.3 m^2

4.34 (a) (i) smallest: c, largest: x/b
    (ii) smallest: ab, largest: ax/b
    (iii) smallest: $c/(ax^2)$, largest: bx^3/a
  (b) (i) $x^2 + a$ (ii) $bx^2 + a/x$ (iii) $a\sqrt{x}$
  (c) (i) $0.01x^3$ (ii) $0.2/x + 1$ (iii) $\sqrt{(0.001x)}$
  (d) (i) $0.1/x^2 + 0.1/x$ (ii) $0.001 + 0.0001x$ (iii) 1

4.35 (a) MLT^{-2}, $\text{kg}\,\text{m}\,\text{s}^{-2}$ or N (b) ML^2T^{-2}, $\text{kg}\,\text{m}^2\,\text{s}^{-2}$ or J
  (c) ML^2T^{-3}, $\text{kg}\,\text{m}^2\,\text{s}^{-3}$ or $J\,\text{s}^{-1}$ or W (d) ML^{-3}, $\text{kg}\,\text{m}^{-3}$
  (e) M^{-2}, $£\,\text{m}^{-2}$ (f) T^{-1}, $K\,\text{s}^{-1}$ (g) MT^{-1}, $\text{kg}\,\text{s}^{-1}$
  (h) $ML^{-1}T^{-2}$, $\text{kg}\,\text{m}^{-1}\text{s}^{-2}$ or Pa

4.36 (a) $ML^{-2}T^{-1}$, $\text{kg}\,\text{m}^{-2}\,\text{s}^{-1}$ (b) ML^{-3}, $\text{kg}\,\text{m}^{-3}$

4.38 (a) klu^2/gd (b) $ML^{-2}T^{-2}$ (c) $\text{kg}\,\text{m}^{-2}\,\text{s}^{-2}$

4.39 16.97 lb

4.40 0.0706 1 km^{-1}

4.41 1.8×10^7

4.42 $0.447/T$ m s^{-2}

4.43 $(1000L - gx)$ cm^3

4.44 $0.1627R/s$ days

4.45 $0.305(N-1)F/(60M)$

4.46 MT^{-2}, $\text{kg}\,\text{s}^{-2}$ (or $N\,\text{m}^{-1}$), $a = -1/2$, $b = 1/2$

4.47 $MT^{-3}K^{-4}$, $\text{kg}\,\text{s}^{-3}\,K^{-4}$ or $W\,\text{m}^{-2}\,K^{-4}$

4.48 $a = 2$, $b = 3$

4.49 Planet's mass $= sd^3 \times$ Earth's mass

4.50 (a) 5.54 (b) about 10.1

5 Discrete Models

5.1 Background

One of the main points of modelling is to predict the future development of a system. A model of the economy, for example, can be used to predict future trends and so provide a basis for policy decisions. Any such model relies on assuming that the rate of change of a variable X is linked to or caused by some or all of:

(1) the present value of X
(2) previous values of X
(3) values of other variables
(4) the rate of change of other variables
(5) the time, t

The relationship that we want to model is the one that describes how X itself varies with time t. There are two very different ways of modelling such a relationship.

(a) We could think of $X(t)$ as a continuous function of continuous time t. In this case the graph of X against t would show some continuous curve and our modelling objective would be to write an explicit formula for $X(t)$ in terms of t. We discuss **continuous** models in Chapter 6.
(b) We could think about values of X only at particular points in time, for example at intervals of one hour or once a month. In this case we use a symbol such as X_n to denote the value of X after n intervals of time have passed. (The n is referred to as a 'subscript'.) A plot of X_n against n is now a set of separated points rather than a curve and we call this a **discrete** model.

For discrete models the essential ingredient is an equation of the form

next value = function of {present value and previous values and possibly time}

or in terms of symbols,

$$X_{n+1} = f(X_n, \ X_{n-1}, \dots, t)$$

This is usually called a **difference equation**. Note that before writing it down a considerable amount of thinking and choosing of modelling assumptions is normally necessary. Solving a difference equation means finding an explicit expression for X_n in terms of n and initial values such as X_0. Note, however, that this can be rather a difficult task and not strictly essential, because a model in the form of a difference equation can be used **without** knowing the mathematical solution of the equation. This is because if we know present and previous values of X we can always use the difference equation to generate the next value, followed by as many values as we like. Of course, the advantage of having a formula for X_n in terms of n is that we can substitute any value of n we like into the formula to get an immediate answer.

As a simple example of a difference equation, suppose P_n represents an industry's production output in year n and that production doubles every year, so that

next year's production $= 2 \times$ this year's production

that is, $P_{n+1} = 2P_n$

If $P_0 =$ production in year 0 then $P_1 = 2P_0$, $P_2 = 2P_1 = 2(2P_0) = 2^2 P_0$ and $P_3 = 2P_2 = 2(2^2 P_0) = 2^3 P_0$. The pattern is clear; the P values are going up in a geometric progression and the general solution is $P_n = 2^n P_0$. A similar equation applies whenever the growth rate is a **constant percentage**; for example, if the growth rate is 25% per annum then the difference equation is $P_{n+1} = (1.25)P_n$ and the solution is $P_n = (1.25)^n P_0$. These are examples of the difference equation $X_{n+1} = aX_n$, which corresponds to the assumption that a variable increases in a fixed *ratio* (or percentage) in each time step. The solution of this is $X_n = a^n X_0$ (as can be verified by changing n into $n + 1$). The two statements $X_{n+1} = aX_n$ and $X_n = a^n X_0$ are in fact equivalent. The first is the difference equation and the second is its solution.

This kind of situation is very common with investments where interest accumulates at a constant $r\%$ per annum. If P_0 is the initial amount of money invested, the amount P_n after n years satisfies the equation $P_{n+1} = (1 + r/100)P_n$ and the solution is $P_n = (1 + r/100)^n P_0$.

The next simplest type of difference equation is the first-order linear constant coefficient case, which we can write as

$$X_{n+1} = aX_n + b$$

Starting with X_0 we get

$$X_1 = aX_0 + b$$

and

$$X_2 = aX_1 + b = a(aX_0 + b) + b = a^2 X_0 + (a+1)b$$

It follows that

$$X_3 = aX_2 + b = a(a^2 X_0 + (a+1)b) + b$$
$$= a^3 X_0 + (a^2 + a + 1)b$$

Continuing in this way:

$$X_n = a^n X_0 + (a^{n-1} + \cdots + a^2 + a + 1)b$$
$$= a^n X_0 + (a^n - 1)b/(a - 1)$$

The last step comes from summing the geometric series, and we have assumed that a does not equal 1. If a does equal 1 then we can see that $X_2 = X_0 + 2b$, $X_3 = X_0 + 3b$ and so on, so in this case the solution is just $X_n = X_0 + nb$.

With some discrete models of this kind we find that as n increases the X_n values are approaching a **limit** or **equilibrium value**, although they never quite reach it. In this case X_{n+1} eventually becomes indistinguishable from X_n. Then $X_{n+1} = X_n = L$, so, from the difference equation, $L = aL + b$ and therefore the equilibrium value is $L = b/(1 - a)$ (provided we are not dealing with the case $a = 1$). Of course, if we happen to start with $X_0 = L$ then we have $X_n = L$ forever.

A difference equation connecting X_{n+1} and X_n and no other X values is called a **first-order** difference equation. If the equation also involved X_{n-1} or X_{n+2} we would call it **second-order**; in other words, the order is the difference between the highest and lowest subscripts appearing in the equation. Not surprisingly, first-order difference equations are the easiest to deal with. More significant than the order is the question of whether the difference equation is **linear**. An example of a linear difference equation (this one happens to be second-order) is

$$X_{n+1} = 2X_n + 3X_{n-1} + n^2 + 7$$

Note that the presence of the n^2 does not make the equation non-linear: the important thing is that all the X terms are only multiplied by constants. A simple (and important) example of a non-linear difference equation is

$$X_{n+1} = aX_n(1 - X_n)$$

where a is a constant. The solutions of non-linear equations reveal a much stranger and more varied behaviour than that of linear equations and in some cases show the kind of behaviour described as 'chaos'.

Difference equations are easiest to solve when they are **homogeneous**. This means that the equation can be satisfied by making all the Xs equal 0. For example, the equation $X_{n+2} - 3X_{n+1} + X_n = 0$ is homogeneous, while $X_{n+1} - 2X_n = 3n + 1$ is not. It also makes things easier if the coefficients are constants. For example, $X_{n+2} - 3X_{n+1} + X_n = 0$ has **constant coeffients**, while $X_{n+2} - 3nX_{n+1} + X_n = 0$ does not.

Mathematical methods for obtaining solutions of difference equations can be found in many textbooks (see the Bibliography for examples) and will not be described in this chapter. Here we are only concerned with the **formulation** of models in terms of difference equations and their possible application.

5.2 More Than One Variable

Suppose that in a battle between two opposing forces each unit of army A is able to destroy a units of army B during one time unit. Similarly each unit of army B is able to destroy b units of army A.

Let A_n denote the number of units of army A surviving after n time steps, and similarly B_n for army B. We therefore have two variables and their fates are obviously linked. How does this connection appear in a mathematical model? The answer is obtained by considering what happens in one time step.

The total number of units of army A destroyed during that time step is bB_n because every one of the B_n units of army B destroys b units of army A. The number of surviving units of army A at the beginning of the next time step is therefore

$$A_{n+1} = A_n - bB_n$$

and similarly for B,

$$B_{n+1} = B_n - aA_n$$

Here we have two explicit but **coupled** difference equations, and neither one can be solved on its own. However, given initial sizes A_0 and B_0 for the two armies, and also given the parameters a and b, we could compute A_1 and B_1 etc. directly from the above difference equations.

An alternative approach is to eliminate one of the variables by substitution. The first equation implies that

$$\begin{aligned} A_{n+2} &= A_{n+1} - bB_{n+1} \\ &= A_{n+1} - b(B_n - aA_n) && \text{(substituting for } B_{n+1}) \\ &= A_{n+1} + abA_n + (A_{n+1} - A_n) && \text{(substituting for } B_n) \end{aligned}$$

This is

$$A_{n+2} - 2A_{n+1} + (1 - ab)A_n = 0$$

a second-order difference equation. From it we can generate a sequence of A_n values provided two starting values, e.g. A_0 and A_1 are available. Alternatively a mathematical solution for A_n in terms of n can be derived. Methods for doing this can be found in the Bibliography, and one example is given in Example 5.9.

5.3 Matrix Models

Linear difference equations involving more than one variable can be neatly expressed using vectors and matrices. The state of the battle in the previous example can be represented by the vector $X_n = [A_n, \ B_n]$ and the pair of simultaneous difference equations can be written

$$\begin{bmatrix} A_{n+1} \\ B_{n+1} \end{bmatrix} = \begin{bmatrix} 1 & -a \\ -b & 1 \end{bmatrix} \begin{bmatrix} A_n \\ B_n \end{bmatrix}$$

so the progress of the battle from one step to the next can be written concisely as $X_{n+1} = M X_n$, where M is the matrix

$$\begin{bmatrix} 1 & -a \\ -b & 1 \end{bmatrix}$$

and the solution can be written $X_n = M^n X_0$.

This approach is especially useful for models representing **transitions** between states or compartments. When developing models for populations, for example, we often want to do more than just predict the total size of the population. At any time a human population will consist of a mixture of individuals of different age, sex, occupation etc. In order to make forward planning for the provision of resources such as schools and hospitals we need to make predictions about the future numbers of individuals in different categories within the population.

Let us take a simple and artificial example of a population of animals which become adult and capable of reproducing at the age of one year. Suppose we represent the population at time step n in terms of the numbers of animals in each of three categories.

B_n = number of babies and young animals up to one year old
A_n = number of young adults up to two years old
S_n = number of 'senior' adults aged two or older

There will be different annual birth and death rates for the three groups. Suppose we have the following information:

Group	Birth rate	Death rate
B	0	0.1
A	0.3	0.2
S	0.1	0.3

This means, for example, that 90% of babies survive to become adults and that 10% of senior adults produce one offspring per year on average.

We can put this information into matrix form as

$$\begin{bmatrix} B \\ A \\ S \end{bmatrix}_{n+1} = \begin{bmatrix} 0 & 0.3 & 0.1 \\ 0.9 & 0 & 0 \\ 0 & 0.8 & 0.7 \end{bmatrix} \begin{bmatrix} B \\ A \\ S \end{bmatrix}_n$$

and to find out what happens to the population we only have to keep multiplying by the matrix (often called the **transition matrix**). The nature of the solution, and whether we eventually reach a steady state depends on the largest eigenvalue, λ, of this matrix.

- If $\lambda > 1$ then the population grows without limit.
- If $\lambda = 1$ then the population converges to the eigenvector associated with λ.
- If $\lambda < 1$ then the population continually decreases.

(See the Bibliography for further information.)

5.4 Worked Examples

5.1 How long does it take a sum of money to double itself if the interest rate is $r\%$ per annum?

Solution We start from the simple model $P_n = (1 + r/100)^n P_0$ and this will be $2P_0$ if $(1 + r/100)^n = 2$. To find n from this, take logs so that $n \ln(1 + r/100) = \ln 2$ from which $n = \ln 2 / \ln(1 + r/100)$.

For example, if $r\% = 10\%$ this gives the doubling time as $n = \ln 2 / \ln(1.1)$, which is about 7.3 years.

Note that $r\%$ per annum is not equivalent to $r/12\%$ per month. Suppose the monthly interest rate is $x\%$ per month; then after 12 months we have $P = (1 + x/100)^{12} P_0$, which must be the same as $(1 + r/100)P_0$, so x and r are related by $1 + x/100 = (1 + r/100)^{1/12}$. For example, an annual rate of 12% is not equivalent to 1% per month but to $x = 100((1.12)^{1/12} - 1) = 0.9489\%$ per month.

5.2   How much does a sum of money grow to if we keep adding regular payments?

Solution   Suppose the initial investment is P_0 and that at the end of each year we add a fixed amount a. If P_n denotes the total value of our savings at the end of n years then

$$\text{this year's amount} = \text{last year's amount} + \text{interest} + \text{latest instalment}$$

i.e.
$$P_{n+1} = (1 + r/100)P_n + a$$

or $P_{n+1} = RP_n + a$ if we use R for $1 + r/100$. This is just a first-order linear difference equation with constant coefficients, so we can write down an expression for P_n in terms of n, namely

$$P_n = R^n P_0 + a(R^n - 1)/(R - 1)$$

5.3   How much do we need to pay back every month to repay a mortgage?

Solution   Let $X_n = $ amount owed after n years
   $m = $ monthly repayment
   $N = $ number of years required to settle our debts
   $r = $ annual % interest rate charged on the amount outstanding

Clearly X_0 is the original amount borrowed and X_N is zero. We can derive a model from the following equation:

$$\text{amount owed next year} = \text{amount owed this year} + \text{interest} - \text{repayments made this year}$$

Putting this into symbols,

$$X_{n+1} = X_n + rX_n/100 - 12m$$
$$= RX_n - 12m$$

where $R = 1 + r/100$. This is the same as Example 5.2, with $a = -12m$, so the solution is

$$X_n = R^n X_0 - 12m(R^n - 1)/(R - 1)$$

The mortgage is to be repaid completely in N years, i.e. $X_N = 0$, so

$$0 = R^N X_0 - 12m(R^N - 1)/(R - 1)$$

and the monthly repayment required to achieve this is

$$m = X_0(R - 1)/(12(1 - R^{-N}))$$

Substituting for m, we find that the amount still owed after n years is

$$X_n = X_0(1 - R^{n-N})/(1 - R^{-N})$$

To take a particular example, if the interest rate is 11%, what is the monthly repayment on a loan of £50 000 to be repaid over 25 years?
   In this case $R = 1.11$ so

$$m = 50\,000 \times (1.11 - 1)/(12(1 - 1.11^{-25}))$$
$$= 494.75$$

The graph in Fig. 5.1 shows how X_n, the amount still owed, decreases slowly at first but drops sharply towards the end of the term.
   In real life, interest rates are liable to change. Suppose there is a 1% cut from 11% to 10%. Does this mean the monthly repayment will also be reduced by 1%?
   Using our formula we find the new monthly repayment is

$$50\,000(1.1 - 1)/(12(1 - 1.1^{-25})) = 459.03$$

which is over 7% less than before.

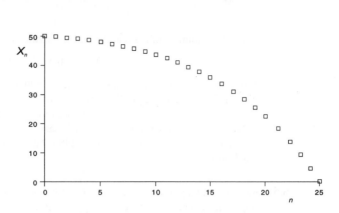

Figure 5.1

If the interest rate goes up, borrowers are sometimes offered the option of continuing to pay the same monthly repayment but lengthening the term, N, of the mortgage. Continuing from our last example, suppose the interest rate now jumps from 10% to 10.5% but we wish to continue paying £459.03 a month. Previously the term was 25 years; what will it now become? We must find N from

$$459.03 = 50\,000(1.105 - 1)/(12(1 - 1.105^{-N}))$$

i.e.

$$1.105^{-N} \approx 0.046\,903$$

from which

$$-N\ln(1.105) \approx \ln(0.046\,903)$$

giving

$$N \approx 30.6$$

It may, however, be impossible to do this. This will be the case if the above equation does not have a solution with a finite positive N. The limiting case is when N is infinite, in other words it takes us forever to pay back the mortgage. What interest rate will cause this to happen? In our last example, keeping our monthly repayment at £459.03 and letting $N \to \infty$ so that $1 - R^{-N} \to 0$ we have

$$459.03 = 50\,000(R - 1)/12$$

which gives

$$R \approx 1.1102$$

so if the interest rate goes above 11% we cannot pay the mortgage back at the rate of £459.03 per month.

Another way of looking at this is to see that we will take forever to pay back the mortgage if

$$\text{amount owed next year} = \text{amount owed this year}$$

so putting $X_{n+1} = X_n = L$ into our model we get

$$L = RL - 12m$$

so

$$L = 12m/(R - 1)$$

For example if the interest rate is 12% and we can afford to repay up to £500 a month, the biggest loan we can repay is $L = 12 \times 500/(1.12 - 1) = 50\,000$ (although it will take us an infinite time to pay it all back!).

5.4 Each year 1000 new cases of a certain disease occur and half the existing cases are cured. At the end of 1994 there were 1200 cases. How many will there be at the end of 1999? What will happen eventually?

Solution We start with a statement based on the facts given:

$$\text{next year's cases} = \text{half of this year's cases} + 1000 \text{ new cases}$$

This becomes our model when we translate the statement into symbols.

Let X_n = number of cases at the end of n years after 1994. Then

$$X_{n+1} = 0.5X_n + 1000 \text{ and } X_0 = 1200$$

From this we can easily calculate $X_1 = 600 + 1000 = 1600$, $X_2 = 1800\ldots$ etc. until we reach $X_5 = 1975$, which is the predicted number of cases at the end of 1999.

Alternatively, we could use the formula for the solution of a linear constant-coefficient first-order difference equation given previously and insert $n = 5$. Note that the X_n values are approaching a limit L, where $L = 0.5L + 1000$, i.e. $L = 2000$. The X_n values approach this value without ever actually reaching it.

5.5   Suppose that a political party loses $p\%$ of its supporters every month while in the same month $q\%$ of its opponents become converted to supporting the party. If X_n is the percentage of the population which supports the party in month n, write down a difference equation satisfied by X_n.

Solution   The percentage of the population which does not support the party in month n is $100 - X_n$ and a fraction $(q/100)$ of these change over to supporting the party. Meanwhile the party loses a fraction $(p/100)$ of its own support. Our model is therefore

$$X_{n+1} = (1 - p/100)X_n + (q/100)(100 - X_n)$$
$$= (1 - p/100 - q/100)X_n + q$$

another first-order linear difference equation.

5.6   A girl eats 2500 calories every day. 1200 cal are used up in basic metabolism and she uses 16 cal per kg of body weight per day in exercise. The rest are converted into body fat (10 000 cal convert to 1 kg fat).

On Sunday morning she weighed 9 stone exactly. On Wednesday she had a bigger than usual meal and her intake was 3500 cal for that day.

Develop a mathematical model for predicting her weight W_n on the morning of day n and use it to estimate:

(a) Her weight on Saturday morning
(b) The most she should eat daily to avoid putting on any weight (when her weight is 9 stone)
(c) The minimum weight she can reduce to in N weeks
(d) The daily intake to which she should restrict herself if she wants to bring her weight down to 8 stone in N weeks for various values of N (starting from 9 stone)

Solution   First, note that for the purpose of this model we will ignore energy intake from respiration.

When her weight is W_n she uses up $16W_n$ calories a day in exercise so her net intake of calories for that day is $1300 - 16W_n$. To convert this from calories into kg of fat we have to divide by 10 000. Her net increase in weight is therefore $(1300 - 16W_n)/10\,000$ and our model is

$$W_{n+1} = W_n + 0.13 - 0.0016W_n = 0.9984W_n + 0.13$$

We also have a mixture of units in the question, so we shall convert stones into kg using the fact that 1 stone $\approx 6.350\,293$ kg.

(a) On Sunday morning we have $W_0 = 9 \times 6.350\,293 = 57.1526$ kg. (Do we need all these decimal places? It is better to be safe and leave the rounding until the end of the calculation.) Using the model we quickly find that her weight on Wednesday morning is $W_3 = 57.268\,119\,4$. On Wednesday her intake is an extra 1000 cal more than usual, so $W_4 = 0.9984W_3 + 0.23 = 57.406\,49$. We then return to the previous model and calculate $W_6 = 57.482\,728$.

(b) Suppose her daily intake is a constant α cal. The difference equation is then $W_{n+1} = W_n + (\alpha - 1200 - 16W_n)/10\,000$.
Putting $W_{n+1} = W_n = 57.1526$ we find $\alpha \approx 2114$.

(c) If she eats nothing at all then the model becomes $W_{n+1} = 0.9984W_n - 0.12$.
We can use our general solution for first-order linear difference equations to write down an expression for

$$W_n = 0.9984^n W_0 - 0.12[1 - 0.9984^n]/0.0016 = 132.1526(0.9984)^n - 75$$

(d) Using the equation from (b), $W_{n+1} = 0.9984W_n + 10^{-4}\alpha - 0.12$, we can again use our general solution for first-order linear difference equations to write down an expression for

$$W_n = (0.9984)^n W_0 + (10^{-4}\alpha - 0.12)[1 - (0.9984)^n]/(1 - 0.9984)$$

Putting this equal to 8 stone $\approx 50.802\,344$ kg and rearranging to solve for α we find

$$\alpha = 1200 + 16[50.802\,344 - 0.9984^n(57.1526)]/[1 - 0.9984^n]$$

Values for $W_N(\alpha = 0)$ and α for various values of N are given in the table below, remembering that N is the number of *weeks*.

N	$W_N(\alpha = 0)$	α
5	49.95	250
10	43.14	1156
20	30.61	1609
30	19.41	1759
40	9.40	1833
50	0.45	1877

Some of the values in the table are obviously not to be taken literally!

5.7 A railway locomotive is connected to a line of stationary wagons and exerts a constant force F. Between every pair of wagons the coupling is slack and movement through a distance d is required before the coupling becomes tight. Obtain an equation satisfied by V_n, the speed of the train immediately after the nth wagon has started to move. Assume that m_n is the mass of the nth wagon.

Solution Just before the nth wagon starts to move the mass of the moving wagons is $M_{n-1} = m_1 + m_2 + \cdots + m_{n-1}$ and their kinetic energy is $M_{n-1}V_{n-1}^2/2$. Immediately afterwards the mass of moving wagons is M_n and their total kinetic energy is $M_n V_n^2/2$. The increase in kinetic energy is $(M_n V_n^2 - M_{n-1}V_{n-1}^2)/2$ and this is accounted for by the work done by the engine, which is force $\times$ distance $= Fd$. This gives us the model

$$V_n = (M_{n-1}/M_n)\sqrt{(V_{n-1}^2 + 2Fd/M_{n-1})}$$

5.8 Suppose an epidemic breaks out in an isolated community of N people. Let I_n represent the number of infected people n days after the start of the epidemic and let S_n represent those who are susceptible but not yet infected. Assume that each day the number of new infections is proportional to the number of contacts between infected and suspected people, which in turn is proportional to how many there are of each. Write down simple models consistent with these assumptions in each of the following cases.

(a) The illness lasts indefinitely but is non-fatal.
(b) Each day a certain percentage of infected persons die.
(c) Each day a certain percentage of infected persons recover and are then immune to reinfection. The illness is non-fatal.
(d) Each day a certain percentage of infected persons recover but then immediately become susceptible to infection again. The illness is non-fatal.

Solution (a) This model can be derived from

$$\text{tomorrow's infectives} = \text{today's infectives} + \text{new infectives}$$

That is, $I_{n+1} = I_n + aS_nI_n$, where a is a constant.

Similarly, $S_{n+1} = S_n - aS_nI_n$, since the newly infected people are no longer classified as simply susceptible. These two difference equations constitute our model. Note that if we add, we get $I_{n+1} + S_{n+1} = I_n + S_n$, so the sum of the numbers of people in the two categories is always constant. This of course, is consistent with our assumptions and the constant number is N, the total size of the community.

(b) Here the first equation must be modified to $I_{n+1} = I_n + aS_nI_n - dI_n$ where d is a constant representing the death rate. This time $I_n + S_n$ is not constant and the population gradually declines.

(c) For this we can introduce another variable, R_n = number recovered and immune on day n. The assumptions lead to

$$I_{n+1} = I_n + aS_nI_n - rI_n$$
$$R_{n+1} = R_n + rI_n$$
$$S_{n+1} = S_n - aS_nI_n$$

Notice that, as in case (a), we have $I_n + S_n + R_n = \text{constant} = N$.
(d) This time we have no R_n and our equations are

$$I_{n+1} = I_n + aS_nI_n - rI_n$$
$$S_{n+1} = S_n - aS_nI_n + rI_n$$

and again $I_n + S_n = N$.

Note that we could not use the matrix method on this problem because the term aS_nI_n makes the equations non-linear.

5.9 A battle is about to start between 10 000 troops of army A and 5000 troops of army B. Given that the destroying rates are $a = 0.1$ and $b = 0.15$, use a simple model to predict the outcome of the battle.

Solution We use the simple model

$$A_{n+1} = A_n - bB_n = A_n - 0.15B_n$$
$$B_{n+1} = B_n - aA_n = B_n - 0.1A_n$$

We can measure in units of 1000 so that $A_0 = 10$ and $B_0 = 5$. The model then gives the following results (rounded to 2 d.p.).

n	0	1	2	3	4	5	6
A_n	10	9.25	8.65	8.19	7.86	7.65	7.55
B_n	5	4.00	3.08	2.21	1.39	0.61	−0.16

At this point we must obviously stop. Sometime during the 6th time step the B army was reduced to zero and our model ceases to be valid. We must remember the limited domain of validity of any model. The other conclusion we can make is that the A army still has a strength of about 7500 at the end of the battle.

We could also consider the mathematical solution of the second-order difference equation derived earlier,

$$A_{n+2} - 2A_{n+1} + (1 - ab)A_n = 0$$

i.e.

$$A_{n+2} - 2A_{n+1} + 0.985A_n = 0$$

The solution for A_n in terms of n is found by substituting $A_n = \alpha x^n$, where α and x are numbers to be found. This gives $\alpha x^n(x^2 - 2x + 0.985) = 0$.

The roots of the quadratic are $x = 1.1225$ and $x = 0.8775$, so there are two answers of this form and the general case is a linear combination of both of them, in other words

$$A_n = \alpha(1.225)^n + \beta(0.8775)^n$$

where the constants α and β are found by using the initial values $10 = A_0 = \alpha + \beta$ and $9.25 = A_1 = 1.225\alpha + 0.8775\beta$. These simultaneous equations for α and β give $\alpha = 1.94$ and $\beta = 8.06$ and finally we can write down an expression for $A_n = 1.94(1.1225)^n + 8.06(0.8775)^n$. This gives the same numerical values as we found before. The corresponding expression for $B_n = 0$ is found from $B_n = (A_n - A_{n+1})/b$ which simplifies to $B_n = -1.58(1.1225)^n + 6.58(0.8775)^n$. Both expressions are of course valid for $n = 0$ up to 5 only, as far as the model is concerned, although the mathematical solution is true for all n.

Yet another approach to this problem is to use the matrix formulation, that is

$$\begin{bmatrix} A \\ B \end{bmatrix}_{n+1} = \begin{bmatrix} 1 & -0.15 \\ -0.1 & 1 \end{bmatrix} \begin{bmatrix} A \\ B \end{bmatrix}_n$$

The numbers 0.8775 and 1.1225 are the eigenvalues of the matrix.

5.10 Suppose that each female adult of a particular species of insect lays 100 eggs every month. Consider female insects only and suppose that 10% of the eggs survive to the larva stage, 20% of the larvae survive to be pupae, and 30% of the pupae grow into adults. Assume that each stage lasts a month and that also

40% of this month's adults are still alive next month. Write down a matrix model for the population vector $X = [E, L, P, A]^T$ where A_n = number of adults in month n etc. If we start with 10 adults what will be the population (a) after 6 months and (b) after a very long time?

Solution   The transition matrix is

$$M = \begin{bmatrix} 0 & 0 & 0 & 100 \\ 0.1 & 0 & 0 & 0 \\ 0 & 0.2 & 0 & 0 \\ 0 & 0 & 0.3 & 0.4 \end{bmatrix}$$

and the model is represented by the difference equation $X_{n+1} = MX_n$
Starting with

$$X_0^T = [0, \qquad\qquad 0, \quad 0, \qquad 10]$$

this produces

$$X_1^T = [1000, \qquad\quad 0, \quad 0, \qquad 4]$$
$$X_2^T = [400, \qquad\quad 100, \quad 0, \qquad 1.6]$$
$$X_3^T = [160, \qquad\quad 40, \quad 20, \qquad 0.64]$$
$$X_4^T = [64, \qquad\quad 16, \quad 8, \qquad 6.256]$$
$$X_5^T = [625.6, \qquad 6.4, \quad 3.2, \quad 4.9024]$$
$$X_6^T = [490.24, \quad 62.56, \quad 1.28, \quad 2.921]$$

We keep the decimal places in the answers even though we cannot have exactly 6.256 insects; the values can be regarded as averages. The answer to (a) is given by X_6, which we can translate to about 490 eggs, 63 larvae, 1 pupa and 3 adults.

To answer (b) we keep on going like this until the X_{n+1} vector is the same as X_n, which is what happens after a while. We get the **steady state** vector [357.1429, 35.7143, 7.1429, 3.5714]. This is an eigenvector of the matrix A. After reaching this state the population does not change from one month to the next.

5.5 Exercises

5.1   For each of the following write down the values of X_1, X_2, X_3 and X_4:

(a) $X_{n+1} = X_n + 3, X_0 = 1$

(b) $X_{n+1} = 0.5X_n + 1, X_0 = 2$

(c) $X_{n+1} = X_n^2 + \sqrt{X_n}, X_0 = 1$

(d) $X_{n+1} = \sin(X_n), X_0 = 1$ (use radians)

5.2   Classify each of the following difference equations by completing the table.

Equation	Order	Linear?	Constant coefficients?	Homoge-neous
(a) $X_{n+1} = 1.2X_n + 30$				
(b) $Y_{n+1} = 5 - Y_n^2$				
(c) $X_{j+1} = 4X_j + X_{j-1}$				
(d) $V_{n+1} = 3V_n + 7$				
(e) $U_k = kU_{k-1} - U_{k-2}$				
(f) $Z_n = 2Z_{n-1}^2 + nZ_{n-3}$				
(g) $W_{n+1} = W_n W_{n-1}$				

5.3   Write down a difference equation connecting X_{n+1} and X_n (the more correct mathematical description is 'a difference equation satisfied by X_n') if

$$X_0 = 2, \ X_1 = 5, \ X_2 = 11, \ X_3 = 23, \ X_4 = 47, \ldots$$

5.4   Suppose that every year, $x\%$ of existing cars are scrapped and N new cars are bought. Write down a difference equation for C_n = number of cars in year n.

5.5   A car does 30 miles per gallon of petrol. Write down a difference equation satisfied by X_n = number of gallons in the tank after going n miles without refuelling.

5.6   A beanstalk grows 3 cm on the first day and its growth on each day after that is half that on the previous day. If B_n is the length of the beanstalk at the end of day n, write down a difference equation satisfied by B_n.

5.7   Suppose the number of insects of a particular species alive in month n depends on the number of eggs laid two months ago and on the number surviving the larval stage (first month). Making the simplest possible assumptions, write down a difference equation satisfied by I_n = number of insects in month n.

5.8   A certain type of tree takes 10 years to grow to maturity. If P_n denotes the number of such trees planted in year n and M_n denotes the number of mature trees in year n, write down an equation connecting M and P. What if C mature trees are cut down every year?

5.9   If production increases by 4% every year and P_n denotes the production level in year n, write down a difference equation satisfied by P_n. If production was 10 million tonnes in 1990 estimate (a) when it will reach 14 million tonnes, (b) when it was below 6 million tonnes.

5.10 A machine depreciates in value by 5% p.a. Write down a difference equation for V_n, its value when it is n years old. If it is worth £10 000 new and is scrapped when its value is down to £3000, calculate (a) its value after 5 years, (b) its useful life.

5.11 A disease spreads in such a way that 100 individuals become infected during any year and 25% of those infected at the beginning of a year die before the end of the year. Write down a difference equation for I_n, the number of people infected at the end of n years. What happens in the long term?

5.12 A firm has just started to manufacture a new product and is stepping up production by 2000 units per month. The first month's production was 5000 units.

(a) In what month will production first exceed (i) 20 000 units per month, (ii) N units per month?
(b) How long will it take to produce a total of more than (i) 80 000 units, (ii) N units?

5.13 A library buys 500 new books at the end of every year and all 10-year-old books are thrown away. Five per cent of the books in the library at the beginning of each year are lost or stolen by the end of the year. Write down a difference equation satisfied by X_n = number of books at the end of year n. (Assume $n = 0$ was a very long time ago.)

5.14 How long does it take a sum of money to treble itself if the interest rate is 9% p.a.?

5.15 If a mortgage is to be repaid over 25 years and the interest rate is r% p.a., by when will half of the original mortgage have been repaid?

5.16 In a factory the time required to carry out a certain task is made up of a fixed set-up time S and a processing time P. The manager finds that new employees all follow a similar 'learning curve'; each time they perform the task the set-up time remains the same but the processing time is reduced by 7%. Write down an equation connecting T_{n+1} and T_n, the time a new employee takes to do the task for the $(n + 1)$th and nth time.

5.17 At the beginning of the year you invest £2000 in an account which pays interest at 9% p.a. At the end of the year, and subsequently every 12 months, you withdraw an amount £W.

(a) Write down a difference equation satisfied by X_n = amount left in the account immediately after the nth withdrawal.
(b) Write down an expression for X_n in terms of n and W.
(c) What happens to the account in the two cases (i) $W = 200$ and (ii) $W = 160$?
(d) What is the maximum W can be and still leave something left in the account at the end of 5 years?
(e) If instead of the exact answer to (c), the nearest whole number of £s are taken out every year, how much will be left in the account at the end of 5 years?

5.18 A carrot which is modelled as a cone is to be sliced up for cooking so that all the slices have the same weight. If the first cut is made at a distance X_0 from the tip, write down an expression for X_n, the distance of the nth cut from the tip.

5.19 A very useful continuous model is the logistic model $P(t) = L/[1 + (L/P_0 - 1)e^{-kt}]$, often used as a basis for models for population growth. This is discussed in Chapter 9. Show that if P_n and P_{n+1} are the values of P at $t = n\delta t$ and $t = (n + 1)\delta t$, where δt is

a finite time step, then $1/P_n$ satisfies a first-order linear difference equation

$$(1/P)_{n+1} = a + b(1/P)_n$$

and find expressions for a and b in terms of $k\delta t$ and L.

5.20 Two neighbouring countries X and Y regard each other as enemies and each year they both spend money on arms for defence. Suppose that for each side, the amount spent is made up as follows:

(a) There is a constant level of spending necessary to maintain a minimum level of defence.
(b) The more was spent last year, the less is spent this year.
(c) The more was spent by the enemy side last year, the more is spent this year.

Write down a simple model consistent with the above assumptions.

5.21 Assume:

(a) The daily growth of a pot plant depends on how much water there was in its pot on the previous day.
(b) The amount of water added per day by the gardener depends on how much water there was in the pot the day before.
(c) The amount of water taken up by the plant depends on its size.

Let P_n = size of plant in day n and W_n = amount of water in its pot in day n. Write down simple equations consistent with the above assumptions.

5.22 Suppose that during every day of an epidemic,

(a) x% of ill people die
(b) y% of ill people recover and become immune
(c) z% of susceptible people become ill

Write down simple models for

I_n = number of ill people on day n
S_n = number of susceptible people on day n
R_n = number of recovered and immune people on day n

5.23 Suppose that a stock-control manager looks at her figures every month. Let P_n = production in month n, S_n = stock in month n and D_n = demand in month n.

(a) Write down an equation connecting S_{n+1} with S_n, P_n and D_n.
(b) The manager decides to adopt a policy of making next month's production proportional to last month's demand. Write down the resulting equation connecting S_{n+1} with S_n and P_n.

5.24 Assume:

(i) National income I is made up from consumption C and investment V.
(ii) Consumption in any year is made up from a constant amount plus an amount proportional to investment.
(iii) Investment in any year is made up from a constant amount plus an amount proportional to national income.

(a) Write down the simplest model consistent with the above assumptions.
(b) How is the model altered if assumption (iii) is changed to: investment in any year is made up from a constant amount plus an amount proportional to the increase in consumption?

5.25 Assume that for a certain agricultural product:

(a) The demand depends on the price.
(b) This year's price depends on last year's supply.
(c) This year's supply depends on last year's price.

Translate these assumptions into simple discrete difference equations.

5.26 Ten thousand troops of army A are confronted on day zero by 8000 troops of army B, who have slightly superior military equipment. The destroying rates are 0.1/day for A and 0.12/day for B. After three days of fighting, 500 troops of army A decide to surrender and are taken prisoner. At the end of day 6 of the battle, army B receives reinforcements of 1500 troops. Use a simple model to predict the outcome.

5.27 One child comes to school on Monday carrying a flu virus. Suppose every infected child has close contact with two uninfected children every day and that at each such contact the virus is passed on. Assume this passing on of the virus happens in the morning and that after two days with the infection a child becomes ill and stays at home until recovered (and is then immune and uninfectious).

Let I_n = number of newly infected children on the morning of day n and S_n = number of susceptible children on the morning of day n. Write down simple equations satisfied by I_n and S_n.

If the total number of children at the school initially was 401, use the equations to predict the number of newly infected children on Friday morning.

5.28 Suppose that in a small town, on any day 50% of ill people become well and 10% of healthy people become ill. Write down a matrix model for $[H, I]^T$ where H_n and I_n represent the number of healthy people and ill people on day n.

If we start with 5000 healthy people and 500 ill people on Monday, what will be the situation on Friday? What happens in the long run?

5.29 Suppose that 80% of the customers who buy Brand A coffee this month will buy the same brand again next month, while 20% will switch to Brand B. Suppose also that 10% of those who this month bought Brand B will buy Brand A next month while the remaining 90% remain loyal to Brand B. Express these statements in the form of a matrix model for $[A, B]^T$ where A = % of shoppers who buy Brand A and similarly for B.

If this month's percentages are $A = 60$ and $B = 40$, what will they be (a) in 3 months time, (b) in 6 months time, (c) eventually?

5.30 Suppose a human population is divided into four age groups and a time step of 20 years is taken. Suppose also that birthrate and survival/transition rates are as follows:

Age	0–20	20–40	40–60	> 60
Birthrate	0.1	1.5	0	0
Survival	0.9	0.8	0.6	0.1

(a) Write down a matrix model incorporating these assumptions.
(b) If the present population vector is $[500, 400, 300, 200]^T$ use the model to predict the population 80 years from now.
(c) Does the model predict a steady state population?

5.31 Suppose that after a certain field has been burnt out by fire, in one year 30% of the bare soil becomes covered with grasses. In subsequent years in 10% of the grass area small shrubs start to grow, while 5% of the grass area reverts to bare soil and 4% of the shrub area reverts to grass.

Write down a simple matrix model for the percentage of ground in each of the three catogories: (i) bare soil, (ii) grass, (iii) shrubs. What happens in the long term?

5.32 Suppose that each year every pair of adult birds from a rare species lays 4 eggs which hatch into two male and two female chicks at the start of the following year. Also 50% of young chicks die in their first year, but if they survive they will breed in their second and subsequent years. Meanwhile 10% of birds aged 1 and 20% of birds aged 2 or older die each year.

Write down a matrix model for female birds using the vector X to represent [chicks, 1-year-olds, > 1-year-olds].

If there are 6 pairs of 2-year-old birds this year, what will be the state of the population (a) in 10 years time and (b) eventually?

5.33 Assume that every day:

(i) 2.6% of the lead in a person's blood is excreted by the kidneys
(ii) 1% of the lead in the blood enters the tissues
(iii) 0.4% of the lead in the blood enters the bones
(iv) 1.2% of the lead in the tissues enters the blood
(v) 1.8% of the lead in the tissues is excreted via the hair, nails and sweat

(a) Write down a matrix model for the percentage of lead in the blood, tissues and bones, which incorporates all the above assumptions.
(b) If a person ingests $100\,\mu g$ one day, what has happened to it, (i) one day later, (ii) a week later?

5.6 Answers to Exercises

5.1 (a) 4, 7, 10, 13   (c) 2, 5.4142, 31.6405, 1006.75
      (b) 2, 2, 2, 2   (d) 0.8415, 0.7456, 0.6784, 0.62757

5.2

Equation	Order	Linear	Constant coefficient?	Homogeneous?
(a)	1	Y	Y	N
(b)	1	N	Y	N
(c)	2	Y	Y	Y
(d)	1	Y	Y	N
(e)	2	Y	N	Y
(f)	3	N	N	Y
(g)	2	N	Y	Y

5.3 $X_{n+1} = 2X_n + 1$ or $X_{n+1} = X_n + 3 \times 2^n$

5.4 $C_{n+1} = (1 - x/100)C_n + N$

5.5 $X_{n+1} = X_n - 1/30$

5.6 $B_{n+1} = B_n + (0.5)^n 3$ or $B_{n+2} - B_{n+1} = 0.5(B_{n+1} - B_n)$

5.7 $I_{n+2} = aI_n + bI_{n+1}$

5.8 $M_n = M_{n-1} + P_{n-10}$ if $n \geqslant 10$. Just subtract C for the cutting.

5.9 (a) 1999   (b) 1977

5.10 (a) £7738   (b) 23.47 years

5.11 $I_{n+1} = 0.75I_n + 100$. Converges to 400.

5.12 (a) (i) 9   (ii) $1 + \text{INT}[(N-3)/2]$
      (b) (i) 8   (ii) $1 + \text{INT}[\sqrt{(4+N)} - 2]$

5.13 $X_n = 500 + 0.95X_{n-1} - X_{n-10}(0.95)^{10}$, assuming $n \geqslant 10$

5.14   About 13 years

5.15 $n = 25 - \ln[2/(1 + R^{-25})]/\ln R$ where $R = 1 + r/100$

5.16 $T_{n+1} = 0.07S + 0.93T_n$

5.17   (a) $X_{n+1} = (1.09)X_n - W$
      (b) $X_n = 2000(1.09)^n - W[(1.09)^n - 1]/0.09$
      (c) (i) decreases and goes into deficit after 27 years
           (ii) increases
      (d) £514.18
      (e) £1.11

5.18 $(n+1)^{1/3}X_0$

5.19 $a = (1 - \text{e}^{-k\delta t})/L, \quad b = \text{e}^{-k\delta t}$

5.20 $X_{n+1} = aY_n - bX_n + c,$
      $Y_{n+1} = dX_n - eY_n + f, (a, \ldots, f > 0)$

5.21 $P_{n+1} = P_n + aW_n, \quad W_{n+1} = bW_n - cP_n, \ a, b, c > 0$

5.22 $I_{n+1} = I_n - (x/100)I_n - (y/100)I_n + (z/100)S_n$
      $S_{n+1} = S_n - (z/100)S_n$
      $R_{n+1} = R_n + (y/100)I_n$

5.23   (a) $S_{n+1} = S_n + P_n - D_n$
      (b) $P_{n+1} = \alpha D_n$ so $S_{n+1} = S_n + (1 - \alpha)P_n$

5.24   (a) $I_n = C_n + V_n, \ C_n = a + bV_n, \ V_n = c + dI_n$
      (b) $I_n = C_n + V_n, \ C_n = a + bV_n, \ V_n = c + d(C_n - C_{n-1})$

5.25 $D_{n+1} = a - bP_{n+1}, \ P_{n+1} = c - dS_n$

5.26 $S_{n+1} = e + fP_n \ (a, \ldots, f > 0)$

5.26   B wins on day 18 with 1398 troops remaining

5.27 $I_n = 2I_{n-1}, S_n = S_{n-1} - I_n, 24$

5.28 $\begin{bmatrix} H \\ I \end{bmatrix}_{n+1} = \begin{bmatrix} 0.9 & 0.5 \\ 0.1 & 0.5 \end{bmatrix} \begin{bmatrix} H \\ I \end{bmatrix}_n, \ [4594, 906]^\text{T}, [4583, 917]^\text{T}$

5.29 $\begin{bmatrix} A \\ B \end{bmatrix}_{n+1} = \begin{bmatrix} 0.8 & 0.1 \\ 0.2 & 0.9 \end{bmatrix} \begin{bmatrix} A \\ B \end{bmatrix}_n,$ (a) [42.48, 57.52],
      (b) [36.47, 65.53],   (c) [33.33, 66.67]

5.30   (a) $P_{n+1} = \begin{bmatrix} 0.1 & 1.5 & 0 & 0 \\ 0.9 & 0 & 0 & 0 \\ 0 & 0.8 & 0 & 0 \\ 0 & 0 & 0.6 & 0.1 \end{bmatrix} P_n$ (b) [1094, 856, 533, 304]
      (c) No (largest eigenvalue ≈ 1.213)

5.31 $\begin{bmatrix} b \\ g \\ s \end{bmatrix}_{n+1} = \begin{bmatrix} 0.7 & 0.05 & 0 \\ 0.3 & 0.85 & 0.04 \\ 0 & 0.1 & 0.96 \end{bmatrix} \begin{bmatrix} b \\ g \\ s \end{bmatrix}_n$
      Tends to [0.04545, 0.2727, 0.6818]

5.32 $X_{n+1} = \begin{bmatrix} 0 & 0 & 2 \\ 0.5 & 0 & 0 \\ 0 & 0.9 & 0.8 \end{bmatrix} X_n$
      (a) Starting with [0, 0, 6] we get [80, 30, 54] after 10 years.
      (b) The population grows without limit (largest eigenvalue ≈ 1.318).

5.33   (a) $\begin{bmatrix} 0.96 & 0.012 & 0 \\ 0.01 & 0.97 & 0 \\ 0.004 & 0 & 1 \end{bmatrix} \begin{matrix} \text{blood} \\ \text{tissues} \\ \text{bones} \end{matrix}$
      (b) (i) [96, 1, 0.4]   (ii) [75.4, 5.7, 2.5]

6 Continuous Models

6.1 Background

In mathematics textbooks, variables usually take any real value (i.e. they 'go from $-\infty$ to $+\infty$'). In modelling this is never so because:

1. Variables represent real quantities and have practical upper and lower limits, and in many cases negative values are physically meaningless.
2. Models have a limited domain of applicability, outside of which some of the assumptions break down and the model should not be used.

Within the usable range of values for a variable we may find that the variable is restricted to particular values (for example integers), in which case it is a **discrete** variable. Models using discrete variables were discussed in Chapter 5. Where a variable is allowed to take any value within a range, we call it a **continuous** variable. The continuous or discrete nature of a variable may be inherent in the real problem *or* it may be a modelling decision. The best choice is not always obvious and partly depends on the balance between realism and convenience. One advantage of using continuous variables is that we can use powerful mathematical tools such as the calculus. For the sake of comparison, the discrete Example 5.6 is resolved as a continuous model in Chapter 9.

In this chapter we are concerned with continuous functions of continuous variables, but note that we could also need to think about a continuous function of a discrete variable. Place a ruler so that one end overhangs the edge of your desk and put a coin on the overhanging end. Push the ruler as far out as it will go without tipping over and record the length y still on the table. Now repeat with two coins, one on top of the other. If you use a pile of n identical coins, what is the relationship between n and y? Clearly n is discrete and y is continuous. There are also examples of discrete functions of a continuous variable, such as the number of customers in a queue at time t.

Very often a model needs to be modified for certain ranges of values so that instead of one equation over the whole range we have a number of equations, each holding over a limited part of the range. At the points where the parts meet, the equations usually agree, so that we have a continuous model (i.e. no sudden jumps).

6.2 Linear Models

These are the simplest continuous models and a lot of modelling is carried out using linear models only. The simplest kind comes from assuming direct proportionality, i.e. $y \propto x$, and its graph is a straight line through the origin. The general linear model relating two variables is characterised by an equation of the form $y = ax + b$ and by having a straight line graph. This general linear model applies when equal changes in x give rise to equal changes in y. A typical application is when x is the number of units used, a is the cost per unit and b is a fixed overhead cost. The total cost is then made up from the sum of the two parts b and ax.

The following facts from coordinate geometry are useful:

Gradient (slope) of straight line $=$ (increase in y)/(increase in x) $= (y_2 - y_1)/(x_2 - x_1)$

if (x_1, y_1) and (x_2, y_2) are two points on the line (Fig. 6.1).

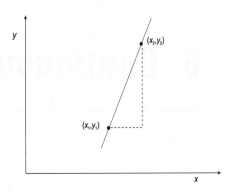

Figure 6.1

Equations of straight line:

1. With slope m and intercept c on the y-axis: $y = mx + c$
2. With intercepts a and b on the x- and y-axes respectively: $x/a + y/b = 1$
3. Passing through the point (x_0, y_0) with gradient m: $y - y_0 = m(x - x_0)$
4. Joining the points (x_1, y_1) and (x_2, y_2): $(y - y_1)/(y_2 - y_1) = (x - x_1)/(x_2 - x_1)$

Linear interpolation can be used to read between the lines in a table of data. Suppose we have:

x	$f(x)$
1.0	0.0000
1.1	0.0414
1.2	0.0792

and we want the values of $f(1.05)$ and $f(1.13)$.

Since $x = 1.05$ comes half-way between $x = 1$ and $x = 1.1$ we could assume that $f(1.05)$ also comes halfway between $f(1.0)$ and $f(1.1)$; that is, we could estimate $f(1.05)$ to be

$$f(1.0) + 0.5[f(1.1) - f(1.0)] = 0 + 0.5[0.0414 - 0] = 0.0207$$

We could make a similar assumption concerning $f(1.13)$ and assume it divides the interval from $f(1.1)$ to $f(1.2)$ in exactly the same proportion as $x = 1.13$ divides the interval from $x = 1.1$ to $x = 1.2$. That is,

$$f(1.13) \approx f(1.1) + \{(1.13 - 1.1)/(1.2 - 1.1)\}[f(1.2) - f(1.1)]$$
$$= f(1.1) + 0.3[f(1.2) - f(1.1)]$$
$$= 0.0414 + 0.3[0.0792 - 0.0414] = 0.0527$$

We can write a general form for this, corresponding to the case where x_1 and x_2 are consecutive values of x in a table and x is some value between them.

$$f(x) \approx f(x_1) + \{(x - x_1)/(x_2 - x_1)\}[f(x_2) - f(x_1)]$$

This corresponds to approximating the graph of $f(x)$ from $x = x_1$ to $x = x_2$ by a linear model.

Linear Models with Several Variables

If the value of variable y is thought to depend on the values of a number of other variables $x_1, x_2, \ldots$ the simplest way of expressing the dependence is through a linear model of the form $y = a + b_1 x_1 + b_2 x_2 + \cdots$. The condition for this kind of model to be valid is that y changes by equal amounts for equal changes in any one of the variables. This model is no more difficult to deal with than the single variable case, except when it comes to graphical interpretation!

Simultaneous Linear Models

We may have two or more *dependent* variables, all of which are modelled as linear functions of x. Questions of interest which then arise are: when are two variables equal (i.e. where do the lines cross) and when does one come above the other?

Suppose, for example, that we have a choice between hiring two machines. Machine A can be hired for £25 a week while machine B can be hired for £150 plus £10 per week. Which is the cheaper machine if we want to use it for x weeks?

The cost of hiring A for x weeks is $y_A = 25x$ and for B the cost is $y_B = 150 + 10x$. The two are equal when $25x = 150 + 10x$, i.e. $x = 10$. Also when $x < 10$ we have $y_A < y_B$ with the opposite being true when $x > 10$. The conclusion from this is that if we need a machine for less than 10 weeks the cheaper choice is A, otherwise choose B.

Piecewise Linear Models

A model does not have to be represented by the same single formula for all values of the variable x. For example, suppose certain items cost £10 each to buy, but if you buy more than 100, the price of any extra items drops to £9 per item. The model for the cost of buying x items is then

$$y = \begin{cases} 10x & 0 \leqslant x \leqslant 100 \\ 1000 + 9(x - 100) = 100 + 9x & x \geqslant 100 \end{cases}$$

The two different linear expressions agree at $x = 100$, so there is no sudden jump (discontinuity) at the changeover point. (Note that x was actually a discrete variable in this example.)

In the previous example a piecewise linear model occurred naturally. We may sometimes choose to model a non-linear function approximately by a piecewise linear function. For example, suppose a car does about 40 miles per gallon of petrol at a speed of 30 m.p.h., decreasing to 20 miles per gallon at a speed of 70 m.p.h. and also decreasing to zero as the speed decreases from 30 m.p.h. to zero. If we do not know the detailed shape of the graph we could represent the mileage rate R as a piecewise linear function of speed (V) using

$$R = \begin{cases} 4V/3 & 0 \leqslant V \leqslant 30 \\ 55 - V/2 & 30 \leqslant V \leqslant 70 \end{cases}$$

This is shown in Fig. 6.2.

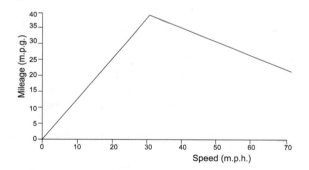

Figure 6.2

6.3 Quadratic Models

When a variable y does not change by equal amounts for equal changes in the x variable then a linear model is not suitable. A simple example of a non-linear model is the quadratic $y = ax^2 + bx + c$, whose graph is a parabola. Three separate pieces of information are needed to determine the three parameters a, b and c. The value of a determines whether the curve is concave upwards (if $a > 0$) or concave downwards. There is a vertical axis of symmetry at $x = -b/2a$, which is also the x value at which the graph has a global maximum or minimum value. The value of the parameter c affects the vertical position of the curve relative to the coordinate axes.

Motion with Constant Acceleration

When something moves with a constant acceleration its velocity is a linear function of time. If u (m s^{-1}) is the velocity when $t = 0$ and a (m s^{-2}) is the constant acceleration, then the velocity at time t is $v = u + at$.

The average velocity over the interval $[0, t]$ is $(u + v)/2$ and so the distance moved is $s = (u + v)t/2$. From these two equations we can also derive equations connecting v and s: $v^2 = u^2 + 2as$; and connecting s and t: $s = ut + at^2/2$.

6.4 Other Non-linear Models

More flexibility is obtained by using higher degree polynomials with $n + 1$ pieces of information being needed to determine the $n + 1$ coefficients of a polynomial of degree n. There are also very simple non-linear models which are not polynomials, for example models expressing inverse relationships between the variables such as $y = k/x$ or $y = k/x^2$. Other examples are models based on rational functions of the form

$$\frac{a + bx}{c + dx}, \quad \frac{a + bx + cx^2}{d + ex + fx^2}, \ldots$$

and models expressed in terms of standard mathematical functions such as square roots, exponentials, and logarithmic and trigonometric functions. The choice of an appropriate *form* is based on a mixture of experience and experimentation (it may help to plot logs). The question of the best *values* to take for the parameters is the subject of fitting models to data (see Chapter 12). It is useful to have insight into the effects of changing each parameter in turn. Note that the effect of replacing the variable x by $x - c$ in a model is to move the curve horizontally c units to the right without altering its shape. The effect of adding c to the dependent variable y is to shift the curve vertically upwards without altering its shape. Replacing x by cx ('scaling') appears to alter the shape of the curve but can also be regarded as 'zooming in' ($c > 1$) or 'zooming out' ($c < 1$). A curve $y = f(x)$ can be reflected in a horizontal line $y = c$ by taking $y = 2c - f(x)$, and for reflection in a vertical line $x = c$ take $y = f(x - c)$.

6.5 Models Tending to a Limit

Very often physical variables increase gradually towards some upper limit or 'ceiling'. An example is a living population whose size is limited by environmental factors. Examples of mathematical models with this kind of behaviour are

1. $a - be^{-ct}$ ($\to a$ as $t \to \infty$)
2. $(at + b)/(ct + d)$ (where $ad > bc$) ($\to a/c$ as $t \to \infty$)
3. $a + b\tan^{-1}(ct)$ ($\to a + b\pi/2$ as $t \to \infty$)
4. $1/(a + be^{-ct})$ ($\to 1/a$ as $t \to \infty$)

In these expressions t is time and a, b, c and d are positive constants. Examples are shown in Fig. 6.3.

The above examples are easily adapted to give curves that *decrease* gradually to a lower limit or 'floor', for example

1. $a + be^{-ct}$ ($\to a$ as $t \to \infty$)
2. $(at + b)/(ct + d)$ (where $ad < bc$) ($\to a/c$ as $t \to \infty$)
3. $a - b\tan^{-1}(ct)$ ($\to a - b\pi/2$ as $t \to \infty$)
4. $1/(a - be^{-ct})$ ($\to 1/a$ as $t \to \infty$)

6.6 Transforming Variables

Starting from a variable with an infinite range, such as $[0, \infty]$ or $[-\infty, \infty]$ we can construct variables with a finite range by using mathematical transformations. Suppose for example,

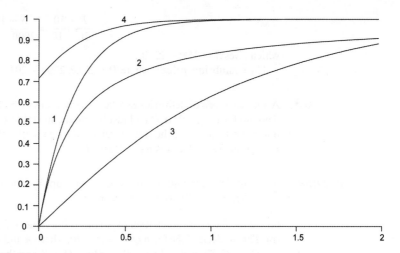

Figure 6.3

that x goes from 0 to ∞. To get a range from 0 to 1 we could use for example $u = x/(1 + x)$. We could make the range $[a, b]$ by taking $u = (ax + b)/(1 + x)$. Alternative ways of achieving the same thing are $u = a + (b - a)(1 - e^{-x})$ and $u = a + 2(b - a)(\tan^{-1}x)/\pi$.

Transforming variables will usually alter the shape of a curve and this can be useful in 'straightening' curves. For example, if $y = kx^n$ then the plot of $\ln y$ against $\ln x$ is a straight line and plotting logs often changes non-linear models into nearly straight lines (see Chapter 12).

To change from $0 < u < 1$ to $a < x < b$, use $x = a + (b - a)u$.

6.7 Worked Examples

6.1 A holiday resort gets 6000 tourists a week when the temperature is 15 °C. Use a simple model to predict how many tourists will come when the temperature is 20 °C. If the actual number of tourists when the temperature is 20 °C is 7250, derive an improved model and use it to estimate the number of tourists when the temperature is 18 °C.

Solution If X is the number of tourists per week when the temperature is T, the simplest model is to assume X is proportional to T. In symbols, $X = kT$ where $6000 = 15k$ so that $k = 400$ and the model is $X = 400T$. This predicts $X = 8000$ when $T = 20$. We could replace it by the linear model $X = aT + b$, which represents a straight line joining the points $(15, 6000)$ and $(20, 7250)$. The equation is therefore given by

$$\frac{x - 6000}{7250 - 6000} = \frac{T - 15}{20 - 15}$$

i.e. $X = 250T + 2250$. This predicts $X = 250(18) + 2250 = 6750$ when $T = 18$.

6.2 As the price of an item goes up the demand often falls. Also, the suppliers are prepared to produce a greater quantity if they get a better price for it. Suppose that the following data applies to a particular product.

Price, P	Demand, D	Supply, S
10	2000	1500
30	1600	2000

Write down linear models for D and S in terms of P and find the **equilibrium** price for which supply = demand.

Solution The equations we need are given by

$$\frac{P - 10}{30 - 10} = \frac{D - 2000}{1600 - 2000}$$

which gives $D = 2200 - 20P$, and

$$\frac{P - 10}{30 - 10} = \frac{S - 1500}{2000 - 1500}$$

which gives $S = 25P + 1250$.

The equilibrium price is where $D = S$, i.e. $2200 - 20P = 25P + 1250$, so $P \approx 21$.

6.3 A retailer receives deliveries regularly every T days which bring his stock up to a level Q_U. The daily demand for his goods is D and just before the next delivery arrives his stock level is Q_L. Write down a linear model for $Q(t)$, the stock level at time t days after the last delivery, (a) given Q_U and D, (b) given Q_U, Q_L and T and (c) given Q_L, D and T.

Solution Since the daily demand is D the stock level drops by amount D every day so the required model is of the form $Q(t) = A - Dt$, where A is a constant.

(a) At $t = 0$ we have stock level Q_L so this is the value of A and our model is $Q(t) = Q_U - Dt$.
(b) The model is of the form $Q(t) = A - Bt$, where A and B are constants. We have $Q_U = Q(0) = A$ and $Q_L = Q(T) = A - Bt$ so $B = (Q_U - Q_L)/T$ and the model is $Q(t) = Q_U - (Q_U - Q_L)t/T$.
(c) Again using the form $Q(t) = A - Dt$ we have $Q_L = Q(T) = A - DT$, from which $A = Q_L + DT$ and the model is $Q(t) = Q_L - D(t - T)$.

6.4 Suppose a storm lasts a total time T during which the rainfall rate increases from zero to a peak of F_* at time $t = t_*$ and then gradually subsides (Fig. 6.4). Using a simple linear model write down expressions for the rainfall rate $F(t)$ at time t after the beginning of the storm.

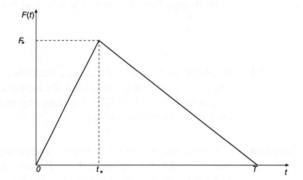

Figure 6.4

Solution While the rainfall is increasing we have $F(t) = \text{constant} \times t$, reaching F_* at $t = t_*$, so the constant is F_*/t_* and the model is $F(t) = F_*t/t_*$ for $0 \leqslant t \leqslant t_*$. (Check that this gives $F(0) = 0$ and $F(t_*) = F_*$.)

From $t = t_*$ until $t = T$ we need a model of the form $F(t) = a - bt$, where $F(t_*) = F_*$ and $F(T) = 0$, that is, $F_* = a - bt_*$ and $0 = a - bT$. It follows that $F_* = bT - bt_*$, so $b = F_*/(T - t_*)$ and $a = F_*T/(T - t_*)$. The complete model is

$$F(t) = \begin{cases} F_*t/t_* & 0 \leqslant t \leqslant t_* \\ F_*(T - t)/(T - t_*) & t_* \leqslant t \leqslant T \\ 0 & t > T \end{cases}$$

6.5 A construction company wants to hire a crane for a certain number of days and considers three offers:

1. Crane A, for which there is a fixed hire charge of £1000 plus £150 per day for the first 30 days, falling to £50 thereafter.
2. Crane B, which has a £2000 hiring charge and a £100 daily charge.
3. A smaller crane C with exactly half the lifting capacity of the other two. For C there is no fixed charge but the daily charge is £175.

Use linear models to advise the company on which crane to choose. Mention any assumptions you make.

Solution Let x be the number of days for which a crane is needed.

For A the cost is

$$y_A = \begin{cases} 1000 + 150x & x \leqslant 30 \\ 5500 + 50(x - 30) = 4000 + 50x & x > 30 \end{cases}$$

For B it is simply $y_B = 2000 + 100x$

For C *assume* that we can do the same job by taking twice the time. This is equivalent to making the daily cost £350, so the model is $y_C = 350x$.

The graphs are plotted in Fig. 6.5 and give rise to the following conclusions:

For	*The cheapest option is*
$x \leqslant 5$	C
$5 \leqslant x \leqslant 20$	A
$20 \leqslant x \leqslant 40$	B
$x > 40$	A

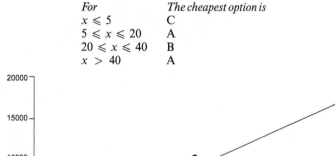

Figure 6.5

6.6 It starts to rain at 2 a.m., slowly at first but gradually increasing to a peak of $1\,\text{cm}\,\text{h}^{-1}$ at 3 a.m. It then gradually subsides until at 5 a.m. (Fig. 6.6) the rainfall rate is $4\,\text{mm}\,\text{h}^{-1}$. It then continues to rain at a decreasing rate until it stops altogether at 9 a.m. Write down equations defining a piecewise linear model for $r(t)$, the rainfall rate $(\text{cm}\,\text{h}^{-1})$ at time t hours after midnight.

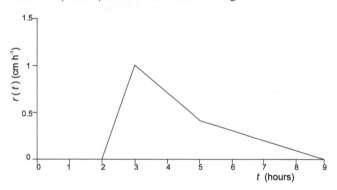

Figure 6.6

Solution Using formulae similar to those of Example 6.2, we derive the equations

$$r(t) = \begin{cases} 0 & 0 \leqslant t \leqslant 2 \\ t - 2 & 2 \leqslant t \leqslant 3 \\ 1.9 - 0.3t & 3 \leqslant t \leqslant 5 \\ 0.9 - 0.1t & 5 \leqslant t \leqslant 9 \end{cases}$$

6.7 Sales of a new daily newspaper were 100 000 on the first day and reached 400 000 per day after 2 months. By 7 months, however, sales were down to 275 000 per day. Use a simple quadratic model to represent the daily sales after t months and use it to find (a) when peak sales were reached and (b) when sales will fall to zero.

Solution Let $S(t)$ represent the daily sales after t months in units of 100 000. We will assume a model of the form $S(t) = at^2 + bt + c$. The information we have is that $S(0) = 1$, $S(2) = 4$ and $S(7) = 2.75$. We use these facts to write down three equations:

$$1 = S(0) = c$$

$$4 = S(2) = a2^2 + b2 + c = 4a + 2b + 1$$

$$2.75 = S(7) = a7^2 + b7 + c = 49a + 7b + 1$$

Solving these, we find $a = -0.25$, $b = 2$ and $c = 1$, so our model is $S(t) = -0.25t^2 + 2t + 1$.

(a) Sales reach a peak when $S'(t) = 0$, i.e. when $-0.5t + 2 = 0$, which is $t = 4$, so we predict the peak to be at 4 months.
(b) The model predicts $S = 0$ when $-0.25t^2 + 2t + 1 = 0$, which has roots $t = 4 \pm \sqrt{20}$. The negative root has no meaning for us and the positive root is $t \approx 8.5$ months. The validity of this conclusion is doubtful because the declining sales of the newspaper are more likely to taper off than to continue to zero along the path marked by the quadratic.

6.8   Let u = average speed (m.p.h.) of vehicles on a motorway and ρ = average density (vehicles per mile) on the motorway at any instant. Write down a simple linear model relating u to ρ.
   If q = traffic flow rate (vehicles per hour passing a fixed point), write down a model for q in terms of ρ.

Solution   Let u_{max} = maximum speed of a vehicle travelling alone (i.e. when $\rho = 0$).
   Let ρ_{max} = maximum density when vehicles are jammed bumper to bumper (i.e. when $u = 0$).
   We want u = a linear function of ρ which gives u_{max} when $\rho = 0$ and 0 when $\rho = \rho_{max}$. The intercepts on the axes are therefore u_{max} and ρ_{max}, so the equation we need is

$$u/u_{max} + \rho/\rho_{max} = 1 \text{ or } u = u_{max}(1 - \rho/\rho_{max})$$

We have cars per hour = (cars per mile) $\times$ (miles per hour); that is,

$$q = \rho u = \rho u_{max}(1 - \rho/\rho_{max})$$

so q is a quadratic function of ρ.

6.9   Choose the most appropriate form of non-linear model to fit the graphs shown in Fig. 6.7.
   (a) $a - bx^2$,   (b) $a/(x + b)$,   (c) $a/(x^2 + b)$ and (d) axe^{-bx}, where a and b are positive parameters.

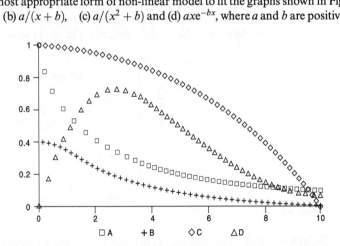

Figure 6.7

Solution   Curve (A) is fitted by (b), which is decreasing for all x and has a gradient which decreases in magnitude with x.
   Curve (B) is fitted by (c), which is decreasing for all x and has a gradient (given by $-2ax/(x^2 + b^2)^2$), which is small for both small x and large x.
   Curve (C) is fitted by (a), which decreases with increasing x, becoming zero at $x = \sqrt{(a/b)}$, and has a negative gradient $(-2bx)$ which gets steeper with increasing x.
   Curve (D) is fitted by (d), which is zero at $x = 0$ and very small for very large x, rising to a maximum at $x = 1/b$.

6.10   Choose appropriate values of the parameters a, b and c so that the models (a) $f(x) = a - 1/(b + cx)$ and (b) $f(x) = a - be^{-cx}$ fit the data shown in Fig. 6.8.

Solution   (a) As $x \to \infty$ we get $f(x) \to a$, which must = 2. When $x = 0$ we have $f(0) = a - 1/b$, which must = 1
   $\therefore b = 1$. At $x = 1$ we have $f(1) = 2 - 1/(1 + c)$ which must = 1.8 $\therefore c = 4$.
   (b) As $x \to \infty$ we get $f(x) \to a$, which must = 2. When $x = 0$ we have $f(0) = a - b$, which must = 1 $\therefore$
   $b = 1$. At $x = 1$ we have $f(1) = a - be^{-c}$, which must = 1.8 $\therefore 2 - e^{-c} = 1.8 \therefore c \approx 1.61$.

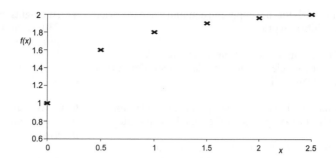

Figure 6.8

6.8 Exercises

6.1 Which of the following data sets have been derived from a linear model? In which cases is *y proportional* to *x*? Write down equations for linear models where appropriate.

(a)

x	0	1	2	4
y	2	2.5	3	4

(b)

x	10	20	30	60
y	2	2.5	3	4

(c)

x	100	200	250	400
y	90	80	75	60

(d)

x	2	4	18	26
y	5	10	45	65

(e)

x	10	12	25	40
y	90	80	60	55

6.2 Which of the following would you model as continuous variables?

(a) Time
(b) The number of wet days in a month
(c) The amount of rainfall in a month
(d) A person's weight
(e) A person's shoe size
(f) The number of fish in a small aquarium
(g) The number of fish in a very large lake
(h) The number of coins in a purse
(i) The amount of money in a country's economy

6.3 A telephone bill is made up from a line rental charge £R and a charge C (pence) per unit used, and VAT at 17.5% is added to complete the bill. Write down an expression for the bill when x units are used.

6.4 A market research survey shows that at a price of £10 per item the demand would be 5 million items, while at a price of £5 per item the demand would be 7.5 million. Fit a linear model for the demand as a function of the price.

6.5 Suppose you receive a cheque for £C on the first day of every month and you spend £S every day. Write down a linear model for the amount of money in your bank account on the xth day of the month. Write down an upper limit on S if you do not wish to be more than £D overdrawn.

6.6 At present 1000 people a day use a local transport service for which a daily ticket costs £1. The managers estimate that for each 10p by which the ticket price is increased, 100 fewer people would use the service. Write down a model for the number $N(P)$ of potential passengers when the ticket price is P (pence).

6.7 Suppose a car costs an average of £S per month in service and repair bills. If petrol costs £P per gallon and the car averages M miles per gallon, write down a linear model for the monthly cost (£y) of using the car if x is the number of miles travelled in the month.

6.8 After heavy rain the water level in a river is rising steadily and people living nearby are worried about the danger of flooding. The level was 1.5 m at 9 a.m. on Monday and 1.6 m at 7 p.m. Write down a linear model for the water level $y(t)$ at time t hours after 9 a.m. on Monday. When will it reach the danger level of 2 m?

6.9 A shop sells N items of a particular kind every week and can order new stock in batches of B items at a time. The shop has room to store a maximum of Q items ($Q > B$) and it takes L days between ordering new stock and its delivery. If $t = 0$ represents the day of delivery, write down a linear model for the stock $y(t)$ on day t. What are (a) the earliest time at which the next batch can be ordered and (b) the latest time at which the next batch can be ordered to avoid running out of stock?

6.10 Use linear interpolation to obtain estimates of $f(1.5)$ and $f(1.7)$ from the following table. Compare your estimates with the exact values, given that $f(x)$ is actually $\sqrt{(1 + x)}$.

x	f(x)
1.0	1.4142
1.5	
1.7	
2.0	1.7321

6.11 A machine costs £A to buy and routine maintenance and running costs come to £R per month. The re-sale value of a second-hand machine decreases by £S per month. It is possible to hire the same machine for £H a month, which includes routine maintenace and running costs. If you need a machine for x months, which is the most economical option, hire or buy?

6.12 Given the following data:

Price (£)	20	30
Supply	1200	1300
Demand	1800	1600

73

Write down linear models for the supply and demand when the price is P. What is the equilibrium price?

6.13 Counts of bird populations on an island revealed 1500 of species A and 2000 of species B. One year later a similar survey showed 1400 of A and 1800 of B.

(a) Use this information to write down simple linear models for the number of birds of each species on the island t years after the first count.
(b) When will there be more A than B birds on the island?
(c) Which species will first become extinct and when?

6.14 A group of students travel from college to attend a football match, a distance of S miles along a motorway. They travel in two cars A and B. Car B starts M minutes later than A but travels at a constant speed V_B (m.p.h.) while car A goes at a slower constant speed V_A (m.p.h.).

(a) Write down linear models for the distances travelled by each car by time t, where $t = 0$ is the time when car A leaves college.
(b) Write down a model for the distance $d(t)$ between the two cars at time t.
(c) Write down a condition for car B to be the first to arrive at the destination.
(d) If the condition in part (c) is satisfied, when and where does car B overtake car A?

6.15 Suppose you wish to hire a car for one day with which you intend to travel x miles.

Firm A offers a car for £40 a day with unlimited mileage.
Firm B offers a car for £20 a day plus 20p per mile.
Firm C offers a car for £30 a day plus 10p for each mile over 100.

Which is the cheapest offer?

6.16 Certain items cost £10 each, but if you buy more than 100 of them you get a 5% discount. If $C(x)$ is the cost of buying x items write down a model for $C(x)$ in terms of x.

6.17 A train leaves a platform at time $t = 0$ and accelerates steadily to a speed of 60 m.p.h. in 30 s. It then travels at a constant 60 m.p.h. for 5 minutes. It begins to slow down at time $t = 5.5$ min and by time $t = 6.5$ its speed is 40 m.p.h. It then steadily reduces speed so that it comes to a halt at $t = 7$. Write down equations representing its speed $V(t)$ at time t (min).

6.18 The height h of a growing plant was measured at various times as follows:

t (months)	0	2	6	12
h (mm)	40	166	1210	2380

Obtain equations for a piecewise continuous linear model for $h(t)$ in terms of t.

6.19 Using the following assumptions:

1. At sea level the Earth's atmospheric pressure is 10^5 Pa and the temperature is 290 K
2. At height h (km) up to 10 km above sea level the temperature $T(h)$ is a linear function of h and the air pressure can be modelled by an equation of the form $p(h) = A[T(h)]^{5.6}$
3. At height 10 km the temperature is 230 K

4. At heights between 10 and 20 km the temperature is constant at 230 K and the pressure is given by a model of the form $p(h) = Be^{-0.15h}$.

Obtain explicit equations in terms of h for $T(h)$ and $p(h)$ for $0 < h < 20$.

6.20 Which of the following data sets have been derived from a quadratic model? For those that have been, write down models for y in terms of x.

(a)
x	1	2	3	4
y	2	11	26	47

(b)
x	0	1	2	3
y	2	4	8	14

(c)
x	10	20	30	40
y	15	20	50	90

(d)
x	5	10	15	20
y	465	380	245	65

(e)
x	0	1	2	4	7
y	2	3	6	18	51

6.21 A car accelerates from 0 to 60 m.p.h. in 10 s, travels at 60 m.p.h. for 20 s, then brakes to 0 in 15 s. Write down models for (a) its speed and (b) its distance from the starting point at time t (s).

6.22 A new monthly magazine sells 12 500 copies in the first month and sales reach a peak at 10 months before dwindling to zero after 25 months. Write down a quadratic model for $S(t) = $ monthly sales t months after the launch. Use the model to find when monthly sales first dropped below 9000.

6.23 Write down a simple quadratic model for the number of people per km^2 living at a distance r (km) from a city centre, given that this number is 4000 at the centre itself and rises to a peak of 20 000 km^{-2} at a distance of 3 km.
Use your model to predict:

(a) The population density at a distance of 1 km from the centre
(b) The distance at which the population density is 10 000 km^{-2}
(c) The outer limit of the population distribution

6.24 A train of length L is stationary at a platform with its rear end at point O. If it moves off with constant acceleration, sketch graphs showing the distances $x_1(t)$ and $x_2(t)$ of the front and rear ends of the train, from point O at time t.

6.25 A new computer game is proving very popular with young children. Ten weeks after first going on sale it is selling at the rate of 500 a day, rising to 1000 a day after 15 weeks. Write down a quadratic model for $S(t)$, the daily sales t weeks after the launch. Use it to predict the daily sales after 25 weeks.

6.26 The driver of a train travelling at a speed V_1 (km h^{-1}) sees on the same track a distance L (m) in front of him, a slow train travelling at V_2 (km h^{-1}). What is the least retardation he must apply to avoid a collision?

6.27 A car travelling with constant acceleration passes a point A moving with speed u (m s^{-1}) and reaches a point B, s metres from A in t seconds. What is its speed when it is half-way between A and B?

6.28 The managing director of a firm producing a commodity for which her firm has a monopoly, finds that the production cost depends on the number of items produced as follows:

Quantity produced Q (millions)	5	8	10
Production cost C (£M)	21.25	37.0	50.0

A market research survey shows that at a selling price of £10 per item the demand would be 5 million items, while at a price of £5 per item the demand would be 7.5 million.

(a) Fit a linear model for the demand as a function of the price.
(b) Fit a quadratic model for C as a function of Q.
(c) Use your models to find what selling price will bring in maximum profit.

6.29 A new toy sold 1000 on the first day and increased at a regular rate reaching daily sales of 3000 after 2 months. Sales eventually peaked at 4 months and then declined to zero at 8 months. Using a linear model for the first 2 months and a quadratic from then on, write down expressions for the daily sales $S(t)$ after t months.

6.30 The population of a town was 6000 five years ago and is now 10 000. Write down two possible models for $P(t)$ = the population of the town at time t years using (a) a linear model and (b) a simple non-linear model. (Take $t = 0$ as five years ago.) Compare their predictions for $t = 10$.

6.31 Match each of the following physical situations to the most appropriate model (in terms of time, t).

(a) The rainfall rate during a shower of rain
(b) The height of a sunflower while it is growing
(c) The depth of water in a bath after the plug is pulled
(d) The depth of water in a bath while being filled
(e) The speed of a car approaching a roundabout
(f) The speed of a car starting from rest

(i) t	(ii) $1 - t^2$	
(iii) $(1 - t)^2$	(iv) $t - t^2$	
(v) $1 - e^{-t}$	(vi) $1/(1 + e^{-t})$	

6.32 Which of the graphs shown in Fig. 6.9 could be a reasonable model of the speed of an athlete during (a) a 100 m sprint, (b) a 400 m track event?

6.33 The temperature of the water coming from a shower is controlled by a single tap which gives very cold water at one extreme and very hot at the other. When you first turn it on, it is too cold. Draw a graph showing the temperature against time as you try to find the position of the tap which gives the ideal temperature.

6.34 Sketch graphs for:

(a) The number of people per m² living a distance x from a city centre
(b) The number of students in a classroom from 8 a.m. to 8 p.m.
(c) The amount of water in a cistern when it is flushed.
(d) The number of cars in a college car park from 6 a.m. to 9 p.m.
(e) The rate of usage of electricity in an average house over a 24 hour period
(f) The time it takes you to drink 1 cm³ of coffee at temperature T
(g) The value of a car of age x

6.35 Figure 6.10 shows the cross-sections of four empty swimming pools, each of width 8 m and 2 m deep at the deepest point. They are each filled with water at a steady rate (m³ s⁻¹). For each case, sketch graphs to show how the depth $h(t)$ of water at the deep end varies with time t.

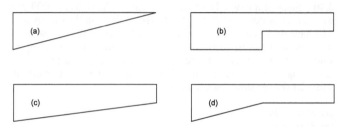

Figure 6.10

6.36 A train accelerates from 0 to 60 m.p.h., then travels at that constant speed for 2 minutes, then slows down to a stop. If the acceleration and deceleration are constants, draw graphs to show (a) the train's speed as a function of time, and (b) its distance from the starting point as a function of time.

6.37 Show the consequences of changing the parameter c in the following:

(a) $1 + cx$	(b) $(1 + c)x$
(c) $1 + c/x$	(d) $c + 1/x$
(e) $1/(1 + cx)$	(f) $cx/(1 + cx)$

6.38 Figure 6.11 shows the graph of $x^2 e^{-x}$ for $0 < x < 10$. Sketch the graphs of (a) $x^2 e^{-x} + 1$, (b) $(x - 1)^2 e^{-(x-1)}$ and (c) $4x^2 e^{-2x}$.

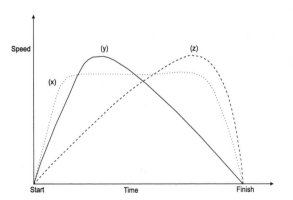

Figure 6.9

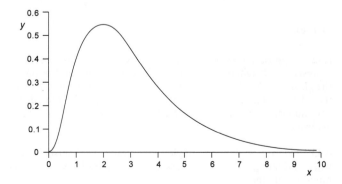

Figure 6.11

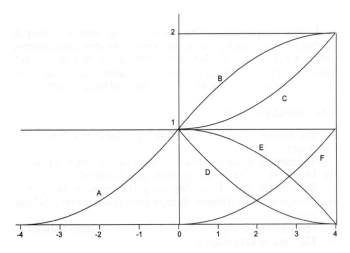

Figure 6.12

6.39 Given that the equation of the curve marked F in Fig. 6.12 is $y = x^2/16$, write down equations for the curves marked A–E.

6.40 Sales of a new CD immediately after release were 6000 per week and it is expected that sales will rise at first but then drop, and will have declined to zero after 12 weeks. Which of the following is likely to be the most realistic model for $S(t)$ the number of copies sold per week, t weeks after release? In each case give a reason for accepting or rejecting the model and write down an appropriate value for the (positive) parameter k.

(a) $6000 - kt$
(b) $6000\, e^{kt}$
(c) $6000\, e^{-kt}$
(d) $k(t^2 - 512t + 6000)$
(e) $k(-t^2 - 488t + 6000)$

6.41 Choose appropriate values of the parameters a, b and c so that the models (a) $a + 1/(b + cx)$ and (b) $a + be^{-cx}$ fit the data of Fig. 6.13.

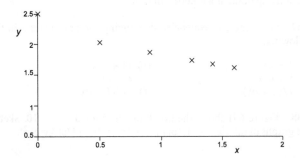

Figure 6.13

6.42 Suppose you are drinking out of a cylindrical glass. Let $h_S(t)$ represent the height of the surface of the drink above the bottom of the glass. Let $h_G(t)$ represent the height of the centre of gravity of the drink *and* glass together. Suppose you sip the drink continuously through a straw. Sketch graphs of $h_S(t)$ and $h_G(t)$ against t.

6.43 Figure 6.14 shows a simple slider–crank mechanism. If the wheel is rotating at a steady rate, sketch the graphs of θ, x, y and z as functions of time.

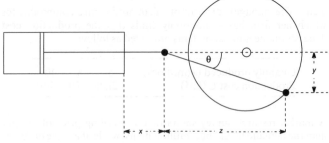

Figure 6.14

6.44 In a human population let L = the percentage of females living from birth to age x and M = the number of female babies born to females of age x. Sketch the graphs of what you think are reasonable models of L and M as functions of x.

6.45 A line of traffic on a straight road is stationary at red traffic lights at $x = 0$. Sketch a graph of $\rho(x)$ = number of cars per m at position x. The light changes to green and the vehicles start to move. Sketch graphs of ρ against x at times (a) 5 s later, (b) 20 s later.

6.46 A tall jar contains muddy water with the same concentration (= number of solid particles per cm^3 of liquid) at all points. As time elapses the mud settles to the bottom of the jar. Sketch graphs of $c(x)$ = concentration at height x above the bottom of the jar (a) initially, (b) a short time later and (c) a long time later.

6.47 In each of the following cases we need to change the variable to u where u goes from 0 to 1 when the original variable ranges over the interval given. In each case write down a linear expression for u in terms of the given variable.

(a) $0 < x < 0.5$
(b) $0.5 < y < 1$
(c) $-3 < z < 2$

6.9 Answers to Exercises

6.1 (a) $y = 2 + 0.5x$, (b) no, (c) $y = 100 - 0.1x$, (d) $y = 2.5x$, (e) no. Only (d) shows $y \propto x$.

6.2 (b), (e), (f) and (h) are discrete. (a), (c) and (d) are in principle continuous but *could* be modelled as discrete. (g) and (i) are in principle discrete but *could* be modelled as continuous.

6.3 $1.175(R + Cx)$

6.4 D (in millions) $= 10 - 0.5P$

6.5 $C - xS$, $S < (D + C)/31$

6.6 $N(P) = 2000 - 10P$

6.7 $y = S + Px/M$

6.8 $y = 1.5 + 0.01t$, 11 a.m. Wednesday

6.9 $y = Q - Nt/7$, (a) $x = 7B/N - L$, (b) $x = 7Q/N - L$

6.10 1.573, 1.637

6.11 Buy if $R + S < H$

6.12 $S = 10P + 1000$, $D = -20P + 2200$, $P = 40$

6.13 (a) $A = 1500 - 100t$, $B = 2000 - 200t$, (b) $t > 5$, (c) B at $t = 10$

6.14 (a) $x_A = tV_A$, $x_B = (t - M/60)V_B$
(b) $d = (V_A - V_B)t + MV_B/60$
(c) $S/V_A > S/V_B + M/60$
(d) $d = 0$ when $t = MV_B/[60(V_B - V_A)]$

6.15 For $0 \leqslant x \leqslant 50$: B, for $50 \leqslant x \leqslant 200$: C, for $x > 200$: A

6.16 Two different answers are possible, depending on the interpretation of the problem statement. If the discount applies to all the items bought, then

$$C(x) = \begin{cases} 10x & x \leqslant 100 \\ 9.5x & x > 100 \end{cases}$$

Otherwise, the answer is

$$C(x) = \begin{cases} 10x & x \leqslant 100 \\ 50 + 9.5x & x > 100 \end{cases}$$

6.17 $V = \begin{cases} 120t & 0 \leqslant t \leqslant 0.5 \\ 60 & 0.5 \leqslant t \leqslant 5.5 \\ 280 - 40t & 5.5 \leqslant t \leqslant 6.5 \\ 560 - 80t & 6.5 \leqslant t \leqslant 7 \end{cases}$

6.18 $h(t) = \begin{cases} 63t + 40 & 0 \leqslant t \leqslant 2 \\ 261t - 356 & 2 \leqslant t \leqslant 6 \\ 195t + 40 & 6 \leqslant t \leqslant 12 \end{cases}$

6.19 $0 < h < 10 : T(h) = 290 - 6h$
$$p(h) = (290 - 6h)^{5.6} \times 1.62 \times 10^{-8}$$
$10 < h < 20 : T(h) = 230$
$$p(h) = e^{-0.15h} \times 7.28 \times 10^{-8}$$

6.20 (a) $y = 3x^2 - 1$, (b) $y = x^2 + x + 2$, (c) no,
(d) $y = 500 - 2x - x^2$, (e) $y = x^2 + 2$

6.21 (a) $V = \begin{cases} 6t & 0 \leqslant t \leqslant 10 \\ 60 & 10 \leqslant t \leqslant 30 \\ 180 - 4t & 30 \leqslant t \leqslant 45 \end{cases}$

(b) $x = \begin{cases} 3t^2 & 0 \leqslant t \leqslant 10 \\ 300 + 60t & 10 \leqslant t \leqslant 30 \\ 180t - 2t^2 + 3600 & 30 \leqslant t \leqslant 45 \end{cases}$

6.22 $2000t - 100t^2 + 12\,500$, month 21

6.23 $N(r) = 4(24r - 4r^2 + 9)/9$ (thousands)
(a) 12 889 km^{-2}, (b) 0.63 km, 5.37 km, (c) 6.35 km

6.24 The curves should be parabolas with constant vertical distance L between them.

6.25 $S(t) = 10t(t + 5)/3$, $S(25) = 2500$

6.26 $1000(V_1 - V_2)^2/L$ km h^{-2}

6.27 $\sqrt{\{u^2t^2 + 2s(s - ut)\}}/t$

6.28 (a) $10 - 0.5P$, (b) $5 + 2Q - 0.25Q^2$, (c) $P = 12$

6.29 Daily sale in thousands:

$$S(t) = \begin{cases} t + 1 & 0 \leqslant t \leqslant 2 \\ 2t - t^2/4 & 2 \leqslant t \leqslant 8 \end{cases}$$

6.30 (a) $P(t) = 6000 + 800t$, $P(10) = 14\,000$
(b) $P(t) = 6000e^{0.102t}$, $P(10) = 16\,639$
or $P(t) = 6000 + 160t^2$, $P(10) = 2200$

6.31 (a) iv, (b) vi, (c) iii, (d) i, (e) ii, (f) v

6.39 A: $(x + 4)^2 16$ B: $2 - (4 - x)^2/16$
C: $1 + x^2/16$ D: $(4 - x)^2/16$ E: $1 - x^2/16$

6.40 (a) Decreases to zero at 12 weeks if $k = 500$, but does not rise to a peak
(b) Carries on increasing for all t, so is unacceptable
(c) Is decreasing for all t and never actually zero
(d) Decreases to zero at 12 weeks but does not peak
(e) Is acceptable for $0 < t < 12$ with $k = 1$

6.41 (a) $a = 1.5$, $b = 1$, $c = 2$, (b) $a = 1.5$, $b = 1$, $c \approx 1.39$

6.47 (a) $u = 2x$, (b) $u = 2y - 1$, (c) $u = (z + 3)/5$

7 Periodic Models

7.1 Background

Figures 7.1–7.4 all show examples of a graph with a repeating pattern; that is, they are graphs of **periodic** functions. In such cases the variable measured along the horizontal axis is nearly always time t, while the other variable plotted could be the strength of an electronic signal, the output of a system or the displacement of a body from a fixed point, to mention just a few of the many possibilities.

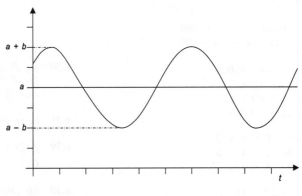

Figure 7.1

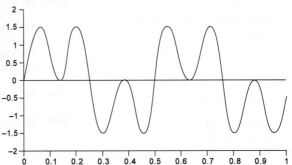

Figure 7.2

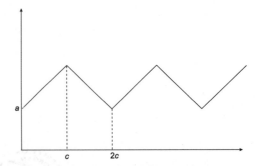

Figure 7.3

The simplest figure to represent by a mathematical model is Fig. 7.1. It is in fact an example of a pure sine wave with the equation:

$$y = a + b \sin \Omega(t - t_0)$$

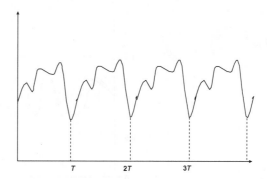

Figure 7.4

The parameter a represents the mean value of y, which lies vertically midway between the peaks and troughs of the wave. The parameter b represents the amplitude of the wave, which is half the vertical distance separating the peaks and the troughs. The parameter Ω is the **angular frequency** (units rad s^{-1}) and the **period** (the interval of time separating one peak from the next) is given by $2\pi/\Omega$. The t_0 value arises from the fact that we do not start with $y = a$ when $t = 0$. The expression for y could also be written as $y = a + b\sin(\Omega t + \phi)$, where $\phi = -\Omega t_0$ is referred to as the **phase**. The **frequency** (as distinct from the angular frequency) is just the reciprocal of the period, i.e. the number of cycles per second (measured in Hz where one Hz = one cycle per second).

The reason why Ω is called the angular frequency derives from the fact that if a point (such as P in Fig. 7.5) travels around a circle with constant angular speed Ω then the angle turned through by the radius in a time t is $\theta = \Omega t$. If $\theta = 0$ is the horizontal direction then the height of the moving point P above the horizontal at time t is $y = r\sin\Omega t$. As P moves round the circle, the point Q oscillates up and down between A and B. The period, T, for the motion of Q, is the time for one revolution for P, that is, $2\pi = \Omega T$ so $T = 2\pi/\Omega$.

The effects of changing the parameters a, b, Ω and t_0 are illustrated in Figures 7.6–7.9.

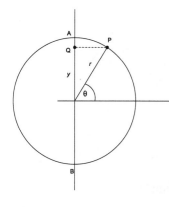

Figure 7.5

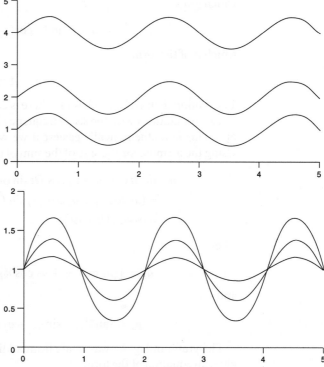

Figure 7.6 Variations in a.

Figure 7.7 Variations in b.

We called this example a sine wave, but a cosine function could be used instead of sine to give a graph with exactly the same shape, since $\cos(\theta - \pi/2) = \sin\theta$. The difference between them is the **phase difference** of $\pi/2$. For example, $b\sin\Omega t$ is 0 and increasing at $t = 0$ while $b\cos\Omega t$ is at its maximum and decreasing at $t = 0$

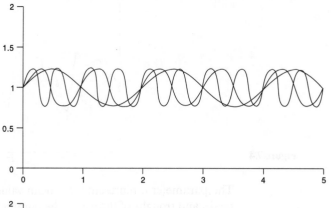

Figure 7.8 Variations in Ω.

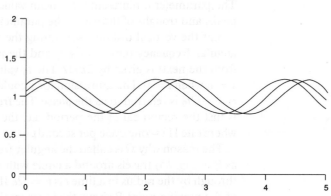

Figure 7.9 Variations in t_0.

Another version of the basic model comes from using the formula

$$\sin(A + B) = \sin A \cos B + \cos A \sin B$$

which gives

$$y = a + b \sin \Omega t \cos(-\Omega t_0) + b \cos \Omega t \sin(-\Omega t_0)$$

which is of the form

$$y = a + A \sin \Omega t + B \cos \Omega t$$

The motion defined by models like these is called **simple harmonic motion.**

Two oscillations with the same frequency but different phases can easily be combined into one. This is mathematically easiest if we write them as $a_1 \sin(\Omega t + \phi_1) + a_2 \sin(\Omega t + \phi_2)$. Using the formula for the sine of the sum of two angles, this is

$$a_1 \sin \Omega t \cos \phi_1 + a_1 \cos \Omega t \sin \phi_1 + a_2 \sin \Omega t \cos \phi_2 + a_2 \cos \Omega t \sin \phi_2$$
$$= (a_1 \cos \phi_1 + a_2 \cos \phi_2) \sin \Omega t + (a_1 \sin \phi_1 + a_2 \sin \phi_2) \cos \Omega t$$
$$= a_3 \sin(\Omega t + \phi_3)$$

where

$$a_3 = \{(a_1 \cos \phi_1 + a_2 \cos \phi_2)^2 + (a_1 \sin \phi_1 + a_2 \sin \phi_2)^2\}^{1/2}$$

and

$$\phi_3 = \tan^{-1}[(a_1 \sin \phi_1 + a_2 \sin \phi_2)/(a_1 \cos \phi_1 + a_2 \cos \phi_2)]$$

The graph in Fig. 7.2 was made from adding two sine waves with **different** periods, which gives an equation of the form

$$y = a_1 \sin \Omega_1 t + a_2 \sin \Omega_2 t$$

(This will be a periodic function provided Ω_1/Ω_2 is a rational number.) The graph in Fig. 7.3 could be described mathematically by

$$y = \begin{cases} a + bt & 0 \leqslant t \leqslant c \\ a + 2bc - bt & c \leqslant t \leqslant 2c \end{cases}$$

After $t = 2c$ the graph repeats itself so we write

$$y = y(t - 2c) \text{ when } t > 2c$$

(that is, it is just like starting at $t = 2c$ instead of $t = 0$).

If $y = f(t), 0 \leqslant t \leqslant T$ describes **one** cycle of the graph in Fig. 7.4, then to describe the whole graph we can write

$$y = \begin{cases} f(t) & 0 \leqslant t \leqslant T \\ f(t - nT) & nT \leqslant t \leqslant (n+1)T \text{ for any integer } n > 0 \end{cases}$$

From the work of Fourier we also have the option of representing graphs like those in Fig. 7.3 and Fig. 7.4 in terms of combinations of sin and cos functions of different frequencies. It may be necessary to take an infinite sum to get a perfect fit. For example, Fig. 7.3 can be represented by

$$y = a + bc\left[\frac{1}{2} - \frac{4}{\pi^2}\left(\frac{1}{1^2}\cos\left(\frac{\pi t}{c}\right) + \frac{1}{3^2}\cos\left(\frac{3\pi t}{c}\right) + \cdots\right)\right]$$

Taking a finite number of terms gives an approximation.

7.2 Fitting a Periodic Model to Data

In practice we may have just a few data points and we want to write down an equation for what we think is an underlying model. It is easier if we have a good reason to believe we know the period T. We then only need to estimate the values of the parameters a and b in $y = a + b\sin\Omega(t - t_0)$ since Ω is given by $2\pi/T$ and the value of t_0 simply serves to adjust the starting point.

Suppose for example, that the average air temperature in °C at a certain point on the Earth's surface is as follows:

Jan	Feb	Mar	Apr	May	Jun	Jul	Aug	Sep	Oct	Nov	Dec
2.8	2.1	3.5	6.9	10.8	12.4	15.2	15.7	14.7	12.8	8.5	5.5

The period is obviously going to be 12 months, so we are looking for a model of the form $y = a + b\sin(\pi(t - t_0)/6)$ if we measure t in months (Fig. 7.10).

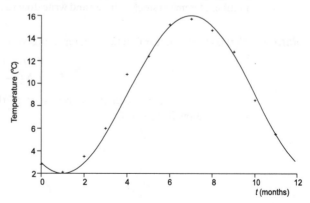

Figure 7.10

The maximum temperature is $y = 15.7$ in August and the minimum is $y = 2.1$ in February, so the annual mean is $a = (15.7 + 2.1)/2 = 8.9$ and the amplitude is b, where $8.9 + b = 15.7$ so $b = 6.8$ and our model is:

$$y = 8.9 + 6.8\sin(\pi(t - t_0)/6)$$

We are measuring the time in months with $t = 0$ being January, so what should we take for t_0? The minimum value of y occurs when $\sin(\pi(t - t_0)/6) = -1$ which is when $\pi(t - t_0)/6 = -\pi/2$ and since February is $t = 1$ this gives $t_0 = 4$ and our model is

$$y = 8.9 + 6.8\sin(\pi(t - 4)/6)$$

Figure 7.10 shows this model plotted alongside the original data. Other methods of fitting periodic models with more difficult examples can be found in Chapter 12.

7.3 Summary

Frequency f and period T are related by $f = 1/T$. t is measured in seconds and f in Hz. The angular frequency is $\Omega = 2\pi/T$ measured in rad s^{-1}.

For a model with period T use one of the forms

$$a + b\sin(2\pi t/T) + c\cos(2\pi t/T)$$
$$a + b\sin(2\pi(t - t_0))$$
$$a + b\sin(2\pi t/T + \phi)$$

The first of these is generally the most convenient when three items of information are given. The sin function in the other two forms can also be replaced by the cos function.

When the minimum and maximum values are known, use $0.5[\max + \min - (\max - \min)\cos(2\pi t/T)]$ when $t = 0$ is a minimum, or $0.5[\max + \min + (\max - \min)\cos(2\pi t/T)]$ when $t = 0$ is a maximum.

7.4 Worked Examples

7.1 In the model $y = \sin 3t + 2\cos 3t + 4$ what are (a) the period, (b) the amplitude and (c) the maximum and minimum values of y?

Solution Here Ω is 3 so the period is $2\pi/\Omega = 2\pi/3$.

The sin and cos terms can be combined by writing

$$y = \sqrt{(1^2 + 2^2)}[\sin 3t/\sqrt{(1^2 + 2^2)} + 2\cos 3t/\sqrt{(1^2 + 2^2)}] + 4$$

Now let ϕ be the angle whose tangent is 2.

Then $\cos\phi = 1/\sqrt{(1^2 + 2^2)}$ and $\sin\phi = 2/\sqrt{(1^2 + 2^2)}$ so $y = \sqrt{5}[\sin 3t\cos\phi + \sin\phi\cos 3t] + 4 = \sqrt{5}\sin(3t + \phi) + 4$. The amplitude is therefore $\sqrt{5}$ and the maximum and minimum values of y are $4 + \sqrt{5}$ and $4 - \sqrt{5}$ respectively.

7.2 A shop regularly sells x items of a certain kind every day and receives deliveries of new stock every T days. Assume that the delivery time coincides with the sale of the last item. Sketch the graph of $N(t) = $ number of items in stock at time t and write down a model for $N(t)$ in terms of x, T and t.

Solution $N(t)$ is clearly a linear function of t, repeating with a period T. We can write it down as

$$N(t) = \begin{cases} (T - t)x & 0 < t < T \\ N(t - T) & t > T \end{cases}$$

Note that the bracket in the second part of the definition stands for functional notation, not multiplication. See Fig. 7.11.

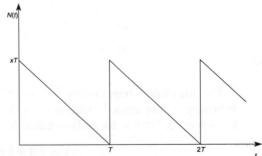

Figure 7.11

7.3 A model is required for the flapping of a bird's wing. If one complete wing beat takes 0.4 s and the wing moves through a total angle of 40°, write down an expression for the angle $\theta(t)$ which the wing makes with the horizontal at time t.

Solution If we measure θ in degrees we can take $\theta = 20 \sin \Omega t$ and the period is $2\pi/\Omega = 0.4$ so $\Omega = 5\pi$ and our model is

$$\theta(t) = 20 \sin(5\pi t)$$

(Note that when we evaluate the sin term we must remember that $5\pi t$ is in radians.)

7.4 At 12 o'clock the two hands of an analogue clock are together. At time t later they make an angle $\theta(t)$ with each other (take this to be the smaller of the two angles). What is $\theta(t)$ in terms of t and at what time after 12 are the two hands first together again?

Solution The minute hand travels at an angular speed of 2π radians per hour, so after t hours $\alpha = 2\pi t$. The hour hand travels at an angular speed of 2π radians in 12 hours, so after t hours, $\beta = \pi t/6$. Now $\theta = \alpha - \beta = \pi t(2 - 1/6) = 11\pi t/6$ until $t = 6/11$ at which time $\theta = \pi$ so the two hands are in line. After that the angle between them is $2\pi - 11\pi t/6$ until $t = 12/11$ when $\theta = 0$ once more.

$\theta(t)$ is therefore given by

$$\theta(t) = \begin{cases} 11\pi t/6 & 0 \leqslant t \leqslant 6/11 \\ \pi(2 - 11t/6) & 6/11 \leqslant t \leqslant 12/11 \end{cases}$$

The graph of $\theta(t)$ is shown in Fig. 7.12.

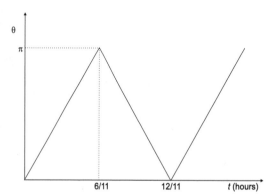

Figure 7.12

7.5 Manufacturers of a certain type of garden furniture find that their sales reach a maximum of £5000 a day in June and fall to a minimum of £600 a day in December. Write down a model for $S(t)$, their daily sales in month t, where $t = 1$ is January. Use the model to predict the daily sales in October.

Solution The period here is 12 months, so $2\pi/\Omega = 12$ and $\Omega = \pi/6$. We can write down the model as $S(t) = a + b \cos(\pi t/6)$. The information we have is that $S(6) = 5000$ and $S(12) = 600$. Substituting these into the model gives us two equations $a - b = 5000$ and $a + b = 600$, so $a = 2800$ and $b = -2200$ and the model is $S(t) = 2800 - 2200 \cos(\pi t/6)$ from which $S(10) = 1700$.

Note that our work was made easy here by the fact that the data was given at the highest and lowest points. A more general problem with data at arbitrary points will require the more general model $a + b \cos \Omega t + c \sin \Omega t$ and **three** data points to determine the three unknown parameters (this is assuming we know Ω!). See Example 7.9.

7.6 A searchlight is fixed at the top of a tower of height h. The beam, which has a constant angular width of 10°, swings regularly backwards and forwards along a horizontal line in such a way that the furthest point reached is a horizontal distance h from the base of the tower. Find an expression for the furthest point reached by the light at time t if the period of the swing is 12 s.

Solution We can model the angle θ shown in Fig. 7.13 by $\theta = 35 \sin \Omega t$, since 35° is the maximum value of θ when the searchlight is at an extremity of its swing. The period is $2\pi/\Omega = 12$, so $\theta = 35 \sin(\pi t/6)$ and the

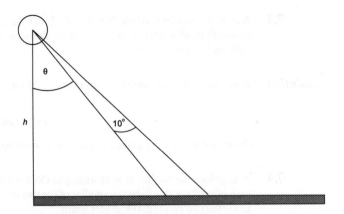

Figure 7.13

furthest point reached by the light at time t is $h\tan(\theta + 10°) = h\tan[35\sin(\pi t/6) + 10]$ where the expression inside the square brackets is in degrees.

A different model for $\theta(t)$ is obtained if we assume that the beam has a constant angular speed ω until it reaches its furthest point, when it instantly reverses direction and returns with the same constant angular speed. Then $\theta = \omega t$ for $0 \leqslant t \leqslant 3$ where $3\omega = 45°$ so $\omega = 15°$ and one complete period is described by

$$\theta = \begin{cases} 15t & 0 \leqslant t \leqslant 3 \\ 90 - 15t & 3 \leqslant t \leqslant 9 \\ 15t - 180 & 9 \leqslant t \leqslant 12 \end{cases}$$

The difference between the two models for θ can be seen by comparing the graphs (Fig. 7.14).

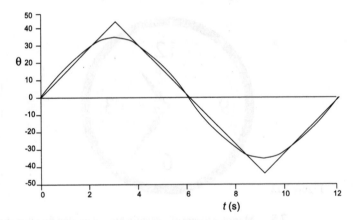

Figure 7.14

7.7 Figure 7.15 shows an in-line slider–crank mechanism. If the wheel is driven at a constant rotational speed, obtain a model for the distance $x(t)$ of the slider from the centre of the wheel at time t.

Solution From the diagram, $x = a\cos\theta + b\cos\phi$. The angle θ is Ωt where Ω is the angular speed of the wheel, if we start at $t = 0$ when $\theta = 0$.

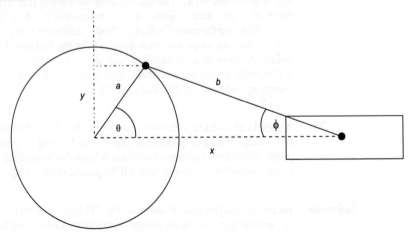

Figure 7.15

84

Also, looking at the direction perpendicular to x,

$$y = a \sin \theta = b \sin \phi$$

Therefore

$$b \cos \phi = \sqrt{(b^2 - b^2 \sin^2 \phi)}$$
$$= \sqrt{(b^2 - a^2 \sin^2 \theta)}$$

The required model is therefore

$$x(t) = a \cos \Omega t + \sqrt{(b^2 - a^2 \sin^2 \Omega t)}$$

The maximum and minimum values of $x(t)$ are clearly $b + a$ and $b - a$ respectively, and the period is $2\pi/\Omega$.

7.8 The following are the times of sunrise and sunset (Greenwich Mean Time) in London on various days at weekly intervals through 1993.

January				February				March			
	2	0806	1604		6	0731	1659		6	0635	1750
	9	0804	1612		13	0718	1712		13	0619	1802
	16	0759	1623		20	0705	1725		20	0604	1814
	23	0751	1634		27	0650	1737		27	0548	1826
	30	0742	1647								

April				May				June			
	3	0532	1837		1	0433	1924		5	0346	2012
	10	0516	1849		8	0420	1935		12	0343	2018
	17	0501	1901		15	0409	1946		19	0343	2021
	24	0446	1912		22	0359	1956		26	0345	2022
					29	0352	2005				

July				August				September			
	3	0349	2020		7	0433	1938		4	0518	1840
	10	0355	2016		14	0444	1925		11	0529	1825
	17	0403	2009		21	0456	1911		18	0540	1808
	24	0413	2001		28	0507	1856		25	0551	1752
	31	0423	1950								

October				November				December			
	2	0603	1736		6	0703	1625		4	0748	1554
	9	0614	1721		13	0715	1614		11	0756	1552
	16	0626	1705		20	0727	1605		18	0802	1553
	23	0638	1651		27	0738	1558		25	0806	1556
	30	0651	1637								

Obtain a formula for the number of hours of daylight in day x, where $x = 0$ is 1 January.

Solution The longest day that we have in the data is 19 June at 998 min, dropping to 997 min by 26 June, but we know from astronomy that the longest day is actually 21 June, which is $x = 172$, so we shall take the longest day to be 999 min. In the data the shortest day was 25 December at 470 min, but 21 December would have been even shorter at, say, 469 min. The period is about 365 days so $\Omega = 2\pi/365$ and the amplitude is $(999 - 469)/2 = 265$ while the mean is $(999 + 469)/2 = 734$, so our model is

$$y = 734 + 265 \cos(2\pi(x - 172)/365)$$

The data and the model are plotted together in Fig. 7.16.

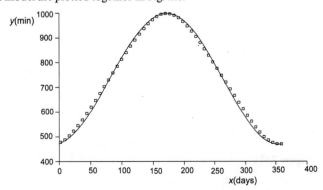

Figure 7.16

7.9 The depth of water in a particular harbour was 5.30 m at 6 p.m., 3.42 m at 9 p.m. and 2.38 m at 10 p.m. Use a simple model to predict:

(a) The depth of water at 1 a.m.
(b) The time of the next high tide
(c) The depth of water at high tide

Solution Tides are caused by the combined effects of the gravitational forces on sea water due to the Moon and the Sun and the rotation of the Earth. An accurate model is rather complicated, but if we consider only the lunar effect combined with simple models for the orbit of the Moon and the rotation of the Earth we get a simple sinusoidal model with $\Omega = 0.505\,89$ (rad h^{-1}). This model predicts high tides every 12.42 h.

We can write the model in the form $y = a + b\sin\Omega t + c\cos\Omega t$ where y is the depth of water in the harbour at time t (hours) and a, b and c are constants. We know the value of Ω but we will have to find a, b and c.

We are given values of y for $t = 6$, $t = 9$ and $t = 10$. Substituting in the model, we get three equations:

$$a + b\sin 6\Omega + c\cos 6\Omega \quad = 5.30$$
$$a + b\sin 9\Omega + c\cos 9\Omega \quad = 3.42$$
$$a + b\sin 10\Omega + c\cos 10\Omega = 2.38$$

Solving these, we find $a = 3.2016$, $b = 0.1161$ and $c = -2.0979$. Our model is therefore

$$y(t) = 3.2016 + 0.1161\sin(0.505\,89t) - 2.0979\cos(0.50589t)$$

(a) To answer this we just put $t = 13$, which gives $y(13) \approx 1.23$ m.
(b) Let us rewrite the model as:

$$y = a + \sqrt{(b^2 + c^2)}\,\sin(\Omega t + \phi)$$

where $\phi = \tan^{-1}(c/b)$. The largest value of y occurs when $\sin(\Omega t + \phi) = 1$, that is, $\Omega t + \phi = \pi/2$, so $t = 6.10$. So we have found that high tide was actually at 6 minutes past 6. We want the *next* high, which will be 12.42 hours later, i.e. at 6:31 a.m.
(c) The depth of water at high tide is $y = a + \sqrt{(b^2 + c^2)}$ which comes to ≈ 5.31 m.

7.10 At the end of May at a particular place it gets dark at 9 p.m. and the Sun rises again at 5 a.m. Write down a model for $L(t)$, the intensity of daylight at time t.

Solution Let us assume an underlying sinusoidal model with a 24 h period. The model we want is obviously a 'cut-off' version of this, since there is no light at all from nightfall to sunrise. The model will represent the variation of light through the day assuming perfect weather conditions.

Let us take $t = 0$ to be 5 a.m. and measure t in hours.
The model can be expressed as

$$L(t) = \begin{cases} a + b\sin(\pi t/12) + c\cos(\pi t/12) & 0 < t < 16 \\ 0 & 16 < t < 24 \end{cases}$$

We want $L = 0$ at $t = 0$, so $a + c = 0$. The graph is shown in Fig. 7.17.

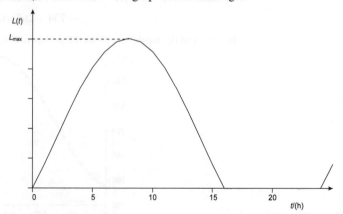

Figure 7.17

Also $L = 0$ at $t = 16$ so $a + b\sin(16\pi/12) + c\cos(16\pi/12) = 0$. We need another equation to make three equations for the three unknowns a, b and c. According to our model, the maximum intensity will occur at $t = 8.5$. If we call this maximum L_{max} then we have $a + b\sin(8.5\pi/12) + c\cos(8.5\pi/12) = L_{max}$.

Solving the three equations, we find $a = 0.3352L_{max}$, $b = 0.5807L_{max}$ and $c = -a$ we can write the model as

$$L(t) = \begin{cases} L_{max}[0.3352\{1 - \cos(\pi t/12)\} + 0.5807\sin(\pi t/12)] & 0 < t < 16 \\ 0 & 16 < t < 24 \end{cases}$$

7.5 Exercises

7.1 Write down simple examples of:

(a) A periodic function with amplitude 2 and period 3 s
(b) A periodic function with amplitude 3 and frequency 2 Hz
(c) A periodic function with amplitude 4 and angular frequency 5 rad s^{-1}

7.2 Find:

(a) The period of a function with angular frequency 20 rad s^{-1}
(b) The frequency of a function with period 20 s
(c) The angular frequency of a function with frequency 100 Hz.

7.3 Find the period and amplitude of the following:

(a) $6\sin 4t$
(b) $4\cos 5t$
(c) $8\sin(2t - 3)$
(d) $4\sin 3t \cos 3t$

7.4 Which of the following models has (a) the shortest period, (b) the highest frequency and (c) the smallest amplitude:

(i) $y = \sin t$, (ii) $y = 10\sin 10t$, (iii) $y = 100\sin 100t$.

7.5 If the electricity supply has a frequency of 50 Hz and maximum voltage 240 V, write down a model for the voltage at time t.

7.6 In the model $y = 3\sin 2\pi t + 4\cos 2\pi t - 2$ what are (a) the period, (b) the amplitude and (c) the maximum and minimum values of y?

7.7 Plot and compare the graphs of (a) $\cos t + \cos 2t$, (b) $\cos t + \cos(\sqrt{2})t$ and (c) $\cos t + \cos(1.41)t$.

7.8 If a clock gains x minutes every hour, every how often will it show the correct time?

7.9 A particular person's blood pressure (mm Hg) at time t (seconds) is modelled by

$$P(t) = 108 + 24\cos(6.2t)$$

What are:

(a) Her systolic (maximum) blood pressure
(b) Her diastolic (minimum) pressure
(c) Her pulse rate in heartbeats per minute?

7.10 A very rough road has bumps regularly spaced at 3 m apart, all with identical shapes and height 10 cm above the average level of the road surface. Write down a model for the height of the road above the average level at any point x.

7.11 A normal healthy resting adult takes about 5 s to breathe in and out (inspire and expire). At the peaks of inspiration and expiration the air flow rate is about 0.5 (l s^{-1}). Write down a model for the air flow at time t. What do you think will be the effects of exercise on the flow and consequently on the model?

7.12 The air temperature T at ground level at a certain point varies in a periodic manner over a 24 h cycle from a maximum of H at noon to a minimum of L at midnight.

(a) Write down a model for $T(t)$ in terms of the time t hours after noon and the values H and L.
(b) If H and L also vary over an annual cycle with mean values H_0 and L_0 write down a model for the temperature at any time t, where $t = 0$ represents noon on the hottest day of the year.

7.13 The water level in a reservoir varies with the seasons, with the summer and winter levels being respectively 5% above and 5% below the mean level L. Write down a model for the expected water level at day t.

7.14 An ice cream salesman finds that his sales have a maximum of 1000 per week in July and a minimum of 50 a week in January. Write down a simple model for $S(t)$, his weekly sales in month t, where January is $t = 0$.

7.15 For a certain type of tree the rate of growth is slow in winter and greatest during the summer months. The rate of growth also decreases every year from a maximum in the first year until there is virtually no growth at all after 10 years. What would be a suitable mathematical model for the rate of growth?

7.16 Trains on a city underground railway arrive at a certain platform regularly, 5 minutes apart. Passengers arrive at this platform at a regular rate of 30 passengers per minute. Write down a model for $N(t)$ = the number of passengers on the platform at time t (minutes).

7.17 An employee receives her £1000 pay cheque on the last day of each month, paid into her bank account. On the third day of each month her mortgage repayment of £250 is paid by standing order. She spends regularly at the rate of £25 per day. Taking a month to be 30 days, write down a model for $A(t)$, the amount of money in her account at *any* time t (days).

7.18 The air temperature in a centrally heated room is controlled by a thermostat. The thermostat cuts off the heater when the air temperature reaches T_1 and switches the heater on when the air temperature falls to T_2. Sketch a graph to show how you think the air temperature in the room varies with time and write down a simple model for $T(t)$, the temperature at time t.

7.19 The Moon's appearance to observers on Earth varies with a period of 29.5 days. In other words, the angle θ shown in Fig. 7.18 goes from 0 to 2π in 29.5 days. At the first quarter, half the Moon appears lit by the Sun, while half-way through its cycle we see the Moon as 'full'.

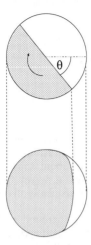

Figure 7.18

(a) What value of θ corresponds to a full Moon?
(b) Sketch the Moon's appearance when $\theta = 3\pi/4$.
(c) Write down a model for the percentage of the Moon's disc which appears lit after t days into the cycle.

7.20 A flying locust flaps its wings with a frequency of about 17 cycles per second. Assume that the hind wings oscillate with an amplitude of 1 radian about the horizontal position while the fore wings oscillate with an amplitude of 0.6 radians. There is also a phase lag of about 0.005 s between the fore and hind wings with the fore wings lagging behind.

(a) Write down expressions for $\theta_F(t)$ and $\theta_H(t)$ the angles made with the horizontal by the fore and hind wings at time t.
(b) For what length of time are the fore and hind wings on opposite sides of the horizontal?

7.21 A star has two planets, the inner one taking a time T_1 to complete one orbit and the outer one taking a longer time T_2. Today the star and its two planets are all in one straight line. How long will it be until they are in a line again?

7.22 A population of birds on an island varies during the year with a minimum at the end of March and a maximum at the end of September.

(a) Write down a suitable model for $P(t)$, the population t months after the beginning of the year.
(b) A team of ornithologists visited the island at the end of February and estimated the number of birds to be 2100. On a return visit at the end of May they estimated 2300. Use your model to predict the number of birds on the island at the end of November.

7.23 The depth of water in a particular harbour was 4.68 m at 2 p.m., 4.79 m at 4 p.m. and 2.08 m at 7 p.m. Use a simple model to predict:

(a) The depth of water at midnight
(b) The depth of water at high tide
(c) The time of the next low tide

7.24 Obtain models for the times of sunrise and sunset on day t, where $t = 0$ is 1 January, using the data of Example 7.8.

7.25 A hospital finds that more babies tend to be born early in the morning than at other times. Given the following data, fit a simple periodic model for the average number of babies born each day at time t hours after midnight.

Hours after midnight	0	3	6	9	12	15	18	21
Average number of babies	5	6	7	6	5	4	3	4

7.26 A string of length l is suspended from a fixed point and carries a heavy mass at the other end. When the string is hanging vertically the mass is at height h above the floor. The string is pulled to one side so that it makes a small angle α with the vertical and then released. In the resulting simple harmonic motion what is the height $y(t)$ of the mass above the floor at time t?

7.27 A small object moves with constant speed in a vertical circle of radius r which meets a horizontal floor at a point P (Fig. 7.19). Suppose the moving point is at the top of the circle at time $t = 0$ and moves with angular speed Ω. If there are parallel rays of light shining from vertically above, write down a model for the distance $x(t)$ of the shadow of the object from the point P at time t. What if the light is emerging from a point source at height $3r$ vertically above P?

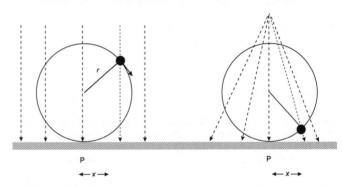

Figure 7.19

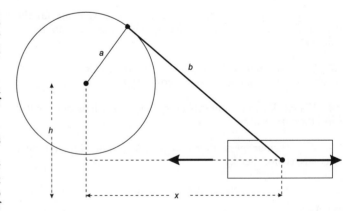

Figure 7.20

7.28 Figure 7.20 illustrates an off-set slider–crank mechanism. If the crank rotates with constant angular speed Ω find an expression for the position $x(t)$ of the slider at time t.

7.29 A woman swings her arm rhythmically with a period of 0.8 s. The angle which her upper arm makes with the vertical (shown as θ

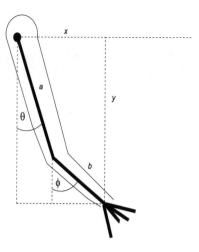

Figure 7.21

in Fig. 7.21) varies from $-20°$ to $+20°$. A model is required to predict the position of her hand at any time t.

(a) Obtain expressions for $x(t)$ and $y(t)$ in terms of t and the other parameters shown in Fig. 7.21, assuming ϕ remains constant.
(b) Obtain the corresponding expressions when ϕ also varies, with a period of 0.8 s, minimum 0 and maximum 50° assuming that $\phi = 0$ at the same time as $\theta = 0$.

7.30 Suppose a binary star system consists of two stars of exactly the same size, but one twice as bright as the other. The dim star can be regarded as orbiting around its bright companion with the plane of its orbit coincident with the line of sight from the Earth. The stars consequently appear to an observer on Earth as shown in Fig. 7.22. When the dim star passes in front of the bright star it shuts off some of the light. An instrument in an observatory on Earth records the total amount of light $L(t)$ received from this system as a function of t. Write down a model for $L(t)$ if the period of the orbit is T_0 days and it takes T_1 days for the dim star to pass in front of or behind the bright star. Sketch the graph of $L(t)$ against t.

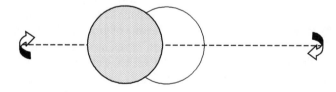

Figure 7.22

7.6 Answers to Exercises

7.1 (a) $2\sin(2\pi t/3)$, (b) $3\sin(4\pi t)$, (c) $4\sin(5t)$

7.2 (a) $\pi/10\,\text{s}$ (b) $1/20\,\text{Hz}$ (c) $200\pi\,\text{rad s}^{-1}$

7.3 (a) $\pi/2$, 6 (b) $2\pi/5$, 4 (c) π, 8 (d) $\pi/3$, 2

7.4 (a) (iii) (b) (iii) (c) (i)

7.5 $240\sin(100\pi t + \phi)$

7.6 (a) 1, (b) 5, (c) 3, -7

7.8 Every $720/x$ hours

7.9 (a) 132, (b) 84, (c) 59.2

7.10 $0.1\sin(2\pi x/3)\,\text{m}$

7.11 $0.5\sin(2\pi t/5)\,1\text{s}^{-1}$. Increased amplitude and frequency.

7.12 (a) $0.5[H + L + (H - L)\cos(\pi t/12)]$
(b) $0.5\cos(\pi t/4380)[H_0 + L_0 + (H_0 - L_0)\cos(\pi t/12)]$

7.13 $L\{1 + 0.05\sin(2\pi t/365.25)\}$

7.14 $525 - 475\cos(\pi t/6)$

7.15 $A\sin^2(\pi t/6)\exp(-0.1t)$

7.16 $N = 30t, 0 \leqslant t \leqslant 5, N(t) = N(t - 5)$ for $t > 5$

7.17 $A(t) = \begin{cases} 1000 - 25t & 0 \leqslant t < 3 \\ 750 - 25t & 3 \leqslant t \leqslant 30 \end{cases}$

7.19 (a) π, (c) $50[1 - \cos(2\pi t/29.5)]$

7.20 (a) $\theta_F = 0.6\sin[34\pi(t - 0.005)], \theta_H = \sin(34\pi t)$
(b) 0.01 s

7.21 $0.5 T_1 T_2/(T_2 - T_1)$ (on opposite sides of the star)

7.22 (a) $a - b\sin(\pi t/6)$, (b) 2846

7.23 (a) 2.46 m, (b) 5.00 m, (c) 9:19 a.m.

7.24 Sunrise: $5.92 - 0.32\ \sin(2\pi t/365) + 2.18\ \cos(2\pi t/365)$
Sunset: $18.16 + 0.47\ \sin(2\pi t/365) - 2.09\ \cos(2\pi t/365)$
(Both in hours)

7.25 $5 + 2\sin(\pi t/12)$

7.26 $y = l + h - l\cos(\alpha\cos(2\pi\sqrt{(g/l)}t))$

7.27 $r\sin\Omega t, 3r\sin\Omega t/(2 - \cos\Omega t)$

7.28 $x(t) = a\cos\Omega t + \sqrt{\{b^2 - (h + a\sin\Omega t)^2\}}$

7.29 (a) $a\sin\theta + b\sin(\theta - \phi), a\cos\theta + b\cos(\theta - \phi)$
where $\theta = (\pi/9)\cos(5\pi t/2)$
(b) as (a), with $\phi = (5\pi/18)\cos(5\pi t/2)$

7.30 Starting $t = 0$ from when the dim star begins its transit across the other star,

$$L = \begin{cases} 3L_0 - 4L_0\{\alpha - \sin\alpha\cos\alpha\}/\pi & 0 \leqslant t \leqslant T_1 \\ 3L_0 & T_1 \leqslant t \leqslant T_0/2 \\ 3L_0 - L_0\{\beta - \sin\beta\cos\beta\}/\pi & T_0/2 \leqslant t \leqslant T_0/2 + T_1 \\ 3L_0 & T_0/2 + T_1 \leqslant t \leqslant T_0 \end{cases}$$

where $\alpha = \cos^{-1}(1 - 2t/T_1)$ and $\beta = \cos^{-1}(1 + T_0/T_1 - 2t/T_1)$.

8 Modelling Rates of Change

8.1 Background

One of the main points of modelling is to try to predict what will happen, that is, we try to model how things change with time. Time itself can be modelled as continuous or discrete, and this is one of the modelling decisions which often have to be made. Sometimes there is a natural time interval at the end of which something happens, for example the breeding season of a living population. In cases like these a discrete model of time is probably appropriate, with a time step equal to the time between breeding seasons. The variable whose rate of change we are modelling can also be continuous or discrete. For a **discrete** variable whose value after n time steps is X_n, the change or increment during the nth step is $\Delta X_n = X_{n+1} - X_n$.

The progression of X_n with time can be shown in a number of ways, the most obvious being a plot of X_n against n. It could also be useful to plot the incremental change ΔX_n against n. Another possibility is to calculate the relative growth in each time interval from $R_n = \Delta X_n / X_n$ which gives the growth as a proportion of the value of the variable at the beginning of the interval. This third possibility could be relevant in modelling the growth of an animal, for example. The table below gives the weight in pounds of one baby during the first few months of her life.

Age (months),	n	0	1	2	3	4
Weight (lb),	X_n	8	10	13	16	20
	ΔX_n		2	3	3	4
	R_n		0.250	0.300	0.231	0.250

We see that the absolute rate of growth for this period (as shown by ΔX_n) was greatest in the fourth month, but the relative rate of growth (as shown by R_n) peaked in the second month.

Discrete models are obtained by making assumptions about the rate of growth which then translate into a difference equation satisfied by X_n. The simplest types are the geometric progression $X_{n+1} = aX_n$ and the linear form $X_{n+1} = aX_n + b$ which were discussed in Chapter 5. It is useful to remember (contrary to common practice by many people) that a **percentage** change is equivalent to a **multiplication**, so if X changes by r% it becomes $(1 + r/100)X$. If, for example, the price of an item goes up by 3%, 4% and 2% in three consecutive years its final price is $(1.03)(1.04)(1.02) = 1.092\,624$ times the original price, so the net increase in price over the three year period is 9.2624%.

The rate of inflation is an indication of the rate of increase in the average level of prices. In the UK this is measured by comparing the Retail Price Index with the value of the Index twelve months earlier. The inflation rate is then calculated as an annual percentage rate, say I%. The actual annual percentage change (say X%) in a particular cost or income can be misleading because it disregards the effect of inflation. The increase 'in real terms' or 'allowing for inflation' is required. A very common mistake is to take the difference $(X–I)$% which comes from forgetting the multiplicative nature of percentage changes as mentioned in the previous paragraph. The fact that this is wrong can be seen by noticing that if inflation is I% the value of £1 decreases to £$1/(1+I/100)$ in one year. An investment yielding an interest of X% p.a. gives for each £1 an amount £$(1 + X/100)$ after one year, but these are deflated pounds worth £$1/(1 + I/100)$ each. The effective rate of interest is therefore given by

$(1 + X/100)/(1 + I/100)$. For example, if $X = 10$ and $I = 4$ this factor is $(1.1)/(1.04) \approx 1.0577$ so the effective rate of interest is 5.77% (not $10 - 4 = 6\%$).

When a **continuous** model is chosen the techniques of differential calculus become very relevant. If $f(t)$ is a function of time then as time changes from t to $t + \Delta t$, $f(t)$ changes from $f(t)$ to $f(t + \Delta t)$ and the change is represented by Δf. The quantities Δt and Δf are referred to as **differentials**.

The average rate of change of f is (change in f)/(change in time), which is the ratio of the differentials or

$$\frac{f(t + \Delta t) - f(t)}{\Delta t}$$

Letting $\Delta t \to 0$ we get

$$\frac{\Delta f}{\Delta t} \to \frac{\mathrm{d}f}{\mathrm{d}t}$$

which is the **instantaneous** rate of change of f with respect to t, often referred to as the **derivative** and abbreviated to f'. The differentials are related by

$$\Delta f \simeq \frac{\mathrm{d}f}{\mathrm{d}t} \Delta t$$

This can be used to calculate approximate changes. For example if $f(t) = 3t^2 - t$ what is the change in f when t changes from 2 to 2.1?

We have $f' = 6t - 1$, so $\Delta f \approx f' \Delta t = (6t - 1)\Delta t = [6(2) - 1](0.1) = 1.1$ gives the approximate change in f. The exact answer is given by $f(2) = 3(2)^2 - 2 = 10$ and $f(2.1) = 3(2.1)^2 - 2.1 = 11.13$ so that the exact change in f is 1.13.

Differentials are useful for estimating errors. Suppose the height of the tree shown in Fig. 8.1 is estimated from measurements of the angle θ and the distance x. In practice x can easily be measured quite accurately, but θ is rather more difficult. Suppose that the measurement of θ is subject to a possible error of 0.1 radians ($\approx 6°$). If θ is measured to be 45° and $x = 20$ m the calculated value of h is $x \tan \theta = 20$ m, but what is the possible error in this measurement? In other words, what is Δh if $\Delta \theta = 0.1$?

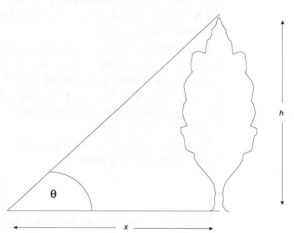

Figure 8.1

We can use

$$\Delta h \simeq \frac{\mathrm{d}h}{\mathrm{d}\theta} \Delta \theta = x \sec^2\theta \, \Delta \theta = 20 \times 2 \times 0.1 = 4 \text{ m}$$

so as a result of the uncertainty of 0.1 radians in θ our estimate of the height of the tree is uncertain by ± 4 m.

When more than one variable changes at the same time we use **partial** derivatives. In this example h is a function of θ and x. If θ changes by $\Delta\theta$ and x changes by Δx the change in h is

$$\Delta h = \frac{\partial h}{\partial \theta} \Delta \theta + \frac{\partial h}{\partial x} \Delta x$$

Suppose $\Delta\theta = 0.1$ as before and that $\Delta x = 0.01$ m. Now $h = x\tan\theta$ and $\partial h/\partial\theta = x\sec^2\theta$ as before, while $\partial h/\partial x = \tan\theta$, so the above formula gives

$$\Delta h = x\sec^2\theta\,\Delta\theta + \tan\theta\,\Delta x = 20 \times 2 \times 0.1 + 1 \times 0.01 = 4.01\,\text{m}$$

The sign of the derivative tells us whether the variable is increasing or decreasing with time.

$f' > 0 \Rightarrow f$ increases

$f' < 0 \Rightarrow f$ decreases

$f' = 0 \Rightarrow f$ has a stationary point which may be a local
maximum or a local minimum or a point of inflection.

In geometric terms the value of f' at any point gives us the gradient of the tangent to the graph of f at that point (Fig. 8.2).

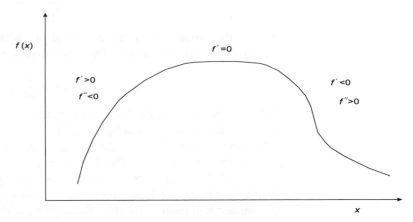

Figure 8.2

If f' is positive and increasing then the graph of f is concave up $\Rightarrow f$ is increasing at an increasing rate ($f'' > 0$).

If f' is positive but decreasing then the graph of f is convex up (or concave down) $\Rightarrow f$ is increasing at a decreasing rate ($f'' < 0$).

The rate of change of f' is the second derivative, f'', which tells us how quickly the rate of change is itself changing.

In economics, if $C(x)$ is the cost of producing x units, $C'(x)$ is often called the **marginal cost** and is the approximate cost of producing the next unit. Another concept from economics is **elasticity of demand**. If $Q(P)$ is the demand when the price is P, the elasticity is $E = -\text{d}(\ln Q)/\text{d}(\ln P) = -(P/Q)(\text{d}Q/\text{d}P)$. Its significance is that if demand is inelastic ($E < 1$) then raising the price will increase the revenue ($= QP$), while the reverse is true for elastic ($E > 1$) demand.

Very often we have $y =$ a function of x, where $x =$ a function of t, in which case we can find the rate of change of y from

$$\frac{\text{d}y}{\text{d}t} = \frac{\text{d}y}{\text{d}x}\frac{\text{d}x}{\text{d}t}$$

For example, suppose an ice cube is melting at the rate of one cubic centimetre per minute. If its edge measures 2 cm at present, how quickly is the edge shrinking?

We are given $\text{d}V/\text{d}t = 1$ and $x = 2$ where $V = x^3$ and we want to find $\text{d}x/\text{d}t$.

Starting from $1 = \text{d}V/\text{d}t = 3x^2\text{d}x/\text{d}t = 3(2)^2\text{d}x/\text{d}t$ we get $\text{d}x/\text{d}t = 1/12$ cm per minute when $x = 2$.

Points where $f' = 0$ are particularly important because we often want to know when a variable will have a local extreme value.

For example, suppose a box is to be constructed from sheet material to have a square base and an open top. If the capacity must be $0.2\,\text{m}^3$ what should the dimensions be in order to use the minimum amount of material?

If $x =$ side of the square base and $y =$ height of the box, its volume is $x^2y = 0.2$. The area of the material used is $A = x^2 + 4xy = x^2 + 4x(0.2/x^2)$ on substituting for y.

$\therefore A' = 2x - 0.8/x^2 = 0$ when $x^3 = 0.4$, i.e. $x \approx 0.737$ m and the corresponding value of y is $0.2/x^2 \approx 0.368$ m.

The fact that we have found a local minimum for the area and not a local maximum is obvious from the observation that we can make A as large as we like by choosing x very small or very large. We do not need to calculate the second derivative etc. in pedantic fashion when we can use practical sense. This is the pragmatic modelling approach as opposed to the pure mathematical.

Numerous examples of the use of differentiation to find maximum and minimum values can be found in any calculus textbook.

8.2 Discrete or Continuous?

In some problems a variable is very obviously discrete and no other way of representing it would be sensible. The harvesting of a crop, for example, usually happens once a year, not continuously through the year. In other cases the choice between a discrete model and a continuous one can be difficult. It is by no means true that the discrete choice is the easiest, it very much depends on the problem being investigated. Generally speaking a continuous model is suitable when the time interval between measurements is small. In going from a discrete model to a continuous one, the change in a unit time interval, which is $y_{n+1} - y_n$, is replaced by y'. One advantage of a continuous model is that a differential equation may be easier to manipulate and solve than a difference equation, and (if we solve it exactly) we finish up with a solution which we can use for any value of t. Paradoxically, if we use a numerical method to solve the continuous differential equation, we are in fact changing the problem back into discrete form! Note that some problems require both discrete and continuous elements together; for example, grass may grow continuously, but is usually only cut on certain days.

The simplest models are

Discrete	Arithmetic	$X_{n+1} = X_n + c$
	Geometric	$X_{n+1} = aX_n$
	Linear first-order	$X_{n+1} = aX_n + b$
Continuous	Linear	$y = a + bt$
	Power law	$y = at^b$
	Polynomial	$y = a + bt + ct^2 + dt^3 + \cdots$
	Exponential	$y = ae^{bt}$

Note the distinction between the power law and exponential models (the t is in the exponent in the exponential model). Also note that $y = a^t$ and $y = e^{kt}$ are equivalent since $\ln y = t \ln a$ in the first case and $\ln y = kt$ in the second, and they are the same if $k = \ln a$.

8.3 Worked Examples

8.1 A lake contains $100\,000$ m^3 of water with 5% pollution by volume. Every day 1000 m^3 of clean water flows into the lake and 1000 m^3 of polluted lake water flows out. How long will it take for the pollution in the lake to drop to a safe level of 1%?

Solution Let P_n represent the volume of pollutant in the lake on day n. Then $P_0 = 0.05 \times 100\,000 = 5000$ m^3.
Each day 1000 m^3 of lake water flows out and every m^3 of this contains $P_n/100\,000$ m^3 of pollutant.

$$\therefore P_{n+1} = P_n - 1000 \times P_n/100\,000$$
$$= (1 - 0.01)P_n$$
$$= (0.99)P_n$$
$$\therefore P_n = (0.99)^n P_0 = (0.99)^n 5000$$

So P_n will be down to 1000 when $1000 = (0.99)^n 5000$. That is, $(0.99)^n = 1/5$ or $n \ln(0.99) = \ln(0.2)$ which gives $n \approx 161$ days.

8.2 Suppose pollution continues to be added to the lake in Example 8.1 at the rate of $5\,m^3$ per day while $995\,m^3$ of clean water flows in every day and the outflow from the lake is $1000\,m^3$ per day. What is now our model for P_n and how does this affect the answer?

Solution We now have

$$P_{n+1} = P_n - 1000 \times P_n/100\,000 + 5$$
$$= (0.99)P_n + 5$$

This first-order linear difference equation has solution

$$P_n = (0.99)^n 5000 + 5[1 - (0.99)^n]/[1 - 0.99]$$
$$= 500[9(0.99)^n + 1]$$
$$= 1000 \text{ when } 9(0.99)^n + 1 = 2$$

which gives $(0.99)^n = 1/9$ or $n\ln(0.99) = -\ln 9$ so that $n \approx 219$ days.

8.3 A plant grows 3 cm on the first day and its growth on each day after that is half that on the previous day. At the same time, a weed grows 1 cm on the first day and its growth on each subsequent day is twice that on the preceding day. When will the weed become taller than the plant, and how tall will they both be at that instant?

Solution Let P_n and W_n represent the heights in cm of the plant and weed respectively at the end of n days.
Let G_n and R_n represent the growth of the plant and weed respectively in day n.
Then $P_{n+1} = P_n + G_n$ and $W_{n+1} = W_n + R_n$.
The question gives us the information that $G_{n+1} = (0.5)G_n$ and $R_{n+1} = 2R_n$, so $G_n = (0.5)^n G_0 = (0.5)^n 3$ and $R_n = 2^n R_0 = 2^n$.
Our models are therefore $P_{n+1} = P_n + (0.5)^n 3$ with $P_0 = 0$, and $W_{n+1} = W_n + 2^n$ with $W_0 = 0$.
The solution of the difference equation for P_n is of the form $P_n = a + b(0.5)^n$ where a and b are constants which we can find by substituting into the difference equation:

$$P_{n+1} = a + b(0.5)^{n+1} = a + 0.5b(0.5)^n$$

which must $= P_n + (0.5)^n 3 = a + b(0.5)^n + 3(0.5)^n$. Comparing both sides, we have $0.5b = b + 3$, $\therefore b = -6$, and since $P_0 = 0$, a must be 6. $\therefore P_n = 6[1 - (0.5)^n]$.
Similarly, trying $W_n = a + b2^n$ we find $a = -1$ and $b = 1$, $\therefore W_n = 2^n - 1$.
These models give:

n	0	1	2	3	...
P_n	0	3	4.5	5.25	...
W_n	0	1	3	7	...

so the weed overtakes the plant somewhere between $n = 2$ and $n = 3$ and their common length at that instant must be between 4.5 and 5.25 cm. We could have obtained these results very easily without any models, but *with* the models we can do more!
Although they only really apply for integer n values, let us put $W_n = P_n$. We then get $2^n - 1 = 6[1 - (0.5)^n]$. If we let x stand for 2^n then $(0.5)^n = 1/x$ and this equation is $x - 1 = 6[1 - 1/x]$ which is $x^2 - 7x + 6 = 0$ or $(x - 6)(x - 1) = 0$ so $x = 1$ or $x = 6$.
The answer $x = 1$ gives $2^n = 1$, so $n = 0$, implying that both the plant and the weed have the same length initially, which is true. The answer $x = 6$ gives $2^n = 6$ and $n = \ln 6/\ln 2 \approx 2.58$. The common length of the plant and the weed at that moment is $2^n - 1 = 6[1 - 1/2^n] = 5$ cm. Our models have enabled us to pinpoint the time and the common length accurately. (For more information on how to solve difference equations see the Bibliography.)

8.4 In exponential growth, if 5 years is the doubling time, (a) what is the tripling time and (b) what is the annual percentage rate?

Solution (a) If $y(t) = y(0)e^{kt}$ the doubling time is $T_2 = \ln 2/k = 5$, so $k = \ln 2/5$.
Let T_3 be the tripling time; then $y(T_3) = y(0)\exp(kT_3) = 3y(0)$. $\therefore \exp(kT_3) = 3$, $\therefore kT_3 = \ln 3$, $\therefore T_3 = \ln 3/k = 5\ln 3/\ln 2 \approx 7.92$ years.

(b) After one year, $y(1) = y(0)e^k = y(0)e^{\ln 2/5} \approx (1.1487)y(0)$. $\therefore$ this represents an increase of 14.87% in one year.

8.5 (a) Figure 8.3 shows the graph of f. What is the graph of f'?

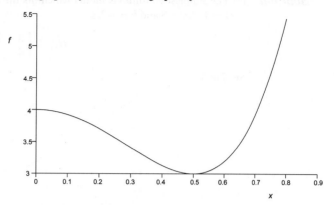

Figure 8.3

(b) Figure 8.4 shows the graph of f'. What is the graph of f? (Assume $f(0) = 1$.)

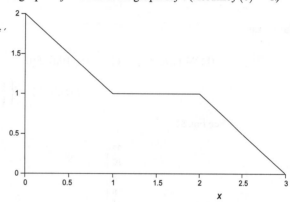

Figure 8.4

Solution The graphs are shown in Figs. 8.5 and 8.6.

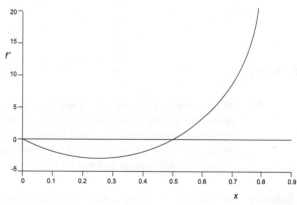

Figure 8.5

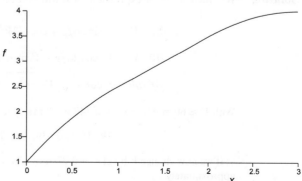

Figure 8.6

95

8.6 In a certain country, inflation decreases gradually from 8% to 4% over a period of 2 years then stays constant at 4%. Draw graphs showing how (a) the rate of inflation and (b) prices change with time.

Solution (a) The simplest continuous model which fits the data is linear, so $I(t) = a + bt$ where $I(0) = 8$ and $I(2) = 4$. $\therefore a = 8$ and $b = -2$, so

$$I(t) = \begin{cases} 8 - 2t & 0 \leqslant t \leqslant 2 \\ 4 & t \geqslant 2 \end{cases}$$

See Fig. 8.7.

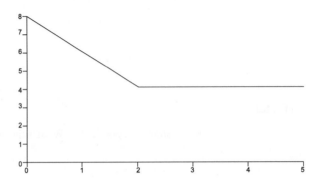

Figure 8.7 Inflation rate.

(b) We have $P(t) = \{1 + I(t)/100\}^t P(0)$

$$\therefore P(t)/P(0) = \begin{cases} (1.08 - 0.02t)^t & 0 \leqslant t \leqslant 2 \\ (1.04)^t & t \geqslant 2 \end{cases}$$

See Fig. 8.8.

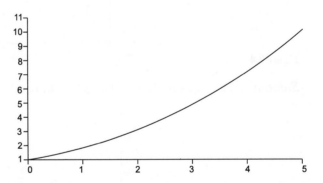

Figure 8.8 Prices.

8.7 When a cricket ball leaves the bowler's hand at a speed V at an angle α to the horizontal at a height h above the ground, a simple mathematical model predicts that it will hit the ground at a point a horizontal distance $R = V \cos \alpha \{V \sin \alpha + \sqrt{(V^2 \sin^2 \alpha + 2gh)}\}/g$ from the initial point. If $V = 60$ m.p.h., $\alpha = 0°$, $g = 9.81 \text{ m s}^{-2}$ and $h = 2$ m find the percentage changes in R caused by a change of (a) 1% in V, (b) 0.01 radians in α and (c) 1% in h.

Solution We differentiate the expression for R with respect to each of V, α and h. This gives us

$$\partial R/\partial V = V \sin 2\alpha/g + \cos \alpha [2V^2 \sin 2\alpha + 2gh]/g\sqrt{(V^2 \sin^2 \alpha + 2gh)}$$

$$\partial R/\partial \alpha = V^2 \cos 2\alpha/g + V \sin \alpha [V^2 \cos 2\alpha - 2gh]/g\sqrt{(V^2 \sin^2 \alpha + 2gh)}$$

$$\partial R/\partial h = V \cos \alpha/\sqrt{(V^2 \sin^2 \alpha + 2gh)}$$

With $V \approx 60$ m.p.h. $\approx 60 \times 0.447 \approx 27 \text{ m s}^{-1}$, $\alpha = 0$, $h = 2$ m and $g \approx 9.81 \text{ m s}^{-2}$ these become

$$\partial R/\partial V \approx 0.639, \quad \partial R/\partial \alpha \approx 74.3 \text{ and } \partial R/\partial h \approx 4.31$$

If we now change V by $\Delta V = 0.27$, α by $\Delta \alpha = 0.01$ and h by $\Delta h = 0.02$ the resulting change in R is approximately

$$\Delta R \approx (\partial R/\partial V)\Delta V + (\partial R/\partial \alpha)\Delta \alpha + (\partial R/\partial h)\Delta h$$
$$\approx 0.639 \times 0.27 + 74.3 \times 0.01 + 4.31 \times 0.02$$
$$\approx 0.17 + 0.74 + 0.09$$

We see that the change in angle has the largest effect, a change of only about half a degree causing R to change by about a metre.

8.8 A snowball of 20 cm diameter is melting at the rate of $1\,\text{cm}^3\,\text{s}^{-1}$. (a) At what rate is its radius shrinking, and (b) how quickly is its surface area changing?

Assume the snowball to be spherical and let r, A and V be its radius (cm), surface area (cm^2) and volume (cm^3) respectively.

Solution (a) The information we are given is $V' = 1$ and $r = 10$.
$$\therefore (4\pi r^3/3)' = 1 \text{ or } 4\pi r^2 r' = 1, \therefore r' = 1/(400\pi) \approx 0.000\,796\,\text{cm}\,\text{s}^{-1}.$$
(b) $A = 4\pi r^2$, $\therefore A' = 8\pi r r' = 8\pi \times 10 \times 1/(400\pi) = 0.2\,\text{cm}^2\,\text{s}^{-1}.$

8.9 A man standing on a wharf is pulling a rope tied to a boat at the rate of 0.5 m s^{-1}. His hands are 2 m above the level of the boat. How fast is the boat moving through the water when there is 4 m of rope between it and the man's hands?

Solution Let L be the length of the rope at any time and x the boat's horizontal distance from the quayside; then $x = \sqrt{(L^2 - 4)}$ and the boat's speed through the water is
$$x' = LL'/\sqrt{(L^2 - 4)} = 4 \times 0.5/\sqrt{(4^2 - 4)} \approx 0.577 \text{ m s}^{-1}$$

8.10 Suppose the demand for a product depends (as it usually does) on the price P. When the price is £3 the demand is 3600 a week, but at £4 the demand falls to 2800 a week. The natural question that arises is 'What is the best price to sell at to maximise the revenue?'

Solution Over a limited range of prices (which in practice is all we would expect) the demand can be modelled as a linear function of the price. Let this be $D(P) = a - bP$.
$$\text{When } P = 3, \; D = 3600 = a - 3b$$
$$\text{When } P = 4, \; D = 2800 = a - 4b$$

Solving these two equations, we find $a = 6000$ and $b = 800$, so our model is $D(P) = 6000 - 800P$.
The revenue is
$$R = \text{price per item} \times \text{number sold}$$
$$= P \times D(P) = 6000P - 800P^2$$

This is a maximum when $0 = \text{d}R/\text{d}P = 6000 - 1600P$, i.e. when $P = 3.75$, so the best price to sell at, from the retailer's point of view, is £3.75.

8.4 Exercises

8.1 A colony of bacteria doubles every hour. If after 8 h there are 33 280 bacteria, how many were there initially?

8.2 In 1970 the Earth's human population was increasing at about 2.1% p.a. In how many years (from 1970) will it have doubled?

8.3 Every year 70% of the branches of a certain tree divide into two and 10% divide into three. Starting with one branch in year 0, write down an expression for the number of branches after n years.

8.4 When the rate of inflation is $I\%$ p.a. in how many years is the £ halved in value?

8.5 A student learning to use a word processor takes 10 s to type the first word but gradually gets increasingly fast. How long will she take to type a 10 000 word report if each word takes (a) 0.001 s less than the previous word and (b) 0.01% less time than the previous word?

8.6 Rewrite the growth equation $y = 3(0.8)^t$ using the exponential function.

8.7 A lake contains $200\,000\,\text{m}^3$ of water, 7% of which is chemical pollution. Every day $2000\,\text{m}^3$ of clean water flows into the lake and

2000 m^3 of polluted water flows out. How long will it take for the pollution to drop to a safe level of 1%?

What is the answer if pollution continues to be added at the rate of 10 m^3 per day while clean water flows in at 1990 m^3 per day?

8.8 Suppose a plant grows 1 cm in the first day and that each subsequent day's growth is 70% of the previous day's growth.

(a) Write this as a discrete model for H_n = the height of the plant at the end of day n.
(b) How tall is the plant after n days?
(c) What is the maximum height the plant can reach?
(d) After how many days does the plant reach 90% of its maximum height?

8.9 A pool measures 5 m × 5 m and contains water to a depth of 0.4 m. Twenty five concrete cubes of 1 m^3 are placed one by one on the bottom of the pool, so that as each cube is added, the water level rises. Write down an expression for d_n, the depth of the water after n cubes have been added.

8.10 Glass X contains 20 spoonfuls of wine and glass Y contains 20 spoonfuls of pure water. One spoonful from X is added to Y and the mixture is stirred. A spoonful of the mixture is then transferred to X. Let X_n = the percentage of wine in glass X after n spoonfuls have been transferred in this way and let Y_n = the percentage of wine in Y. Find:

(a) A difference equation satisfied by X_n
(b) Expressions for X_n and Y_n in terms of n
(c) What happens eventually

8.11 A motorist drives a distance of x_1 miles in t_1 hours, then stops for s minutes before travelling a further x_2 miles in t_2 hours. What was his average speed in miles per hour for the whole journey?

8.12 A company's profit in 1994 was £X_1 and in 1995 it was £X_2. What was the average rate of increase of profit over the two year period?

8.13 At the beginning of 1994 the population of a town was P_1. During 1994, d_1 people died, b_1 were born, m_1 people moved into the town and l_1 left. The corresponding values for 1995 were d_2, b_2, m_2 and l_2. Write down an expression for the average rate of change of the population over the two year period.

8.14 For the function $f(t) = 2t^2 - t^3$ what are:

(a) The average rate of change over the interval $0 < t < 4$?
(b) The instantaneous rate of change at the point $t = 2$?

8.15 Refer to the graphs of $f_1(t)$ and $f_2(t)$ shown in Fig. 8.9. At which of the three times t_1, t_2, t_3 shown is:

(a) f_1 greatest?
(b) f_2 least?
(c) $f_1 > f_2$?
(d) $f_1 < f_2$?
(e) f_1' greatest?
(f) f_2' greatest?
(g) f_1' least?
(h) f_2' least?
(i) $f_2' > f_1'$?
(j) $f_2' < f_1'$?
(k) f_1 changing faster than f_2?
(l) f_2 changing faster than f_1?
(m) f_1 changing fastest?
(n) f_2 changing fastest?

8.16 (a) Figure 8.10 shows the graph of f. Can you sketch the graph of f'?

(b) Figure 8.11 shows the graph of f'. Can you sketch the graph of f?

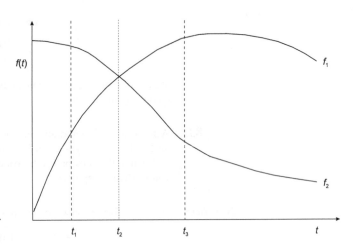

Figure 8.9

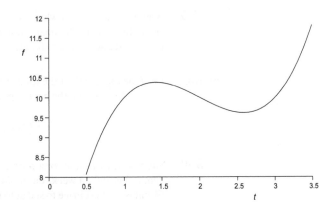

Figure 8.10

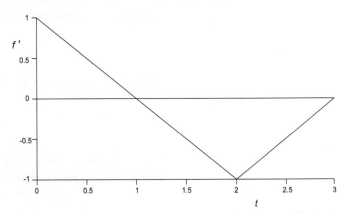

Figure 8.11

8.17 Figure 8.12 shows roughly the rate of increase of house prices in the UK over the years 1986–1993.

Over this period, when were house prices:

(a) Rising most quickly?
(b) At their peak?
(c) Decreasing most quickly?
(d) At their lowest?

8.18 There are two models for the population (in millions) of a certain country at time t years after 1990: (a) $P(t) = 14 + 0.23t$ and

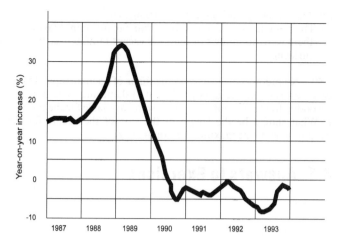

Figure 8.12

(b) $P(t) = 14e^{0.02t}$. What is the instantaneous rate of change of the population in 1993 according to each model?

8.19 If $y = 6x^3$ use differentials to find the approximate change in y when x changes from 1 to 1.002. Check with the exact answer.

8.20 Suppose that the number Q of certain items sold daily when the price is £P can be modelled by

$$Q = 1000 - 0.4P^2$$

If the price is currently £10 what will be the drop in sales if the price is increased to £10.50?

8.21 If $f_1(t) = 2000/t^2$ and $f_2(t) = 1000/t^3$, which of f_1 and f_2 decreases most (a) absolutely and (b) relatively as t increases from 1 to 2?

8.22 Suppose that the weekly sales of a new computer game, x weeks after launch, can be modelled by $S(x) = 900x + 30x^2 - x^3$.

(a) What does the model predict for the weekly sales after 5 weeks?
(b) How quickly are the weekly sales increasing after 5 weeks?
(c) When are the weekly sales increasing fastest?
(d) When do the weekly sales reach their peak?

8.23 Suppose that the number of fish in a certain lake at time t (days) can be modelled by $F(t) = 1000/(1 + 99e^{-0.1t})$.

(a) How many fish were in the lake initially (at $t = 0$)?
(b) How quickly is the population increasing after 10 days?
(c) When is the population increasing most rapidly?
(d) What is the maximum number of fish the lake can support?

8.24 The intensity of illumination on a screen due to light falling on it from a lamp a perpendicular distance r from the screen can be modelled as inversely proportional to r^2. What is the percentage change in the illumination caused by a small increase $p\%$ in the value of r?

8.25 In measuring a rectangular block the dimensions were found to be 10.0, 12.0 and 20.0 cm with a possible error of ± 0.05 cm in each of the measurements. Estimate the possible error in:

(a) The calculated surface area of the block
(b) The calculated volume of the block

Check your answers by calculating the greatest and least possible values in each case.

8.26 The volume of a cone is calculated from measurements of its height h and the angle α which its slant side makes with the vertical, using the formula $V = \pi h^3 \tan^2 \alpha/3$. If the measurement of h is accurate to $p\%$ and the measurement of α is accurate to $q\%$, what is the percentage error in the calculated value of V? (Assume p and q are small and that α is very close to 30°.)

8.27 A darts player stands 8 ft from the board and throws from a height of 6 ft with a speed of 20 ft s^{-1} at an angle of 30°.
Find the effect of changing the speed of throw by $s\%$ and the angle of throw by $a\%$ on the point where the dart hits the board.

8.28 Water is flooding into your leaking boat at the rate of f m^3 s^{-1}. You have a bucket which when full contains b m^3 and it takes you T seconds to fill it and throw the water overboard. What is the condition that you do not sink?
If you *do* sink and your boat's capacity is V (m^3), how long does it take from when the leak started?

8.29 (a) The length, x of each side of a square is increasing at the rate of b m s^{-1}. How fast is its area increasing?
(b) The dimensions x and y of a rectangle appearing on a computer screen are increasing at the rate of a and b (pixels per second) respectively. How fast are (i) its area, (ii) its perimeter increasing?

8.30 A cylindrical tank of radius 20 cm is supplied with water at the rate of 0.001 m^3 s^{-1}. How fast is the water level in the tank rising?

8.31 Suppose a car does $(s - s^2/100)$ miles per gallon of petrol when travelling at a constant speed s.

(a) How fast is it using up petrol (in gallons per hour)?
(b) What is its most economical speed?

8.32 Suppose each edge of a melting ice cube decreases in length by 1 mm in one minute. What is the melting rate of the ice cube in cubic centimetres per minute when its edge is one centimetre long?

8.33 Suppose that when a solid metal cube of mass 1 kg is heated it expands uniformly so that the length of each edge (which was initially 5 cm) expands at the rate of 2 mm per hour. How fast are (a) its volume and (b) its density changing after 3 hours?

8.34 A conical tank of angle 90° at its apex is supplied with water at the rate of 0.002 m^3 s^{-1}. When the depth of water is 0.5 m, how fast are (a) the depth and (b) the area of water surface increasing?

8.35 Suppose a forest fire spreads in such a way that at any time it covers a circular area of the forest.

(a) If the radius, r of the circle increases at a constant rate k (m s^{-1}) how quickly does the area of fire increase?
(b) If the area of fire increases at a constant rate c (m^2 s^{-1}) how quickly is the radius of the fire increasing?

8.36 A balloon is blown up by pumping in 100 litres of air per second. When its radius is 1 m how fast are (a) its radius and (b) its surface area increasing?
Two points on the balloon's surface are 10 cm apart at the instant when the radius is 1 m. (c) How quickly is the distance between them increasing at that moment?

8.37 A drawbridge of length l, hinged at its lower end, is lowered with constant angular speed Ω. Find the rate of change of the height of the top end above the hinge when the angle between the drawbridge and the vertical is α.

8.38 An aircraft flying horizontally with a constant speed U at a constant height h is currently at a straight line distance r from a fixed point on the ground. How fast is r changing?

8.39 Suppose a spider spins a spiral web with a constant linear speed b m s^{-1}. If the equation of the spiral is $r = k\theta$, find the rate of change of the area of the web.

8.40 A fir tree is modelled as a cone with constant angle α between its slant side and the vertical. If its height, h at time t is increasing at the rate b (m s^{-1}), find the rate of change of:

(a) Its (slant) surface area
(b) The area of its base
(c) The diameter of the base
(d) The volume of space it occupies

8.41 Sand flows through a chute at a constant rate of f m^3 s^{-1} and forms a conical pile on the ground.

(a) If the area, A of the base of the cone increases at a constant rate k (m^2 s^{-1}), how quickly is the height h of the pile increasing?
(b) If the height of the pile is increasing at a constant rate of c (m s^{-1}) how quickly is the area of the base increasing?

8.42 The volume of a cylinder of radius r and height h is $V = \pi r^2 h$. How quickly is the volume changing when $r = 20$ cm and $h = 50$ cm if the radius is shrinking at the rate of 1 mm s^{-1} and the height is increasing at 4 mm s^{-1}?

8.43 How fast is the shadow of a 100 m tall building at the equator increasing at 1 p.m.?

8.44 A person's area of skin, S (m^2) can be modelled by $S = 2W^{0.4}H^{0.7}$ where W (kg) is the weight and H (m) is the height. A girl 150 cm tall weighs 58 kg. If her weight is increasing at 6 kg yr^{-1} and her height is increasing at 5 cm yr^{-1}, estimate the rate at which her skin area is increasing.

8.45 The speed of a falling object increases by about 9.81 m s^{-1} every second. How fast is its height decreasing after it has fallen through a distance of 5 m from rest?

8.46 A lift descends with a uniform acceleration a for the first part of its journey and a uniform retardation b for the remainder. If the total time taken is T, what is the distance from start to stop?

8.47 A boy standing on a wall drops a ball from a height H above the ground and at the same moment his friend throws a ball vertically upwards with speed U from a height h above the ground. If both balls move in the same vertical line, how far above the ground will they meet? If they happen to have equal speeds when they meet, show that one of them will have travelled three times as far as the other.

8.48 Show that a conical tent of a given capacity will require the least amount of material when the height is $\sqrt{2}$ times the radius of the base.

8.49 Suppose that the depth of water in a certain lake t hours after midnight last night can be modelled by $h(t) = 15 + 0.2t - 0.01t^2$. Assuming the area of the water surface is constant at 50 000 m^2, find:

(a) The net amount of water that entered the lake between 7 a.m. and 8 a.m. this morning

(b) The inflow rate at 7 a.m. this morning in m^3 s^{-1}
(c) The rainfall rate at 8 a.m. this morning in mm min^{-1} (assuming there were no inflows or outflows except rainfall over the lake surface).

8.50 A window is to be made in the shape of a square topped by an isosceles triangle. The glass will be cut to shape and surrounded by a wooden frame. The total length of wood available for the frame is L. What should be the length of the side of the square for the window to let in the maximum amount of light?

8.5 Answers to Exercises

8.1 130

8.2 About 34

8.3 $(2.7)^n$

8.4 $2/\ln(1 + I/100)$

8.5 (a) 50 005 s, (b) 63 214 s

8.6 $y = 3e^{-0.223t}$

8.7 About 194 days; about 255 days

8.8 (a) $H_{n+1} = H_n + (0.7)^{n+1}$, $H_0 = 1$, (b) $[10 - 7(0.7)^n]/3$,
(c) 10/3, (d) $-\ln 7/\ln(0.7) \approx 5.45$ days

8.9 $1/(25 - n)$ for $0 \leqslant n \leqslant 15$, $1 + (n - 15)/25$ for $15 \leqslant n \leqslant 25$

8.10 (a) $X_{n+1} = (19X_n + 100)/21$
(b) $X_n = 50[1 - (19/21)^n]$, $Y_n = 100 - X_n$
(c) X_n and Y_n become 50.

8.11 $(X_1 + X_2)/(t_1 + t_2 + s/60)$

8.12 $(X_2 - X_2)/2$ p.a.

8.13 $(b_1 + b_2 + m_1 + m_2 - d_1 - d_2 - l_1 - l_2)/2$

8.14 (a) –8, (b) –4

8.15 (a) t_3 (b) t_3 (c) t_3 (d) t_1 (e) t_1 (f) t_1
(g) t_3 (h) t_2 (i) none (j) t_1, t_2, t_3 (k) t_1 (l) t_1, t_3
(m) t_1 (n) t_2

8.16 (a) See Fig. 8.13.

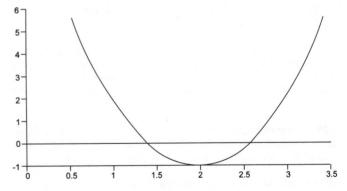

Figure 8.13

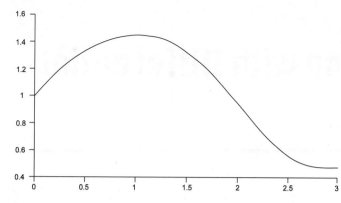

Figure 8.14

(b) See Fig. 8.14.

8.17 (a) End of 1988, (b) End of 1989, (c) End of 1992, (d) End of 1993

8.18 (a) $0.23y - 1$, (b) $0.2973y - 1$

8.19 0.036 (exact answer = 0.036 072 048)

8.20 -4 per day

8.21 (a) f_1 (by 1000), (b) f_2 (by a factor of 8)

8.22 (a) 5125, (b) 1125, (c) week 10, (d) week 30

8.23 (a) 10, (b) $2.6\,\text{day}^{-1}$, (c) 45.95 days, (d) 1000

8.24 $2p\%$

8.25 $\pm 8.4\,\text{cm}^2$, $\pm 28\,\text{cm}^3$

8.26 Approximately $(3p + 2.42q)\%$

8.27 $0.5943a + 0.25104s$ in

8.28 $b > fT$, $\{V + b\text{INT}[V/(fT - b)]\}/f$

8.29 (a) $2bx$; (b) (i) $ax + by$, (ii) $2(a + b)$

8.30 $0.0079577\,\text{m s}^{-1}$

8.31 (a) $1/(1 - s/100)$, (b) 50 m.p.h.

8.32 $0.3\,\text{cm}^3\,\text{min}^{-1}$

8.33 (a) $5.227 \times 10^{-9}\,\text{m}^3\,\text{s}^{-1}$ (b) $0.1695\,\text{kg m}^{-3}\,\text{s}^{-1}$

8.34 (a) $0.002\,546\,\text{m s}^{-1}$, (b) $0.008\,\text{m}^2\,\text{s}^{-1}$

8.35 (a) $2\pi rk$, (b) $c/2\pi r$

8.36 (a) $0.007\,957\,7\,\text{m s}^{-1}$, (b) $0.2\,\text{m}^2\,\text{s}^{-1}$, (c) $0.000\,795\,77\,\text{m s}^{-1}$

8.37 $-l\Omega \sin \alpha$

8.38 $(U/r)\sqrt{(r^2 - h^2)}$

8.39 $2\pi kb$.

8.40 (a) $2\pi bh \sin \alpha / \cos^2 \alpha$ (b) $2\pi bh \tan^2 \alpha$ (c) $2b \tan \alpha$ (d) $\pi h^2 b \tan^2 \alpha$

8.41 (a) $(3f - kh)/A$, (b) $(3f - Ac)/h$

8.42 $-125.66\,\text{cm}^3\,\text{s}^{-1}$

8.43 $0.0074\,\text{m s}^{-1}$

8.44 $0.872\,\text{m}^2\,\text{yr}^{-1}$

8.45 About $9.9\,\text{m s}^{-1}$

8.46 $abT^2/2(a + b)$

8.47 $H - 0.5g[(H - h)/U]^2$

8.49 (a) $250\,\text{m}^3$, (b) $5\,\text{m}^3\,\text{s}^{-1}$, (c) $0.1\,\text{mm min}^{-1}$

8.50 Approximately $0.224L$

9 Modelling with Differential Equations

In most of the examples of Chapter 8 we were given or assumed that our variable was modelled by a particular function of time, $y = f(t)$, and then we found the rate of change, $y' = f'(t)$. Very often our modelling **assumptions** are expressed in terms of **rates of change**. For example, we may assume that the rate of change, y', is related to the value of y itself at any time t. The rate of change of the size of a population, for example, clearly depends on the existing size of the population. This gives us the problem of working back from y' to find y. (Note that in all the examples in this chapter we use ' to stand for d/dt.)

A **first-order differential equation** is an equation expressing a connection between y, y' and t which applies at any time t. Starting from this differential equation our task is to obtain y explicitly in terms of t. This varies from being easy to very difficult or even impossible to do mathematically. However, we can always obtain approximate answers by numerical methods, in which case we produce estimates of $y = f(t)$ for a set of t values, usually going up in equal steps.

The exact solution of a differential equation is an equation connecting y and t which is obtained (in principle) by integration, which also brings in an arbitrary constant, c. In other words, there is a **set** of solution curves, each corresponding to a different value of c. Usually there will be information about the value of y at a particular time t (often $t = 0$). This information, together with the differential equation, gives us an **initial value problem**. If we have found the mathematical solution set to the differential equation, substituting the initial condition into our equation will give us the value of the constant c. If we use numerical methods the initial value is automatically included.

Sometimes one differential equation $y' = f_1$ applies from $t = 0$ to $t = t_1$ and then another equation, $y' = f_2$ from $t = t_1$ onwards. We can tackle this problem by first solving the initial value problem $y' = f_1$, $y(0) = y_0$ (given) to find the value y_1 of $y(t_1)$. The second step is to solve the initial value problem $y' = f_2$, $y(t_1) = y_1$ for $t > t_1$.

The procedure of modelling with differential equations requires the following steps.

1. **Translate** your assumptions into differential equations. This is a crucially important step and must be done with care. It often helps to use the principle

$$\text{net rate of change} = \text{rate of input} - \text{rate of output}$$

Note that a negative net rate of change means that the variable concerned is decreasing with time.

2. Choose the **unit** of time and make sure that all constants of proportionality are in the correct units. Also check that all the terms in the differential equation have the same units. Suppose, for example, that the volume of water in a tank is assumed to be decreasing at a rate proportional to the volume of water in the tank at any instant. Our differential equation then is $V' = -kV$. If V is measured in m^3 and we measure time in seconds then k must be in units of s^{-1}. Suppose that k has the value $0.1\,s^{-1}$; then the model is $V' = -0.1V$. (Note that both sides of the equation have units $m^3\,s^{-1}$.) If we decide to

change the unit of time to a minute then k must be in units of min^{-1} and the differential equation must be $V' = -0.1V/60$.

3. Explore the implications of the model **before** trying to solve the differential equation. With the equation in the form $y' = $ RHS, examine the RHS carefully. What is its value initially? This tells you the slope of the solution curve at the initial point. Is RHS always positive? If it is, then y is always increasing. Does RHS increase as t increases? If so, then the solution curve gets steeper as t increases. Conversely, if RHS decreases, your solution curve flattens out. Are there any special values of the parameters or variables that make $y' = 0$? In that case y may have a local maximum or a local minimum. Note that, physically, the condition $y' = 0$ means that y does not change with time, a condition often described as **steady state** or **equilibrium**. This is often the state to which a system evolves after a very long time ($t \to \infty$). In that case the solution curve flattens out gradually as y approaches its steady state value.

4. Decide whether the differential equation is simple enough to be solved mathematically or whether a numerical method is to be used.

9.2 Exponential Growth and Decay

One of the simplest differential equation models applies when the rate of change of a variable at any time is proportional to the value of the variable at that time. We can write this as $y' = ky$ and the solution is $y(t) = y(0)e^{kt}$. We get very different graphs depending on whether the constant k is positive (giving exponential growth) or negative (exponential decay). To fit one of these models to data we need the values of $y(0)$ and k. To find them we need only the values of y at two different times. Shortening $y(0)$ to y_0 and so on, we can write $y_1 = y_0 \exp(kt_1)$ and $y_2 = y_0 \exp(kt_2)$. By dividing we get $y_1/y_2 = \exp(k(t_1 - t_2))$, so $k = [\ln(y_1/y_2)]/(t_1 - t_2)$. Substituting for k into the expression for y_1 then gives y_0.

A simple feature of the exponential model is that it always takes the same time T for y to double (in exponential growth) or halve (in the case of decay). We see this from $y(t) = y_0 e^{kt}$ so that if $y(T) = 2y_0$ then $2 = e^{kT}$, so $T = \ln 2/k$, which is independent of y_0. Clearly $y(2T) = y_0 e^{2kT} = y_0 e^{2\ln 2} = y_0 e^{\ln 4} = 4y_0$. T is the 'doubling time' for exponential growth or 'half-life' for exponential decay (Figs 9.1 and 9.2).

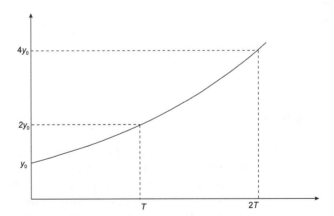

Figure 9.1

Exponential growth is seen (approximately) in the size of a population of bacteria, since the rate at which new individuals are produced is proportional to the number already present until limitations of space and other essential resources begin to have an effect. A good example of exponential decay is seen in the natural decay of radioactivity, where the rate of decay of radioactive nuclei is proportional to the number of nuclei remaining at that time. This is used in the technique of carbon dating, which is based on the principle that a constant proportion of the carbon atoms in **living** tissue is the radioactive isotope ^{14}C. Once the organism dies there is no replenishment of the ^{14}C so as it decays the ratio of ^{14}C to normal ^{12}C in its remains drops exponentially at a known rate (the half-life of ^{14}C is

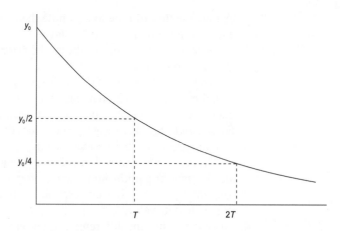

Figure 9.2

about 5568 years). By measuring the present ratio and comparing it with that of a living sample we can work out how long the ratio has been dropping, in other words the age of the sample.

9.3 Linear First-Order

A simple variation of the exponential model is obtained when the rate of change of y is assumed to be proportional to the difference between the present value of y and some fixed value L; in symbols: $y' = k(L - y)$, which has a solution $y(t) = L + (y_0 - L)e^{-kt}$ with $y \to L$ as $t \to \infty$. The shape of the solution curve depends on whether we start with $y_0 > L$ or $y_0 < L$ (Fig. 9.3).

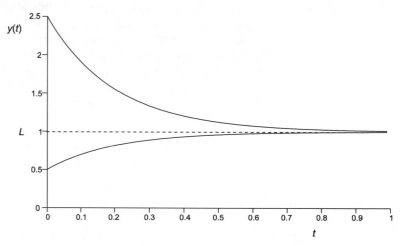

Figure 9.3

A common example of this model is seen in the transfer of heat energy by convection. The amount of heat energy contained in a body of mass M at temperature T is McT, where c is a constant called the specific heat capacity of the material from which the body is made. The transfer of heat energy by convection at the interface between a body and its environment can be very effectively modelled by assuming that the rate of transfer per unit area is proportional to the difference in temperature between the body and the outside. In other words, $(McT)' = hA(T_{out} - T)$, where T_{out} is the outside temperature, A is the area of the interface and h is the heat transfer coefficient, which depends on the nature of the interface. If M, c, h and A are constants the equation can be written $McT' = hA(T_{out} - T)$ or $T' = \alpha(T_{out} - T)$, where α is a constant, and in this form it is sometimes referred to as **Newton's Law of Cooling**. Note that it applies only when $T > T_{out}$, so that the body is hotter than its surroundings and loses heat. This is reflected by the fact that, from the equation, $T' < 0$. A similar equation applies to heat transfer by conduction when there is a constant temperature gradient.

The above equation is a simple case of the more general form

$$y' + a(t)y = b(t)$$

which is the class of linear first-order differential equations, solvable by the **integrating factor method** (see the Bibliography). If a and b are constants, the selection is $y = A\mathrm{e}^{-at} + b/a$, where A is an arbitrary constant.

Other simple cases occur in the modelling of the flow of water containing a chemical into and out of a tank. Suppose a tank contains initially M_0 (kg) of salt in $V(\mathrm{m}^3)$ of water. A solution containing S (kg) of salt per m^3 enters at the rate $f(\mathrm{m}^3\,\mathrm{s}^{-1})$. The contents of the tank are continuously and thoroughly mixed and the solution leaves the tank at the same rate f, so the volume of liquid in the tank remains constant throughout (Fig. 9.4).

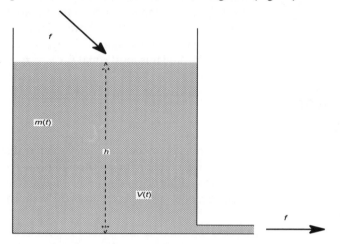

Figure 9.4

Let $m(t)$ be the mass of salt in the tank at time t. The rate of change of $m(t)$ must equal the rate at which salt enters the tank minus the rate at which it leaves. So

$$\text{mass flow rate of salt } in = S\,(\mathrm{kg\,m^{-3}}) \times f(\mathrm{m^3\,s^{-1}})$$
$$= Sf\,(\mathrm{kg\,s^{-1}})$$

Each cubic metre of solution in the tank contains (m/V) kg of salt, so

$$\text{mass flow rate of salt } out = (m/V)(\mathrm{kg\,m^{-3}}) \times f(\mathrm{m^3\,s^{-1}})$$
$$= mf/V(\mathrm{kg\,s^{-1}})$$
$$\therefore\ m' = Sf - mf/V \text{ or } m' + (f/V)m = Sf$$

This can be solved by the integrating factor method and the solution is

$$m(t) = M_0\mathrm{e}^{-ft/V} + SV[1 - \mathrm{e}^{-ft/V}]$$

The first term on the right-hand side shows how much of the original salt remains in the tank at time t. As $t \to \infty$ this decreases to zero and we get $m \to SV$, that is the same mass as we would get by filling the tank with the input salt solution containing $S\,\mathrm{kg\,m^{-3}}$.

An important feature of the above problem was the fact that the input and output flow rates were equal, so that the volume of liquid in the tank remained constant. Suppose now that these rates are not equal. The volume in the tank therefore changes and its rate of change is $V' = f_{\mathrm{in}} - f_{\mathrm{out}}$. If these flow rates are constant then the solution of this equation is

$$V(t) = V_0 + (f_{\mathrm{in}} - f_{\mathrm{out}})t$$

The equation for $m(t)$ is

$$m' = Sf_{\mathrm{in}} - (m/V)f_{\mathrm{out}}$$
$$= Sf_{\mathrm{in}} - mf_{\mathrm{out}}/[V_0 + (f_{\mathrm{in}} - f_{\mathrm{out}})t]$$

This is again a linear first-order differential equation, although slightly more difficult to solve than before.

Another feature which can complicate the model slightly is that the input of chemical may suddenly stop. Suppose that in the above constant volume example, the input of salt is stopped at time $t = T$ and that from then onwards pure water flows in. The model then becomes

$$m' = \begin{cases} Sf - mf/V & t < T \\ -mf/V & t > T \end{cases}$$

The solution for $m(t)$ will be represented by two different expressions for $t < T$ and $t > T$, but they must of course match up at $t = T$. This kind of phenomenon is quite common when modelling pollution with differential equations.

For problems of the above kind, a useful concept is the **mass concentration** $C(t) = m(t)/V(t)$. The rate of change of mass of the chemical inside a compartment is then $m' = (CV)'$ and this must equal $f_{in} C_{in} - f_{out} C_{out}$.

9.4 Non-linear Differential Equations

Although linear models are very useful, realistic models tend to involve differential equations where the expression for y' is not simply a linear function of y. A common form which occurs in the modelling of growing individual animals or plants or a population of individuals is the **logistic** model (also referred to as the **Verhulst** model)

$$y' = ky(1 - y/L)$$

The logical justification for using this model is that it predicts a low rate of growth when y is small and also when y is close to L. Living things also start growing slowly then gradually faster until a natural limit L is approached, so that $y' \to 0$ as $y \to L$. For populations, L is called the 'carrying capacity of the environment'. The behaviour of solution curves of the logistic model depends on whether we start with $y(0) > L$ or $L/2 < y(0) < L$ or $y(0) < L/2$. In all cases the mathematical solution is

$$y(t) = L/[1 + (L/y(0) - 1)e^{-kt}]$$

See Fig. 9.5.

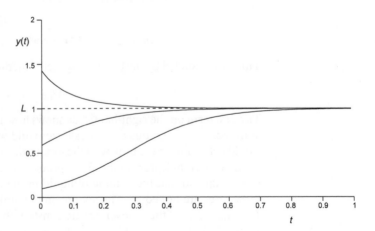

Figure 9.5

Simple modifications to this basic model can be made to account for a migration of animals into or out of the area, or hunting, harvesting or fishing by humans. For example, if a population of fish is depleted by fishing at a constant rate f, the model could be $y' = ky(1 - y/L) - f$.

Alternative forms of the logistic model are

$$y' = ky(L - y) \text{ with solution } y = L/[1 + (L/y(0) - 1)e^{-kLt}]$$

$$y' = ay - by^2 \text{ with solution } y = a/[b + (a/y(0) - b)e^{-at}]$$

Non-linear differential equations also apply to flow problems where a liquid flows out of a tank by gravity. If $a\,(\text{m}^2)$ is the area of the outlet at right angles to the outflow and the speed of the outflow is $u\,(\text{m s}^{-1})$ then the rate at which water flows out is $V' = a\,(\text{m}^2) \times u\,(\text{m s}^{-1}) = au\,(\text{m}^3\,\text{s}^{-1})$.

If h is the depth of liquid in the tank, then measuring potential energy from the bottom, a small particle of water of mass m has potential energy mgh at the water surface and is hardly moving, so its kinetic energy is zero and its total energy is mgh. When it has reached the outlet its potential energy is zero and its kinetic energy is $mu^2/2$. By energy conservation, $mu^2/2 = mgh$ so that $u^2 = 2gh$ and the rate of outflow of liquid is therefore $V' = a\sqrt{(2gh)}$. This is often called **Torricelli's Law**.

For containers with variable cross-section it is often useful to remember the connection between area, depth and volume in the form $\mathrm{d}V/\mathrm{d}h = A$. When the area of the liquid surface is A, the rate of change of depth is

$$h' = \mathrm{d}h/\mathrm{d}t = (\mathrm{d}h/\mathrm{d}V)(\mathrm{d}V/\mathrm{d}t) = (1/A)(\mathrm{d}V/\mathrm{d}t)$$

and $\mathrm{d}V/\mathrm{d}t$ is usually known (for example from Torricelli's Law).

A simple form of non-linear equation occurs in economics, where the demand Q for an item can be considered as a function of its price P. If a price rise of 1% leads to a drop in demand of 2%, we say the 'elasticity of demand' is $E = 1/2$. In general terms, $E = (-\mathrm{d}Q/Q)/(\mathrm{d}P/P)$. If we assume that E is a constant, then to find $Q(P)$ we solve the differential equation $\mathrm{d}Q/\mathrm{d}P = -EQ/P$.

9.5 Mechanics

The principles of Newtonian mechanics, which result in second-order differential equations, enable us to model problems involving moving objects very successfully. A large number of examples can be found in any textbook on mechanics (see the Bibliography), and similar examples will not be repeated in this book. When regarded as a first-order equation in velocity, v, Newton's second law for a single body of mass m, moving in one dimension, can be written $mv' = \text{force}$. Many different forces can be modelled, but the most common are that due to gravity ($-mg$ if v is measured vertically upwards and the body is close to the Earth's surface) and resistance to motion by the fluid through which the body moves. Commonly used models for the force of resistance are (a) $-kv$ and (b) $-kv^2$. The constant k includes the area of the body at right angles to the motion. Model (a) is the best choice for small bodies at low speeds.

9.6 Systems of Differential Equations

We often find that our models contain several dependent variables $y_1(t)$, $y_2(t) \ldots$ and we clearly need as many equations as we have unknowns. It may be that all of these are differential equations. If each equation involves only one y, then all we have to do is solve each differential equation separately, but more commonly all the y variables will be mixed up together. This is inevitable when one tank feeds into another tank or populations interact with each other. The result is that we have to solve the differential equations simultaneously, as a *system*, and this usually requires numerical techniques. Any equilibrium states that might exist are found by solving the simultaneous equations $y_1' = 0$, $y_2' = 0, \ldots$ etc., and an interesting question is whether such equilibrium states are *stable* (see the Bibliography for further details).

One of the most well-known models involving a system is that representing two interacting populations. If x and y stand for the sizes of two populations sharing the same living space, the equations for x' and y', as well as representing birth rates, must also model the interaction between the two populations. This can take a number of forms because the two populations may be competing for the same food or one species may be eating the other. The predator–prey case is often modelled by the **Lotka–Volterra** equations

$$x' = ax - bxy$$
$$y' = -cy + dxy$$

where the interaction is represented by the xy terms and the constants are all positive. The ratio of b to d represents how many prey are needed to produce one new predator.

Simpler equations can be used for **conflict** models, where there are no births, so the equations take the form $x' = -ay$, $y' = -bx$, which were used by **Lanchester** in 1916. Here the constants a and b represent the relative strengths or 'firing power' of individuals on each side.

Similar equations can also be used to model chemical reactions, which are best discussed in terms of the concentrations of various chemicals present at any time. Suppose we have a reaction between two chemicals A and B which combine to form a compound C.

We write

$$\mathrm{A} + \mathrm{B} \xrightarrow{k} \mathrm{C}$$

meaning a molecule of A and a molecule of B combine to form a molecule of C and k is the rate constant. We have three variables a, b and c (the concentrations of the three chemicals involved) and we assume the rate of reaction is proportional to a and to b. C is therefore being created at the rate $c' = kab$. At the same time, A and B are being used up at the rate kab, so $a' = -kab$ and $b' = -kab$.

Many reactions are reversible, for example $\mathrm{A} + \mathrm{B} \leftrightarrow \mathrm{C}$. The differential equations in this case are

$$a' = -k_1 ab + k_2 c$$
$$b' = -k_1 ab + k_2 c$$
$$c' = k_1 ab - k_2 c$$

Biological processes in living organisms can often be modelled using a number of compartments. Each compartment is assumed to be homogeneous and receives flows of material into it and out of it. The flow rates are often assumed to be proportional to the concentration difference; in other words the flow rate from compartment 1 to compartment 2 is $k(C_1 - C_2)$. This is sometimes called **Fick's Law**. In ecological modelling the various components of an ecosystem are often modelled as compartments with flows of energy and nutrients between various compartments.

9.7 Worked Examples

9.1 Write down differential equations corresponding to the following hypothetical statements:

(a) A town's population increases by 1000 every year.
(b) A town's population increases by 10% every year.
(c) The rate at which the radius of a circular area of forest fire increases is proportional to the perimeter.
(d) The rate at which the area of a circular forest fire increases is proportional to the perimeter.
(e) As part of an economic model it is assumed that the rate of change of output is proportional to the difference between demand and output. It is also assumed that demand is made up of a constant part and a part which is proportional to output.
(f) The number of rabbits in a field would double every 50 days except for the fact that 10 rabbits are caught and killed every day.
(g) Two different species of insects live together and eat the same food. They do not interfere with each other apart from the fact that they are competing for food. Assume that for both species the net birth rate is proportional to the population size and to the amount of food (F) available. Assume that there is initially a large amount of food available but that it steadily decreases as it is eaten by the insects. Write down differential equation models for X, Y and F, where X and Y represent the number of insects of each type.

Solution   (a) $P' = 1000$ (note that the unit of time is one year).

(b) At first glance it might be thought that the answer here is $P' = 0.1P$, but this is not correct for the reason explained in Chapter 8. Let the equation be $P' = kP$; then the solution is $P = P(0)e^{kt}$, so after one year the population becomes multiplied by e^k. This will $= 1.1$ if $k = \ln(1.1) \approx 0.0953$, so the correct model in accordance with the statement is $P' = 0.0953P$.

(c) If the radius is r its rate of change is r' and the perimeter is $2\pi r$, so $r' = kr$ where k is a constant.

(d) If the radius is r the area is πr^2 and its rate of change is $2\pi rr'$, while the perimeter is $2\pi r$, so if these two things are proportional to each other we have $r' = k$.

(e) Let x represent output and let demand be represented by y. The first assumption is that $x' = k(y - x)$ and the second is that $y = a + bx$. Here a, b and k are constants and there is only one **differential** equation, which we can write as $x' = k[a + (b-1)x]$, or equivalently, with just two parameters as $x' = cx + d$.

(f) If none were caught we would have $y' = ky$ so $y = y(0)e^{kt}$ which $= 2y(0)$ when $t = 50$; $\therefore\ e^{50k} = 2\ \therefore\ k \approx 0.0139$. The required model is therefore $y' = 0.0139y - 10$.

(g) In accordance with the assumptions, $X' = aXF$ and $Y' = bYF$ where a and b are constants. If we assume the two types of insects eat at constant but different rates then $F' = -cX - dY$. More realistically, a and b will be functions of F and will decrease when F becomes small. Also c and d are unlikely to be really constants.

9.2   Obtain differential equations satisfied by the radius of a sphere if its rate of change of volume is proportional to (a) its volume, (b) its surface area and (c) its radius.

Solution   If the radius of the sphere is r, its volume is $4\pi r^3/3$, so its rate of change of volume is $4\pi r^2 r'$. Case (a) is therefore $4\pi r^2 r' \propto 4\pi r^3/3$ or $r' = kr$. Case (b) is $4\pi r^2 r' \propto 4\pi r^2$, so $r' = k$, and case (c) is $4\pi r^2 r' \propto r$, so $r' = k/r$.

9.3   If y satisfies the given differential equation write down the differential equation satisfied by (i) $z = 5y$ and (ii) $w = y - 3$ in each of the following cases:

(a) $y' = 2y + 7$,   (b) $y' = y(y - 1)$ (c) $y' = \sqrt{(y^2 + 1)}$

Solution   (a) $z' = 5y' = 5(2z/5 + 7) = 2z + 35$
$w' = y' = 2(3 + w) + 7 = 2w + 13$

(b) $z' = 5y' = 5(z/5)(z/5 - 1) = z(z - 5)/5$
$w' = y' = (w + 3)(w + 2)$

(c) $z' = 5y' = 5\sqrt{[(z/5)^2 + 1]} = \sqrt{(z^2 + 25)}$
$w' = y' = \sqrt{[(w + 3)^2 + 1]} = \sqrt{(w^2 + 6w + 10)}$

9.4   A driver tested 3 hours after an accident was found to have 56 mg/100 ml of alcohol in his blood. After another 2 hours this had decreased to 40 mg/100 ml. Was he over the legal limit (80 mg/100 ml) at the time of the accident?

Solution   Let $c(t) = $ concentration (in mg/100 ml) of alcohol in the person's blood at time t. A simple model for the rate at which this decreases with time is $c' = -kc$. This implies $c(t) = c(0)e^{-kt}$ and $c(0)$ is the value we want. The information we have is that $c(3) = 56$ and $c(5) = 40$. We therefore have $56 = c(0)e^{-3k}$ and $40 = c(0)e^{-5k}$, from which, by division, we get $e^{2k} = 56/40$ and so $k \approx 0.17$. Finally, $c(0) = 56e^{3k} \approx 94$, so he *was* clearly over the limit (assuming the validity of our model) at the time of the accident.

9.5   Police officers discover a body at 1 a.m. and measure its temperature to be 29 °C while the outside air is at 21 °C. One hour later the body's temperature has dropped to 27 °C. Taking the temperature of a living body to be 37 °C, estimate the time of death.

Solution   We can use Newton's law of cooling, $T' = \alpha(T_{\text{out}} - T)$ with solution $T = T_{\text{out}} + (T_0 - T_{\text{out}})e^{-\alpha t}$, where T_0 is the temperature at time $t = 0$, which we take to be the time of death. Inserting the given data, we have

$$29 = 21 + (37 - 21)e^{-\alpha t}$$

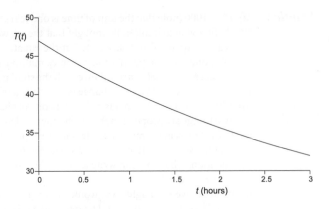

Figure 9.6

and

$$27 = 21 + (37 - 21)e^{-\alpha(t+1)}$$

These simplify to $e^{-\alpha t} = 8/16$ and $e^{-\alpha(t+1)} = 6/16$, from which, by division, $e^{\alpha} = 4/3$ so $\alpha \approx 0.2877$. The value of t is $-\ln(1/2)/\alpha \approx 2.409$ h so we estimate the time of death to be 10:35 p.m. Figure 9.6 shows the cooling curve.

9.6 Figure 9.7 represents a small lake which contains $2000\,\text{m}^3$ of water. Water flows in at the rate of $0.1\,\text{m}^3\,\text{s}^{-1}$ through stream A, and there is another stream B through which water flows out of the lake at $0.1\,\text{m}^3\,\text{s}^{-1}$.

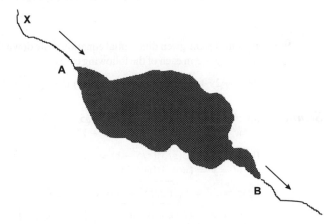

Figure 9.7

At 11.05 a.m. as a result of a road accident a tanker overturns and spills a toxic chemical into the lake at X.

By the time police and emergency services have brought the situation under control it is 11.35 a.m. and an unknown amount $z\,(\text{m}^3)$ of the chemical has leaked into the lake. The value of z is estimated to be anything from 5 to 20.

Develop a mathematical model which you can use to predict the concentration of the pollutant in the lake at any time and use it to estimate (for a range of possible initial pollution amounts z):

(a) The maximum pollution level in the lake and the time at which the maximum is reached.
(b) The time it will take for the pollution to fall below the safe level of 0.05%.

Solution The pollution level in the lake at any time can be measured by the **concentration** $C(t)$ of pollutant by volume (so each m^3 of polluted water contains $C\,\text{m}^3$ of chemical and $(1 - C)\,\text{m}^3$ of pure water).

Let us take a minute as the unit of time.

The rate of flow of pollutant into the lake is $z/30\,(\text{m}^3\,\text{min}^{-1})$ for $0 < t < 30$.

The rate of outflow of pollutant from the lake is $60 \times 0.1C\,(\text{m}^3\,\text{min}^{-1})$, since every m^3 of outflowing polluted water contains $C\,\text{m}^3$ of pollutant.

The volume of the lake remains constant at $2000\,\text{m}^3$, so the rate of change of the mass of pollutant in the lake is

$$2000C' = \text{rate in} - \text{rate out} = z/30 - 6C$$

This is a first-order linear differential equation, and its solution, using the initial condition $C(0) = 0$, is

$$C(t) = z[1 - e^{-6t/2000}]/180$$

The maximum pollution level in the lake is obviously reached at time $t = 30$ and the maximum level is $C(30) = (4.782 \times 10^{-4})z$. After that the differential equation changes to $2000C' = -6C$, which has solution $C(t) = C(30)e^{-6(t-30)/2000}$. This falls to 0.0005 when $t = T$, where

$$T - 30 = -(2000/6)\ln[0.0005/C(30)]$$

or

$$T = 30 + (2000/6)\ln[0.9653z]$$

The table below gives values of $C(30)$ and T for some values of z.

z (m^3)	$C(30)$ (m^3)	T (min)
5	0.002 39	552
10	0.004 78	738
15	0.007 17	918
20	0.009 56	1014

9.7 The International Whaling Commission has been fairly successful in controlling the overfishing of whale stocks, which in past years has sometimes led to some species of whales becoming endangered. Suppose the estimated present size of a particular population of whales is 10 000 and that the rate of growth can be modelled by the equation $P' = 0.12P(1 - P/100\,000)$ (measuring in units of 1000 for whales and 1 year for time).

(a) Obtain an expression for $P(t)$.
(b) When is the rate of growth increasing?
(c) When is the rate of growth decreasing?
(d) What will happen eventually?
(e) How would you modify the differential equation to take account of a fishing rate of f whales per year?
(f) What is the maximum rate of fishing which would not cause this species to become extinct?

Solution (a) Referring to the general solution of the logistic equation quoted earlier, we have $L = 100$, $P(0) = 10$ and $k = 0.12$. The required expression is therefore $P(t) = 100/[1 + 9e^{-0.12t}]$.

(b) The rate of growth is P' and this is increasing when $P'' > 0$. From the answer to (a),

$$P' = 108e^{-0.12t}/(1 + 9e^{-0.12t})^2$$

(which we note is always positive) and

$$P'' = 12.96e^{-0.12t}(-1 + 9e^{-0.12t})/(1 + 9e^{-0.12t})^3$$

It follows that P' is increasing when $9e^{-0.12t} - 1 > 0$, that is, when $e^{-0.12t} < 1/9$, which is true when $t < 18.3$ years.

(c) This is the opposite of (b), i.e. $t > 18.3$ years.
(d) From (a), as $t \to \infty$ we get $P \to 100$.
(e) $P' = 0.12P(1 - 0.1P) - 0.001f$.
(f) From (e), $P' = 0$ if $f > 120P(1 - 0.1P)$. Using the current estimate of $P = 10$, this gives $P'(0) < 0$ for $f > 1080$. It follows that the whale population will decline to zero when fishing exceeds 1080 whales per year.

9.8 Hot and cold water taps are turned on at time $t = 0$ in order to fill a bath which can be modelled as a rectangular tank. The hot tap is turned off after one minute, while the cold tap is allowed to run for a further minute.

(a) Make a list of the variables and parameters you would need in order to set up a simple model whose purpose is to predict the temperature of the bath water at any time.
(b) Make a list of the assumptions you would make in order to set up the necessary equations and then write down your differential equations.

Solution (a) We can make up a list of factors as follows.

Description	Type	Symbol	Units
Volume of water in bath	output variable	V	m^3
Surface area of bath water	output variable	A	m^2
Temperature of bath water	output variable	T	K
Temperature of hot water	input parameter	T_1	K
Temperature of cold water	input parameter	T_2	K
Ambient air temperature	input parameter	T_a	K
Inflow rate of hot water	input parameter	F_1	$m^3\,s^{-1}$
Inflow rate of cold water	input parameter	F_2	$m^3\,s^{-1}$
Heat transfer coefficient	input parameter	h	$W\,m^{-2}K^{-1}$
Density of water	input parameter	ρ	$kg\,m^{-3}$
Specific heat capacity of water	input parameter	c	$W\,kg^{-1}K^{-1}$

(b) Assume:

- Heat is lost by convection from the water surface only.
- The temperatures and flow rates of the hot and cold water from the taps do not vary.
- The temperature of the ambient air is constant.
- The temperature of the bath itself is constant.
- There is instant mixing of the hot and cold water.

For the volume of water in the bath we can write down the equations

$$V' = \begin{cases} F_1 + F_2 & 0 < t < 60 \\ F_2 & 60 \leqslant t < 120 \\ 0 & t \geqslant 120 \end{cases}$$

For the heat energy of the water in the bath, we can write

$$(c\rho VT)' = \begin{cases} (\rho F_1 T_1 + \rho F_2 T_2)c - hA(T - T_a) & 0 < t < 60 \\ \rho F_1 T_1 c - hA(T - T_a) & 60 \leqslant t < 120 \\ -hA(T - T_a) & t \geqslant 120 \end{cases}$$

To solve the problem, we need to solve these differential equations for T and V.

9.9 The following problem was discussed in Chapter 5 as a **discrete** model. Let us repeat it here, modelling the weight as a **continuous** function of time and using a differential equation model.

A girl eats 2500 calories every day. 1200 cal are used up in basic metabolism and she uses 16 cal per kg of body weight per day in exercise. The rest are converted into body fat (10 000 cal convert to 1 kg fat).

On Sunday morning she weighed 9 stone exactly. On Wednesday she had a bigger than usual meal and her intake was 3500 cal for that day.

Develop a mathematical model for predicting her weight $W(t)$ at time t and use it to estimate:

(a) Her weight on Saturday morning.
(b) The most she should eat daily to avoid putting on any weight (when her weight is 9 stone).
(c) The minimum weight she can reduce to in N weeks.
(d) The daily intake to which she should restrict herself if she wants to bring her weight down to 8 stone in N weeks for various values of N (starting from 9 stone).

Solution First, note that for the purpose of this model we will ignore energy intake from respiration. Taking 1 day as the time unit, let $W(t)$ represent her weight in kg after t days and let β be her **net** daily intake (cal). Her daily intake in cal is $\beta - 0.0016W$, which in kg is $(\beta - 16W)/10\,000$. For $0 < t < 3$ we have $\beta = 1300$ so the differential equation is $dW/(1300 - 16W) = dt/10\,000$. We can integrate this to $-\ln(1300 - 16W)/16 = 10^{-4}t + C_1$, or $W(t) = 81.25 - C_1 e^{-0.0016t}$.

We know that 9 stone $= 57.1526$ kg $= W(0) = (81.25 - C_1)$ kg. Therefore, $C_1 = 24.0974$.

Using this value for C_1 and putting $t = 3$, we find $W(3) = 57.26799$. For $3 < t < 4$ (Wednesday) we change β to 2300 and the new differential equation gives $W(t) = 143.75 - C_2 e^{-0.0016t}$. We must choose the value of C_2 so that this gives the correct value for $W(3)$. We find $C_2 = 86.89812$, and putting $t = 4$ we then get $W(4) = 57.40625$.

For $t > 4$, the original differential equation applies again, so we get $W(t) = 81.25 - C_3 e^{-0.0016t}$. Note that C_3 is not the same as C_1; we must find it from the fact that $W(4) = 57.406\,25$, which gives $C_3 = 23.9968$. We can now write down a complete description of our model for $W(t)$, which is:

$$W(t) = \begin{cases} 81.25 - 24.0974e^{-0.0016t} & 0 < t < 3 \\ 143.75 - 86.8981e^{-0.0016t} & 3 < t < 4 \\ 81.25 - 23.9968e^{-0.0016t} & t > 4 \end{cases}$$

To answer (a) we put $t = 6$, which gives $W(6) = 57.482\,47$ kg.

For (b) $W' = 0$ when $\beta = 16W = 16 \times 57.1526 \approx 914$, so her gross daily intake is 2114 cal.

For (c) the model is $W' = -0.0016W$, with solution $W(t) = W(0)e^{-0.0016t} = 57.1526e^{-0.0016t}$. After n weeks this will be $57.1526e^{-0.0016 \times 7n}$.

(d) With a net daily intake of β we have $-\ln(\beta - 16W)/16 = 10^{-4}t + C$, so $W(t) = [\beta - Ce^{-0.0016t}]/16$. Since $W(0) = 57.1526$ we have $\beta - C = 914.4416$. After N weeks W will be $[\beta - Ce^{-0.012N}] = 8 \times 6.350\,293$. Substituting for C and solving for β we find $\beta = [812.8375 - 914.4416e^{-0.0112N}]/[1 - e^{-0.0012N}]$.

9.10 Figure 9.8 shows a cylindrical tank and a hemispherical bowl, both with diameter 1 m. Water drains from the cylinder through a hole of diameter 2 cm into the bowl below. The bowl has an identical hole at its lowest point. At time $t = 0$ the height h_1 of water in the cylinder is 1.5 m. When does it become empty? Write down differential equations needed to find when the bowl becomes empty if it contains water to a depth of 0.2 m initially.

Solution

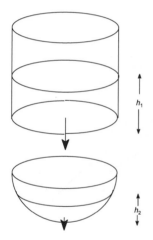

Figure 9.8

The first part of the question can be answered separately. The volume flow rate from the cylinder is

$$\text{area of outlet} \times \text{speed of outflow} = 0.25\pi(0.02)^2 \times \sqrt{(2gh_1)} \text{ (m}^3 \text{ s}^{-1})$$

The volume of water in the tank is $0.25\pi(1)^2h_1$, so the volume flow rate is also equal to $0.25\pi h_1'$, and therefore h_1 satisfies the differential equation

$$h_1' = -(0.02)^2\sqrt{(2gh_1)}$$

(note the minus sign for the outflow). By first writing it as $dh_1/\sqrt{(h_1)} = -0.001\,772\,dt$, we can integrate both sides to give $\sqrt{h_1} = \sqrt{1.5} - 0.000\,886t$ (making use of the fact that $h_1 = 1.5$ when $t = 0$). This tank will therefore be empty when $t = \sqrt{1.5}/0.000\,886 \approx 1383\,\text{s} \approx 23\,\text{min}$.

For the bowl,

$$V' = Ah_2' = \pi r^2 h_2' = \pi[(0.5)^2 - (0.5 - h_2)^2]h_2'$$
$$= \pi(h_2 - h_2^2)h_2'$$
$$= \text{flow in} - \text{flow out}$$
$$= 0.25\pi(0.02)^2\sqrt{(2g)}(\sqrt{h_1} - \sqrt{h_2})$$

We can now write down a differential equation for h_2 (for $0 < t < 1383$):

$$h_2(1 - h_2)h_2' = 0.000\,442\,9[\sqrt{1.5} - 0.000\,886t - \sqrt{h_2}]$$

This could be solved numerically, using the initial value $h_2(0) = 0.2$. We have assumed that the bowl does not overflow or become empty during the 23 minutes while the tank is emptying. We could check these assumptions after solving the differential equation for h_2.

When $t > 1383$, we must change the differential equation to $h_2(1 - h_2)h_2' = -0.000\,442\,9\sqrt{h_2}$, and this will apply until h_2 becomes zero.

9.8 Exercises

9.1 Write down differential equations corresponding to the following (hypothetical) statements:

(a) The rate of change of height of a tree is proportional to its height.
(b) The speed of a particle is proportional to the distance it travels.
(c) The acceleration of a particle is proportional to its speed.

9.2 If y satisfies the given differential equation write down the differential equation satisfied by $z = 2y + 3$ in each of the following cases:

(a) $y' = 4y + 1$
(b) $y' = 2(1 - y^2)$
(c) $y' = \cos(6y + t)$

9.3 Suppose $y(t)$ represents the water level (in metres) in a tank at time t (days) and that it is modelled by the differential equation

$$y' = 0.2 + 0.1\sin(10t)$$

What does this differential equation become if we measure y in cm and t in hours?

9.4 In 1798 Thomas Malthus made the assumptions that 'Population when unchecked increases in geometrical ratio, substinence increases only in arithmetic ratio'. Translate these assumptions into:

(a) Discrete difference equations
(b) Differential equations

9.5 Assume that:

(a) A population P increases at a rate proportional to the difference between the amount of food available and the amount of food consumed.
(b) The amount of food consumed is proportional to the size of the population.
(c) The amount of food available increases at a constant rate as time elapses.

Write down a differential equation model for P.

9.6 Assume that the rate at which a chemical dissolves is proportional to how much of it remains undissolved. If M is the maximum mass of the chemical that can be dissolved in a certain solution, write down a differential equation for $m(t)$, the mass dissolved at time t.

9.7 Some economists argue that the rate of change of wage rates (a) decreases when the level of unemployment goes up, (b) decreases when the rate of change of the level of unemployment goes up, and (c) increases when the rate of change of retail prices increases. Let W = wage rates, U = unemployment level and R = Retail Price Index. Write down the simplest differential equation model which conforms with the above assumptions.

9.8 Assume that a car driver:

(i) Brakes when the car in front is travelling at a slower speed than she is.
(ii) Accelerates when the car in front is travelling faster than she is.

If V_1 and V_2 are the speeds of cars 1 and 2, where car 2 is behind car 1, and k is a positive constant, which of the following models is consistent with both assumptions?

(a) $V_1' = k(V_1 - V_2)$ (b) $V_1' = k(V_2 - V_1)$
(c) $V_2' = k(V_1 - V_2)$ (d) $V_2' = k(V_2 - V_1)$

What further assumption is implied in these models?

9.9 The growth of a living cell depends on the flow of nutrients through its surface wall and therefore depends on its surface area. Suppose the rate of growth is directly proportional to the surface area. Assuming a cell can be modelled as a sphere, write down a differential equation for $m(t)$, the mass of the cell at time t.

9.10 Although it does not rain every day, suppose the averaged out daily rainfall over a reservoir can be modelled as a periodic function with a minimum of r_0 (m) in July and a maximum of r_1 (m) in January. The area of the water surface is A (m^2) (assumed constant) and f (m^3) of water leaves the reservoir every day. Write down a differential equation for $V(t)$, the volume of water in the reservoir at any time t (days).

If the sides of the reservoir can be modelled as the surface of a sphere of radius R, obtain a differential equation for $h(t)$, the depth of water at the deepest point.

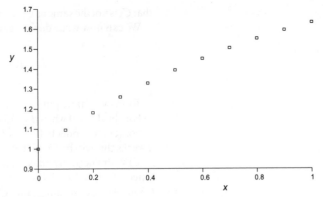

Figure 9.9

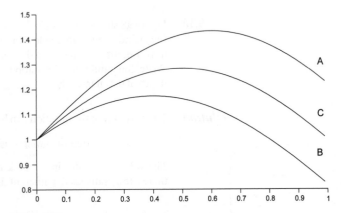

Figure 9.10

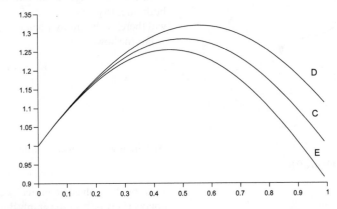

Figure 9.11

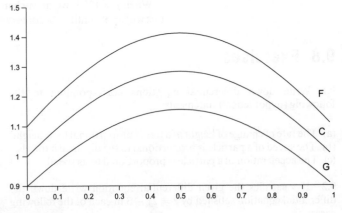

Figure 9.12

114

9.11 Given some data which looks like Fig. 9.9, which of the following models appears to you to be correct?

(a) $y' = y + 2$ (b) $y' = -y + 2$
(c) $y' = -2 - y$ (d) $y' = y - 2$

9.12 In each of Figs. 9.10, 9.11 and 9.12, curve C represents the solution of the initial value problem

$$y' = (a - bx)y, \ y(0) = c$$

with all parameters $a, b, c = 1$.

Without solving the differential equation, indicate which is the correct option in each of the following statements:

(a) Increasing the value of parameter a will give a solution curve
    (i) closer to curve A   (ii) closer to curve B
(b) Increasing the value of parameter b will give a solution curve
    (i) closer to curve D   (ii) closer to curve E
(c) Increasing the value of parameter c will give a solution curve
    (i) closer to curve F   (ii) closer to curve G

9.13 **Without** solving, match the curves shown in Fig. 9.13 to the differential equations.

(a) $y' = -4y$ (b) $y' = 4y(2 - y)$
(c) $y' = y - x$ (d) $y' = y + x$

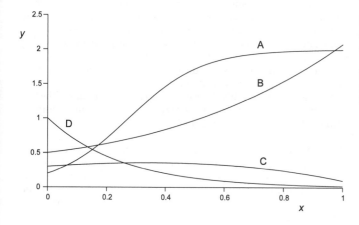

Figure 9.13

9.14 Water flows into a conical tank at a rate $f \ (\text{m}^3 \ \text{s}^{-1})$ and flows out by gravity through an opening of area A at the lowest point. The side of the tank is inclined at an angle α to the vertical.
    (a) Write down a differential equation for $h(t)$, the height of water in the tank at time t.
    (b) What value of f will keep the tank in a steady state?

9.15 Assume that a hormone is secreted into the blood at a rate which varies with a 24 hour period and that the hormone leaves the blood at a rate proportional to the current level, $h(t)$, of the hormone. Write down a differential equation for h which is consistent with these assumptions.

9.16 Assume that:

(a) If no toxins are present, bacteria grow at a rate proportional to the amount present.

(b) Toxins destroy bacteria at a rate proportional to the number of bacteria present and proportional to the amount of toxin.
(c) Toxins are increasing at a constant rate.

Write down a continuous differential equation model for $N(t)$, the number of bacteria present at time t.

9.17 Assume that in a competitive market a particular firm's share of the market increases at a rate which is proportional to:

(a) The size of the existing share
(b) The fraction of the market remaining

If there are only two firms in the market, write down equations for their respective shares of the market, s_1 and s_2, consistent with assumptions (a) and (b).

9.18 Assume that:

(a) If no money is spent on advertising, a firm's sales at time t, $S(t)$, decrease exponentially with time.
(b) The maximum possible sales (saturation) is M.
(c) The rate of change of sales is proportional to the amount $A(t)$ spent on advertising.
(d) The rate of change of sales is proportional to the fraction of the market left unsaturated.

Using these assumptions, write down a differential equation model for $S(t)$.

9.19 Water flows into a conical lake at a constant rate $f \ (\text{m}^3 \ \text{s}^{-1})$. It also evaporates at a rate proportional to the surface area. Write down a differential equation for the depth (h) of water in the lake.

9.20 Write down differential equations for the amounts of water in the three tanks shown in Fig. 9.14. The volume flow rates are indicated as f_1 etc. Note that $f_3 = f_1 + f_4$.

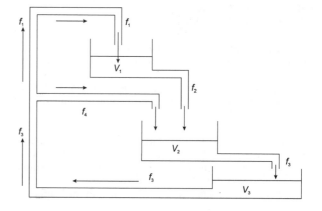

Figure 9.14

9.21 Obtain differential equations satisfied by the radius $r(t)$ of a sphere at time t in the following cases:

(a) The rate of change of the surface area of the sphere is proportional to time.
(b) The rate of change of the surface area of the sphere is proportional to its radius.
(c) The rate of change of the volume of the sphere is inversely proportional to its radius.

In each case find $r(t)$ in terms of $r(0)$ and a constant.

9.22 Assume the growth rate of a colony of bacteria is directly proportional to the size of the colony. If the number of bacteria increased from 200 to 800 in 12 hours, (a) what was the population size after 6 hours?

(b) What will the population size be after 18 hours?

9.23 If N_0 bacteria are present at time $t = 0$ and N_1 at time $t = t_1$, what is the doubling time?

9.24 The half-life of lead-210 is 22 years.

(a) What percentage of the original amount is left after 10 years?
(b) In how many years will there be only 10% left?

9.25 A chemical reaction converts A into B at a rate proportional to the amount of A present at any instant. Five minutes after the start of the reaction it is found that 3% of A has been converted.

(a) How much of A will have been converted 10 minutes after the start of the reaction?
(b) At what time will 50% of A have been converted?

9.26 A certain population increases its size by 5% every year.

(a) What are the appropriate values of a and b in the discrete model?

$$P_{n+1} = aP_n + b$$

(b) What are the appropriate values of a and b in the continuous model?

$$dP/dt = aP + b$$

(c) How long does it take the population to double in size?

9.27 A town has a present population of 21 000, which is steadily decreasing. Assuming the population decreases:

(a) By a constant 2000 every year
(b) By a constant 9% every year

write down differential equation models for both cases.
  Which model predicts the larger population at the end of 3 years?

9.28 Archaeologists dig up a piece of very old bone and measure its radioactive carbon-14 content to be 20% that of living bone. How old is the specimen?

9.29 Water flows into a tank at a rate $f_1(t)$ $(\mathrm{m^3\,s^{-1}})$ and out through an exit pipe at a rate of $f_2(t)$. Write down a differential equation for the height $h(t)$ of water in the tank at time t if the tank has a uniform cross-sectional area A $(\mathrm{m^2})$.
  If the height of the water is 1.5 m at $t = 0$, find the height after 8 minutes if $A = 0.6, f_1 = 0.007$ and $f_2 = 0.006$.

9.30 Assume an ice cube of side $a(0)$ at time $t = 0$ melts at (a) a constant rate, (b) a rate proportional to its surface area, and (c) a rate proportional to its volume. For each model use k as the constant of proportionality and find (i) an expression for $a(t)$ in terms of t and (ii) the time it takes the cube to melt completely.

9.31 A dealer estimates that for every 1% by which he increases his price he gets 3% fewer customers. Obtain an expression for $Q(P)$, the number of customers when the price is P.

9.32 Assume a spherical raindrop evaporates at a rate proportional to its surface area and k is the proportionality constant. If it has radius r_0 at time $t = 0$, what will its radius be at time t according to this assumption? How long would it take to disappear altogether?

9.33 After 10 minutes a cup of coffee initially at 60 °C has cooled to 45 °C. What will its temperature be after another 20 minutes?

9.34 Police officers discover a body at 10 p.m. and measure its temperature to be 18 °C, while the outside air is at 11 °C. Two hours later the body's temperature has dropped to 15 °C.

(a) Taking the temperature of a living body to be 37 °C, estimate the time of death.
(b) How sensitive is the above answer to the figure assumed for the living temperature (assume $\pm\,0.5\,°C$)?

9.35 Tom pours a cup of coffee for himself and another for Francine. Tom immediately adds milk to his coffee but Francine waits 5 minutes before adding milk to hers. Who has the hotter coffee?

9.36 A thermometer shows a temperature T_1 inside a room and when placed outside it reads T_2 after 10 minutes and T_3 after another 10 minutes. If T_0 is the outside temperature, show that

$$(T_2 - T_0)^2 = (T_1 - T_0)(T_3 - T_0)$$

Find T_0 if $T_1 = 18$, $T_2 = 12$ and $T_3 = 9$.

9.37 Suppose a room is heated by a system controlled by a thermostat which is set to switch on when the room temperature falls to T_1 and to switch off when the temperature reaches T_2. While the heating is on, the room receives heat energy at the rate of Q (measured in watts). The temperature outside the room is T_{out} and the total wall area is A. Write down differential equations for $T(t)$, the temperature in the room at time t.
  How would you modify these equations to take account of the fact that the outside temperature varies daily with a minimum at midnight and a maximum at noon?

9.38 Assume that a drifting canoe experiences no forces except the resistance of the water, which is proportional to the canoe's velocity. At time $t = 0$ you stop paddling your canoe. At time $t = t_1$ your canoe has drifted a total distance x_1 and by the time $t = 2t_1$ you have drifted a total distance x_2. Show that the maximum total distance you will drift is $x_1^2/(2x_1 - x_2)$.

9.39 Assume that the percentage of incident light absorbed in passing through a material is proportional to the thickness, x of the material. Translate this into a differential equation model for $I(x)$, the light intensity after passing through a thickness x.
  If 1 cm reduces light to 40% of its original intensity, how much additional material is needed to reduce it to 10% of its original intensity?

9.40 A gas storage tank has volume $5000\,\mathrm{m^3}$ and is full of gas A. Gas B, which does not react with A, is pumped in at one end at a constant rate $f\,(\mathrm{m^3\,s^{-1}})$, while an opening at the other end lets gases escape. Write down differential equations for the volumes of A and B in the tank at any time.
  What is the total amount of gas B that needs to be pumped in to reduce the proportion of A in the tank to 1%?

9.41 A tank contains $1000\,\mathrm{m^3}$ of pure water. If toxic waste is pumped into the tank at the rate of $1\,\mathrm{m^3\,min^{-1}}$ and the mixture leaves the tank at the same rate, how long will it take the toxic concentration to reach 20%?

If, at that moment, the source of toxic waste is removed and pure water is pumped in at the same rate, how long will it take the toxicity to fall to 2%?

9.42 A room with capacity $3000 \, m^3$ contains 0.02% carbon dioxide by volume. A window is opened and fresh air containing 0.005% carbon dioxide comes in at the rate of $10 \, m^3 \, min^{-1}$ while the air in the room flows out at the same rate.

(a) What is the percentage of carbon dioxide in the room after 10 min?
(b) When does the room have 0.01% carbon dioxide?

9.43 A tank contains 3 kg of salt dissolved in $2 \, m^3$ of water. Starting at time $t = 0$ a solution containing 1 kg of salt per m^3 enters the tank at the rate of $0.001 \, m^3 \, s^{-1}$ and the well-stirred solution leaves the tank at the same rate.

(a) Write down a differential equation for $m(t)$, the mass of salt in the tank at time t, and obtain its solution with the initial value $m(0) = 3$.
(b) If the tank has a maximum capacity of $3 \, m^3$ and the inflow rate is $0.002 \, m^3 \, s^{-1}$ while the outflow rate is $0.001 \, m^3 \, s^{-1}$, write down a differential equation for $m(t)$ and obtain its solution with the initial value $m(0) = 3$.
(c) What is the mass of salt in the tank at the moment when it first overflows?

9.44 Match each of the statements below to the most appropriate model from the following.

(i) $P' = f - kP(1 - P/M)$ (ii) $P' = kP(P/L - 1)(1 - P/M)$
(iii) $P' = kP(1 - P/M) - fP$ (iv) $P' = kP(1 - P/M) - f$
(v) $P' = kP(1 - P/M) + f$ (vi) $P' = kP(1 - P/M)(1 - P/L)$

(a) A population of fish naturally follows a logistic model but is fished at a constant rate.
(b) A population of fish naturally follows a logistic model but is fished at rate proportional to the population size. (This is to be expected if the fishing is carried out for a fixed period of time.)
(c) A population of fish has a natural upper limit of M and also a lower limit L so that the rate of growth becomes zero if the population size approaches either limit (and there is no fishing).

9.45 At time $t = 0$, 2000 of fish type A and 800 of fish type B are put into a tank. Let $A(t)$ and $B(t)$ represent the sizes of the two populations at time t and assume that they do not interfere with each other. Population A grows at the rate $A' = 0.1A - 0.0001A^2$, while for B the growth rate is $B' = 0.2B - 0.0001B^2$. For each of A and B find:

(a) An expression for the population size at time t
(b) At what times the population is increasing
(c) At what times the population is decreasing
(d) At what times the rate of growth is increasing
(e) At what times the rate of growth is decreasing
(f) At what times there are more A fish than B
(g) What happens after a long time

How would you modify the differential equations to take account of a fishing rate of 50 fish per unit of time, assuming that the proportion of the two types in the catch is the same as the proportion in the tank at that time?

9.46 Assume that the rate at which a rumour spreads is proportional to (i) the number of people who have heard it, and (ii)

the number of people who have not heard it. If a town contains M people, write down a differential equation for the number $n(t)$ of town-dwellers who have heard the rumour by time t.

Suppose that $M = 10\,000$ and that at time $t = 0$ only one person knows. If after 1 day, 500 people have heard, write down an expression for $n(t)$.

How long will it be before 90% of the town's population will have heard?

9.47 At time $t = 0$ a pebble of mass 1 g and diameter 1 cm is dropped from rest in still air at the top of a well. At $t = 4$ s a splash is heard as it reaches the water at the bottom of the well.

Estimate the depth of the well:

(a) Using a simple model
(b) Taking account of air resistance (proportional to $(speed)^2$)
(c) Taking account of the finite speed of sound ($330 \, m \, s^{-1}$),
(d) Taking account of varying gravity.

What percentage difference does each of (b), (c), (d) make to the answer? (Take $g = 9.81 \, m \, s^{-2}$.)

9.48 When a bath is emptied by gravity it takes longer to empty the last half than the first half. By how much?

9.49 A cylindrical drum full of oil is to be drained as quickly as possible by making a single small hole and letting the oil flow out by gravity. Is it better to make the hole in one of the flat ends and stand the drum vertically or lay the drum on its side with the hole at the lowest point of the curved side of the drum? Express the condition in terms of the radius r and height h of the drum.

9.50 Snow starts to fall at time $t = 0$ and continues to fall at a constant rate $k \, (m \, s^{-1})$ so that in a time t a flat area of ground becomes covered with snow to a depth kt (m). When the depth is b, a woman starts clearing snow from a 1 m wide path at the front of her house and clears c (m^3) of snow every second.

How long does it take her to clear the whole path, which is L (m) long?

She then works her way back to the house. At what time does she reach the doorstep and what is then the depth of snow at the furthest point of the path?

9.51 The X army is about to attack the Y army, which has only 5000 troops while the X army has 10 000. The Y army however has superior military equipment, which makes each Y soldier about 1.5 times as effective as an X soldier. Assume that the battle stops only when one side is completely destroyed and that 0.1 Y soldiers are killed by each X soldier in one hour. Write down a mathematical model and use it to answer the following questions:

(a) Which army do you predict will win and how many troops of the winning army will be left at the end?
(b) How long will the battle last?
(c) How many troops would the other army have needed initially in order to win the battle?
(d) The Y army can fly in paratroop reinforcements three hours after the start of the battle. How many reinforcements do they need to win?
(e) If reinforcements could be made available at a *uniform* rate, what would that rate have to be in order to change the outcome of the battle?
(f) How long would the battle last if the Y army received reinforcements at the rate of 400 troops per hour?

9.52 The top tank shown in Fig. 9.15 contains water and a concentration C_1 of salt.

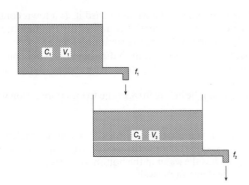

Figure 9.15

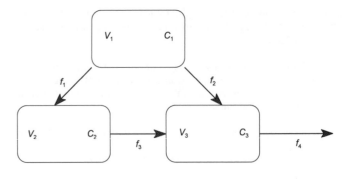

Figure 9.16

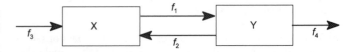

Figure 9.17

(a) Obtain a differential equation for $C_2(t)$, the concentration of salt in the bottom tank at time t, if the outflow rates are constant values f_1 and f_2 and the initial volume in the bottom tank was V_0.
(b) Suppose the flows are driven by gravity in both cases. If both tanks have the same constant cross-sectional area A and both exit pipes have cross-sectional area a, write down differential equations for h_1, h_2 and C_2.

9.53 The more Juliet loves him, the more Romeo dislikes her, but when Juliet loses interest, his feelings for her warm up. Juliet behaves differently. Her love for Romeo grows when he loves her more and turns to hate when he hates her. Translate these statements into differential equations for $R(t)$ = Romeo's love for Juliet and $J(t)$ = Juliet's love for Romeo at time t.

9.54 A simple model of the heart can be built up from the following simple assumptions.

(a) During the systolic (contraction) period which lasts T_1 seconds, there is no inflow of blood.
(b) During the diastolic (relaxed) period, which lasts T_2 seconds, there is a constant inflow I_0.
(c) The outflow rate is always proportional to the pressure.
(d) The pressure is always proportional to the excess volume of the heart over a base volume V_0.

Translate these assumptions into a differential equation model for $V(t)$, the volume of blood in the heart at time t over one complete heartbeat.

9.55 At time $t = 0$ a freezer breaks down. Write down differential equations for

(a) $T_f(t)$ = the temperature in the freezer at time t
(b) $T_r(t)$ = the temperature in the room at time t

Assume the temperature outside the room is a constant T_{out}.

9.56 In Fig. 9.16 the Vs are volumes, the fs represent volume flow rates $(m^3 s^{-1})$ and the Cs are mass concentrations of a pollutant $(kg\, m^{-3})$.
Write down differential equations for V_1, V_2, V_3, C_1, C_2, C_3.

9.57 At time $t = 0$ the tank X shown in Fig. 9.17 contains x_0 kg of a chemical while tank Y contains pure water only. Both tanks contain the same volume (V) of solution and there are equal flow rates between them (so that $f_1 = f_2 = f$).

(a) Write down differential equations for $x(t)$ and $y(t)$, the mass of chemical in each tank at time t.
(b) Solve the differential equations. What happens eventually?

(c) Suppose that $f_1 \neq f_2$ and that fresh water flows into tank X at the rate f_3 while there is an outflow f_4 from tank Y.
(i) Write down connections between the fs for the volumes in both tanks to remain equal and write down differential equations for $x(t)$ and $y(t)$.
(ii) What do the differential equations become if the fs do not satisfy the conditions of part (i)?

9.58 Given the following chemical reactions involving four compounds A, B, C and D, write down differential equations for the concentrations of each chemical at any time.

$$A + B \xrightarrow{k_1} C, \quad A + C \xrightarrow{k_2} D, \quad D + B \xrightarrow{k_3} A.$$

9.59 Suppose an epidemic of a non-fatal disease breaks out in a population of N people. Let $I(t)$ = the number infected at time t and $S(t)$ = those who are susceptible but have not yet been infected. Obtain equations relevant to the following cases.

(a) Assume the rate of increase of the number infected is proportional to the number already infected and to the number susceptible.
(b) In addition to (a), assume that every day a constant proportion of infected people recover (but are then susceptible again).
(c) As (b) except that those who recover become immune to the disease.

9.60 An isolated community of 999 people living on an island receives a visitor who carries a flu virus. After 5 days, 10 people are infected. Assume the rate of spreading of the virus is proportional to the number infected and to the number not infected. Use a simple differential equation model to answer the following questions.

(a) What will be the total number of people infected after 20 days?
(b) How soon will 99% of the population be infected?
(c) If 20% of infected people recover every day and are then immune to infection, write down differential equation models for

$I(t)$ = number of individuals infected at time t
$S(t)$ = number of individuals susceptible to infection at time t
$R(t)$ = number of individuals recovered at time t

9.9 Answers to Exercises

9.1 (a) $h' = kh$, (b) $x' = kx$, (c) $v' = kv$

9.2 (a) $z' = 4z - 10$, (b) $z' = 6z - z^2 - 5$,
(c) $z' = 2\cos(3z - 9 + t)$

9.3 $y' = [5 + 2.5\sin(5t/12)]/6$

9.4 (a) $P_{n+1} = aP_n, F_{n+1} = F_n + b$
(b) $P' = kP, F' = c$

9.5 $P' = at - bP$

9.6 $m' = k(M - m)$

9.7 $W' = -aU - bU' + cR'$ $(a, b, c > 0)$

9.8 (c) It is implied that the acceleration or braking is directly proportional to the relative speed.

9.9 $m' = km^{2/3}$

9.10 $V' = 0.5A[r_0 + r_1 + (r_1 - r_0)\cos(\pi t/182.5)] - f$
$h' = r_0 + (r_1 - r_0)\sin(\pi t/182.5) - f/[\pi(2Rh - h^2)]$

9.11 (b)

9.12 (a) A, (b) E, (c) F

9.13 (a) D, (b) A, (c) C, (d) B

9.14 (a) $h' = (f - A\sqrt{(2gh)})/(\pi h^2 \tan^2 \alpha)$ (b) $A\sqrt{(2gh)}$

9.15 $h' = a\sin(\pi t/12 + b) - ch$ (t in hours)

9.16 $N' = aN - (bt + c)N$

9.17 $s_1' = ks_1 s_2, s_2' = -ks_1 s_2$ (or $s_1 + s_2 = 1$)

9.18 $S' = kA(1 - S/M) - bS$

9.19 $h' = f/(\pi h^2 \tan^2 \alpha) - k$

9.20 $V_1' = f_1 - f_2, V_2' = f_2 + f_4 - f_3, V_3' = f_3 - f_4 - f_1$

9.21 (a) $r' = at/r$, (b) $r' = b$, (c) $r' = c/r^3$
(a) $r = \sqrt{(r_0^2 + at^2)}$, (b) $r = r_0 + bt$, (c) $r = (r_0^4 + 4ct)^{1/4}$

9.22 (a) 400, (b) 1600

9.23 $t_1 \ln 2/(\ln N_1 - \ln N_0)$

9.24 (a) 72.97%, (b) 73.08 yr

9.25 (a) 5.91%, (b) 113.78 min

9.26 (a) $a = 1.05$, $b = 0$, (b) $a = 0.04879$, (c) 4.21 yr

9.27 (a) $P' = -2000$, (b) $P' = -0.0943106P$
(a) predicts 15 000, (b) predicts 15 825 ($0.91^3 \times 21\,000$)

9.28 About 13 000 yr

9.29 $Ah' = f_1 - f_2$, 2.3 m

9.30 (a) (i) $(a_0^3 - kt)^{1/3}$, (ii) a_0^3/k
(b) (i) $a_0 - 2kt$, (ii) $a_0/2k$
(c) (i) $a_0 e^{-kt/3}$, (ii) ∞

9.31 $Q_0 P^{-3}$

9.32 $r_0 - kt, r_0/k$

9.33 29 °C

9.34 (a) 5:19 p.m., (b) ± 0.5 °C leads to uncertainty of ± 4 min

9.35 Tom

9.36 6 °C

9.37 $McT' = -hA(T - T_{out})$ when $T > 2$ or $T' > 0$
$McT' = Q - hA(T - T_{out})$ when $T > 1$ and $T' > 0$
For variable T_{out} the equations are the same with T_{out} replaced by $0.5[\max + \min - (\max - \min)\cos(\pi t/(12 \times 60 \times 60))]$ ($t = 0$ seconds is midnight)

9.39 $dI/dx = kIx$, 1.513 cm

9.40 $B' = (1 - B/5000)f$, $A' = -B'$, 11 513 m^3

9.41 223 min, 2302.6 min

9.42 (a) 0.0195%, (b) $300 \ln 3 \approx 330$ min

9.43 (a) $m' + 0.0005m = 0.001$, $m(t) = 2 + e^{-0.0005t}$
(b) $m' = 0.002 - 0.001m/(2 + 0.001t)$
$m(t) = (6000 + 4t + 0.001t^2)/(2000 + t)$
(c) $m(1000) = 3\frac{2}{3}$ (kg)

9.44 (a) iv, (b) iii, (c) ii

9.45 (a) $A(t) = 1000[1 - 0.5e^{-0.1t}]^{-1}$
$B(t) = 2000[1 + 1.5e^{-0.2t}]^{-1}$
(b) no t, all t
(c) all t, no t
(d) all t, $t < 13.54$
(e) no t, $t > 13.54$
(f) $t < 12.34$
(g) $A \to 1000$ $B \to 200$
$A' = 0.1A - 0.0001A^2 - 50A/(A + B)$
$B' = 0.2B - 0.0001B^2 - 50B/(A + B)$

9.46 $n' = kn(M - n)$, $n(t) = (0.1 + 9999.9e^{-2.3t})^{-1}$, about 6 days

9.47 (a) 78.48 m (b) 78.88 m
(c) 76.27 m (d) 78.480 312 7 m
0.5%, 3%, 0.004%

9.48 $1 + \sqrt{2}$ times

9.49 $r/h < 32/9\pi^2$

9.50 $[e^{Lk/c} - 1]b/k$

9.51 (a) $X = 7906$ (b) 5.82 h (c) $Y > 8165$
(d) > 4570 (e) 388 h^{-1} to Y (f) 34.3 h

9.52 (a) $C_2' = f_1(C_1 - C_2)/[V_0 + (f_1 - f_2)]$

(b) $Ah_1' = -a\sqrt{(2gh_1)}$, $Ah_2' = a\sqrt{(2g)}(\sqrt{h_1} - \sqrt{h_2})$
$C_2' = a\sqrt{(2gh_1)}(C_1 - C_2)/Ah_2$

9.53 $R' = -aJ$, $J' = bR$, $a, b > 0$

9.54 $V' = \begin{cases} -k(V - V_0) & 0 < t < T_1 \\ I_0 - k(V - V_0) & T_1 < t < T_2 \end{cases}$

9.55 (a) $T_f' = \alpha(T_r - T_f)$, (b) $T_r' = -\alpha(T_r - T_f) - \beta(T_r - T_{out})$

9.56 $V_1' = -F_1 - F_2$, $V_2' = F_1 - F_3$, $V_3' = F_2 + F_3 - F_4$
$C_1' = 0$, $(C_2 V_2)' = F_1 C_1 - F_3 C_2$,
$(C_3 V_3)' = F_3 C_2 + F_2 C_1 - F_2 C_3$

9.57 (a) $x' = (y - x)f/V$, $y' = (x - y)f/V$
(b) $x = 0.5x_0[1 + e^{-2t}]$, $y = 0.5x_0[1 - e^{-2t}]$, $x \to y \to 0.5x_0$
(c) (i) $f_2 + f_3 = f_1 + f_2 + f_4$
$x' = (-f_1 x + f_2 y)/V$, $y' = (f_1 x - f_2 y - f_4 y)/V$

(ii) $x' = -f_1 x/V_x + f_2 y/V_y$,
$y' = f_1 x/V_x - f_2 y/V_y - f_4 y/V_y$
$V_x' = f_3 + f_2 - f_1$, $V_y' = f_1 - f_2 - f_4$
(or $V_x = V_0 + (f_3 + f_2 - f_1)t$,
$V_y = V_0 + (f_1 - f_2 - f_4)t$)

9.58 $d' = -k_1 ab - k_2 ac + k_3 bd$, $b' = -k_1 ab - k_3 bd$
$c' = k_1 ab - k_2 ac$, $d' = k_2 ac - k_3 bd$

9.59 (a) $I' = aIS$, $I + S = N$
(b) $I' = aIS - bI$, $I + S = N$
(c) $I' = aIS - bI$, $R' = bI$, $I + R + S = N$

9.60 $I' = kI(1000 - I) \Rightarrow I(t) = 1000/[1 + 999e^{-0.4623t}]$
(a) 912, (b) 25 days
(c) $I' = KIS - 0.2I$
$S' = -KIS$
$R' = 0.2I$

10 Modelling with Integration

10.1 Background

In many of the examples of Chapters 8 and 9 the rate of change of a variable was modelled by some function which could involve the present value of the variable as well as the time t. In this chapter we deal with the slightly easier case where we have an explicit model in terms of t for the rate of change of our variable, $y' = f(t)$. To find an expression for the variable in terms of t we can then integrate to give

$$y(t) = y(0) + \int_0^t f(x)\,\mathrm{d}x$$

In the integral we use the 'dummy variable' x temporarily to take the place of t, since t is the upper limit of the integral.

A simple example of a rate of change is the speed of a moving vehicle, which is clearly the rate at which its distance from a fixed point is changing. If its speed $v(t)$ changes with time we can work out the distance s it travels between any two times t_1 and t_2 from

$$s = \int_{t_1}^{t_2} v(t)\,\mathrm{d}t$$

If we start with information about the **acceleration**, $a(t)$, of a moving vehicle, which is its rate of change of speed, then one integration produces $v(t)$ and we need a further integration to find s. That is, $v' = a(t)$ and so

$$v(t) = v(0) + \int_0^t a(x)\,\mathrm{d}x, \quad s = \int_{t_1}^{t_2} v(t)\,\mathrm{d}t$$

Note that x is a dummy variable again.

Sometimes the rate of change is not with respect to time but with respect to some other variable, such as distance. If the problem is one-dimensional then there is no essential difference from the case of time. Suppose, for example, that the value of a square metre of land decreases with distance x (m) from the seashore. We could model it as $f(x) = a - bx$, for $0 \leqslant x \leqslant a/b$, which implies the following:

1. Land on the coast is worth an amount £a per m^2.
2. For each metre you move away from the coast the value of a square metre of land decreases by £b.
3. Land at a distance of a/b is worthless.
4. The model does not apply for $x > b/a$.

If we accept all these assumptions, the total value of a strip of land of width w and length l ($< a/b$) at right angles to the coastline (Fig. 10.1) is then given by

$$V = w \int_0^l (a - bx)\,\mathrm{d}x$$

Note that this calculation depends on the assumption that the value of land decreases *continuously* with x. It is this assumption that allows integration to be used. If the value of

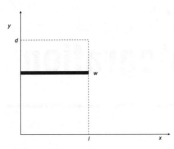

Figure 10.1

land is constant within certain spatial 'bands' then the total value of a region will be a sum of amounts for each band rather than an integral.

If the value of the land depended on two directions we would need to do two integrations to solve the equivalent problem. For example, suppose the value of land at position (x, y) is modelled by $a - bx - cy$ (implying that the value of land decreases as you go north of the favourite spot $(0, 0)$ as well as decreasing as you go inland). The value of a strip of width dy at right angles to the coast is given as before (with dy in place of w) by

$$dy \int_0^l (a - bx - cy) dx$$

and the total value of a rectangular plot of land with opposite corners at $(0, 0)$ and (l, d) is given by integrating the values of all such strips from $y = 0$ up to $y = d$. In other words, the total value is given by the double integral

$$
\begin{aligned}
V &= \int_0^d dy \int_0^l (a - bx - cy) dx \\
&= \int_0^d dy [ax - bx^2/2 - cxy]_0^l \\
&= \int_0^d (al - bl^2/2 - cly) dy \\
&= [aly - bl^2 y/2 - cly^2/2]_0^d \\
&= ald - bl^2 d/2 - cld^2/2
\end{aligned}
$$

Sometimes there is radial symmetry in a spatial distribution, which simplifies the integration. Suppose that a circular plate is made of a material whose density at positions a distance r from the centre is $\rho(r) = a \exp(-br^2)$. The mass of a ring-shaped piece of the plate at radius r and of width dr is $2\pi r \rho(r) dr$ and the mass of the plate up to radius R is

$$\int_0^R 2\pi r \rho(r) dr = \int_0^R 2\pi r a e^{-br^2} dr = [-\pi a e^{-br^2}/b]_0^R = \pi a \{1 - e^{-bR^2}\}/b$$

In a population there will be individuals of all ages from newly born to the elderly. We can model the age distribution using a function $N(x)$ such that $N(x)dx$ is the number of individuals with ages between two very close values, x and $x + dx$. (Roughly speaking, $N(x)$ is the number of individuals of age x.) The number of individuals with ages between two values x_1 and x_2 with a finite separation between them is given by

$$\int_{x_1}^{x_2} N(x) dx$$

If x_{max} is the age of the oldest individual then the total size of the population is given by

$$N_T = \int_0^{x_{max}} N(x) dx$$

(The function $N(x)/N_T$ is akin to the probability density functions used in Chapter 11.)

The **median** age in a population is the age M such that half the population are older than M and half are younger than M. We can (in principle) find M from

$$\int_0^M N(x) dx = N_T/2$$

In practice this is easier said than done because the integral is unlikely to give a simple linear function of M. To find M we will instead have to solve a non-linear equation using the Newton–Raphson method, for example (see the Bibliography).

The speed of flow V $(\mathrm{m\,s^{-1}})$ of fluid through a pipe of circular cross-section is greatest $(= V_{max}$ say) on the central axis of the pipe and is zero at the pipe walls because of friction.

By symmetry we would expect V at any point to depend only on the distance r of that point from the central axis. What would be a suitable model (usually referred to as a 'velocity profile') for $V(r)$ in terms of r? A possible model is $V(r) = V_{max}(1 - r^2/a^2)$ where a is the radius of the pipe. This gives the right answer at $r = 0$ and is zero at $r = a$.

The **volume flow rate** measures the volume of fluid per second flowing through the pipe. If $V(r)$ happened to be the same for all r we would just multiply the cross-sectional area πa^2 by V to get the volume flow rate. With $V(r)$ depending on r, we get the answer by integration. Consider a ring-shaped area between radii r and $r + dr$. The cross-sectional area for fluid flowing through this ring is $2\pi r dr$, so the volume flow rate is $2\pi r V(r)dr$. The total volume flow rate is obtained by integrating over all such rings from $r = 0$ to $r = a$ which is

$$\int_0^a 2\pi r V_{max}(1 - r^2/a^2)dr = \pi V_{max}[r^2 - r^4/2a^2]_0^a = \pi V_{max}a^2/2$$

Sometimes we find it impossible to express an integral in terms of standard mathematical functions and in such cases **numerical integration** can be used to give an approximate (but can be very accurate) answer. The simplest methods are the trapezoidal and Simpson's rules (see the Bibliography).

The **mean value** of a continuous function $f(x)$ over the interval $a \leqslant x \leqslant b$ is given by

$$\frac{1}{b - a}\int_a^b f(x)dx$$

10.2 Worked Examples

10.1 A rocket accelerates vertically from its launch pad at 5 m s^{-2} and has enough fuel to burn for 3 minutes.

(a) How high will the rocket be when its fuel runs out?
(b) How fast will it be climbing then?
(c) When will it reach its highest point?
(d) How high will it be then?
(e) When will it return to ground level and with what speed?

Solution The variables in this problem are:

t = time since launch (s)
$v(t)$ = vertical velocity of rocket at time t (m s^{-1})
$h(t)$ = height of rocket above ground at time t (m)

While it has fuel to burn the rocket's acceleration is $v' = 5$. Integrating, we get $v = 5t$ (assuming $v = 0$ at $t = 0$). The rate of change of height is $h' = v = 5t$ so $h = 2.5t^2$ (since $h = 0$ when $t = 0$).

(a) At time $t = 3 \times 60$ (s) we have $h = 2.5(180)^2 = 81\,000$ (m), and (b) its speed at that moment is $5 \times 180 = 900$ (m s^{-1}).

(c) After the fuel has finished, $v' = -g \approx -9.81(\text{m s}^{-2})$ and to get v we integrate this equation with respect to t. If, for convenience, we now measure t from this point, we have $v = 900 - 9.81t$. Alternatively, keeping the original meaning of t as being the time since launch, this is equivalent to $v = 900 - 9.81(t - 180)$. At the highest point, $v = 0$ so $t \approx 271.7$ s and the highest point is reached 271.7 s after launch.

(d) Its height $h(t)$ at time t is given by integrating v. We can represent $v(t)$ by the piecewise continuous model

$$v(t) = \begin{cases} 5t & 0 \leqslant t \leqslant 180 \\ 900 - 9.81(t - 180) & t > 180 \end{cases}$$

By integrating, we have

$$h(t) = \begin{cases} 2.5t^2 & 0 \leqslant t \leqslant 180 \\ 900t - 9.81(t - 180)^2/2 - 81\,000 & t > 180 \end{cases}$$

At time $t = 271.7$ this gives the height as $\approx 122\,300$ (m).

(e) Putting $h(t) = 0$ (for $t > 180$) gives the quadratic $-4.905t^2 + 2665.8t - 239\,922 = 0$ whose roots are $t = 429.64$ and $t = 113.85$. The only answer which applies is the one bigger than 180, so we conclude that the model predicts that the rocket finally reaches the ground after about 430 s. Its speed at that moment is $900 - 9.81(429.64 - 180) \approx -1549$ m s^{-1}. See Fig. 10.2.

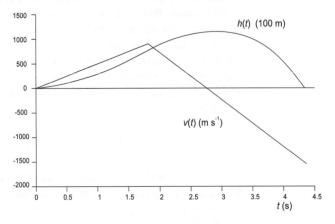

Figure 10.2

10.2 A wall of length L has a curved top edge which is at a height b above the ground at the middle point of the wall and at height a above the ground at the two ends $x = 0$ and $x = L$.

(a) Write down a simple model for $h(x) =$ the height of the wall above the ground at position x.
(b) How much paint is needed to paint the wall if one litre of paint covers A m^2 of wall?

Solution (a) If we assume that the curved edge of the wall can be modelled by a quadratic function we can write $h(x) = a + cx(L - x)$ (which gives $h = a$ at both $x = 0$ and $x = L$) and find c from the fact that $b = h(L/2) = a + c(L/2)(L/2)$. This gives $c = 4(b - a)/L^2$ and our model is therefore $h(x) = a + 4x(L - x)(b - a)/L^2$.

(b) The area of the wall is given by

$$\int_0^L h(x)\mathrm{d}x = \int_0^L \{a + 4(b - a)(xL - x^2)/L^2\}\mathrm{d}x$$
$$= [ax + 4(b - a)(x^2L/2 - x^3/3L^2)]_0^L$$
$$= L(a + 2b)/3$$

So the amount of paint needed is $L(a + 2b)/3A$ litres.

10.3 A normal healthy resting adult takes about 5 s to breathe in and out (inspire and expire). At the peaks of inspiration and expiration the air flow rate is about $0.5\,1\,\mathrm{s}^{-1}$. Write down a model for the air flow at time t and use it to calculate the total amount of air breathed in one minute.

Solution A simple model for the air flow rate $F(t)$ as a function of t is periodic, e.g. of the form $a \sin \Omega t$ where the period is $2\pi/\Omega = 5$ and the peak flow is $a = 0.5\,1\,\mathrm{s}^{-1}$. We shall therefore take $F(t) = 0.5 \sin(0.4\pi t)\,1\,\mathrm{s}^{-1}$.
The inspiration takes 2.5 s and the amount of air breathed in is given by

$$\int_0^{2.5} 0.5 \sin(0.4\pi t)\mathrm{d}t = (5/4\pi)[-\cos(0.4\pi t)]_0^{2.5}$$
$$= (5/2\pi)\,1$$

This amount is breathed in and out every 5 s, so in one minute we breathe $12 \times (5/2\pi) \approx 9.6$ litres of air.

10.4 A new CD sells 12 500 copies in the first week of its release and sales reach a peak 10 weeks later before dwindling to zero after 25 weeks. Write down a continuous quadratic model for $S(t) =$ weekly sales, t weeks after release, and use it to calculate:

(a) The total sales
(b) The average number sold per week

(c) The peak weekly sales
(d) The total sales in the first 12 weeks
(e) The week when weekly sales drop below 9000
(f) The week when total sales reach 300 000

Solution Let us interpret the given information to mean that $S(0) = 12\,500$. The form of $S(t)$ must then be $12\,500 + at + bt^2$.

We also know that $S'(t) = 0$ when $t = 10$ and that $S(25) = 0$. These facts give equations $a + 2b(10) = 0$ and $12\,500 + 25t + 25^2 b = 0$, from which we find $a = 2000$ and $b = -100$, so our model is $S(t) = 12\,500 + 2000t - 100t^2$. (Note that we are using a continuous model for a function which in reality will be a discrete one.)

(a) Total sales are given by:

$$\int_0^{25} S(t)\mathrm{d}t = \int_0^{25} (12\,500 + 2000t - 100t^2)\mathrm{d}t$$
$$= [12\,500t + 1000t^2 - 100t^3/3]_0^{25} = 416\,667$$

(b) The total sales found in (a) are spread over 25 weeks, giving an average of 16 667 per week.
(c) The weekly sales peak at $t = 10$ when $S = S(10) = 22\,500$.
(d) The total sales after 12 weeks are given by:

$$\int_0^{12} S(t)\mathrm{d}t = \int_0^{12} (12\,500 + 2000t - 100t^2)\mathrm{d}t$$
$$= [12\,500t + 1000t^2 - 100t^3/3]_0^{12}$$
$$= 236\,400$$

(e) Weekly sales drop below 9000 when $S(t) < 9000$. Either from sketching the graph of $S(t)$ or by solving the quadratic $S(t) = 9000$, we find that this first happens at $t = 21$ weeks.
(f) The total sales after t weeks are given by:

$$\int_0^t S(x)\mathrm{d}x = \int_0^t (12\,500 + 2000x - 100x^2)\mathrm{d}x$$
$$= 12\,500t + 1000t^2 - 100t^3/3$$

Trying various values of t in this expression we find that it first reaches 300 000 in week 12.

10.5 Figure 10.3 represents the flow of water in a river following a storm which lasted 12.5 hours. If the storm covered the entire catchment area of 100 km², what was the average rainfall rate during the storm?

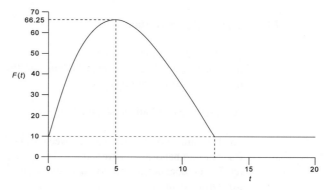

Figure 10.3

Solution Let us use a function $F(t)$ to model the flow rate (m³ s⁻¹) in the river at time t (hours). The following items of information are clear from the diagram.

(i) $F(0) = 10$
(ii) F has a maximum value at $t = 5$
(iii) The maximum value of F is 66.25
(iv) $F(12.5) = 10$

Since we have four items of information we can fit a cubic model for $F(t) = a + bt + ct^2 + dt^3$.

Item (i) gives $a = 10$ and since $F'(t) = b + 2ct + 3dt^2$, (ii) implies that $0 = F'(5) = b + 10c + 75d$. Items (iii) and (iv) give respectively, $66.25 = F(5) = 10 + 5b + 25c + 125d$ and $10 = F(12.5) = 10 + 12.5b + 156.25c + 1953.125d$.

Solving these equations, we find $b = 25$, $c = -3.25$ and $d = 0.1$. The model is therefore $F(t) = 10 + 25t - 3.25t^2 + 0.1t^3$. This gives the flow rate in $m^3 \, s^{-1}$, so the flow in one hour is $3600 \, F(t)$ and the total *excess* water which flows through the river due to the storm is given by

$$\int_0^{12.5} 3600(F(t) - 10)dt = 3600 \int_0^{12.5} (25t - 3.25t^2 + 0.1t^3)dt$$
$$= 3600[25t^2/2 - 3.25t^3/3 + 0.1t^4/4]_0^{12.5}$$
$$\approx 1.6 \times 10^6 \, m^3$$

This is spread over an area of $10^8 \, m^2$ over a period of 12.5 hours, so the average rainfall per hour was

$$1.6 \times 10^6/(12.5 \times 10^8) \approx 1.3 \times 10^{-3} \, m \, h^{-1} = 1.3 \, mm \, h^{-1}$$

10.6 Suppose that the rate of growth of grass (m/day) on a hillside can be modelled by $A \sin^2(\pi t/365)$, where t is the number of days since the beginning of the year and A is the maximum daily rate of growth. Find an expression for the height of the grass on day n. What is the answer if the grass is grazed by sheep at a constant rate of B (m) of grass per day?

Solution   Assuming the grass has zero height at the beginning ($n = 0$), its height after n days will be

$$h(n) = \int_0^n A \sin^2(\pi t/365)dt$$
$$= (A/2) \int_0^n \{1 - \cos(2\pi t/365)\}dt$$

leading to $A\{n/2 - (365/4\pi)\sin(2\pi n/365)\}$.

With the sheep also grazing we must change our starting assumption (otherwise the grass height will immediately become negative!) to $h = h(0)$ say; then the answer is

$$h(n) = h(0) + \int_0^n \{A \sin^2(\pi t/365) - B\}dt$$
$$= h(0) + A\{n/2 - (365/4\pi)\sin(2\pi n/365)\} - Bn$$

In effect we are assuming that the sheep do not start to graze until the grass has reached the minimum height $h(0)$.

10.7   Suppose that in a certain town

(i)   Nobody is aged 90 or more
(ii)   There are more people aged 20 than any other age
(iii) The total population is 12 000

Write down a quadratic model for $N(t) = $ number of people of age t years and use it to calculate:

(a) The number of children aged between 5 and 11
(b) The number of adults over 60
(c) The number of babies less than one year old
(d) The median age

Solution   Let us take the model to be $N(t) = a + bt + ct^2$. We need to find values of the parameters a, b and c so that this model is consistent with the assumptions given. According to assumption (i) there is no one aged 90 or more, although there may be 89-year-olds who are very close to their 90th birthday. We therefore want $N(t)$ to be zero at $t = 90$, i.e. $0 = N(90) = a + 90b + 8100c$.

Assumption (ii) means that we want $N(t)$ to have a maximum at $t = 20$. Since $N'(T) = b + 2ct$, this implies that $0 = N'(20) = b + 40c$.

We now have two equations involving a, b and c. We get a third from assumption (iii), which gives the total size of the population to be

$$12\,000 = \int_0^{90} N(t)\mathrm{d}t = \int_0^{90} (a + bt + ct^2)\mathrm{d}t$$
$$= [at + bt^2/2 + ct^3/3]_0^{90}$$
$$= 90a + 4050b + 243\,000c$$

Solving the three equations gives $a = 500/3$, $b = 1.481\,48$, $c = -0.037\,037$, so our model is $N(t) = 166.667 + 1.481\,48t - 0.037\,037t^2$.

(a) The answer is given by

$$\int_5^{11} N(t)\mathrm{d}t$$

which comes to 1056.

(b) This is given by

$$\int_{60}^{90} N(t)\mathrm{d}t$$

which works out to 2000.

(c) This is represented by

$$\int_0^1 N(t)\mathrm{d}t$$

which gives 168 (the nearest integer).

(d) If M is the median then

$$\int_0^M N(t)\mathrm{d}t = 6000$$

that is, $166.67M + 0.740\,74M^2 - 0.037\,037M^3/3 = 6000$, which gives (for example by using the Newton–Raphson method) $M \approx 33.8$.

10.8 At 1 a.m. the depth of water in a reservoir is 5 m. It starts to rain at 2 a.m., slowly at first but gradually increasing to a peak of $1\,\mathrm{cm\,h^{-1}}$ at 3 a.m. It then gradually subsides until at 5 a.m. the rainfall rate is $4\,\mathrm{mm\,h^{-1}}$. It then continues to rain at a decreasing rate until it stops altogether at 9 a.m. Obtain equations defining a model for $d(t)$, the depth of water in the reservoir at time t hours after midnight. How deep is the water at 9 a.m.?

Solution The question is given in terms of three different units of length, namely m, cm and mm. If we choose to measure in cm then, according to the data given, the rainfall rate at time t (in $\mathrm{cm\,h^{-1}}$) is

$$r(t) = \begin{cases} 0 & 0 \leqslant t \leqslant 2 \\ t - 2 & 2 \leqslant t \leqslant 3 \\ 1.9 - 0.3t & 3 \leqslant t \leqslant 5 \\ 0.9 - 0.1t & 5 \leqslant t \leqslant 9 \end{cases}$$

Assuming $r(t)$ to be adequately modelled by this piecewise linear function, the depth of water in the reservoir at time t is given by

$$d(t) = 500 + \int_0^t r(x)\mathrm{d}x$$

For $0 \leqslant t \leqslant 2$ the rainfall rate is zero and d remains at 500. For $2 \leqslant t \leqslant 3$ we get

$$d(t) = 500 + \int_2^t (x - 2)\mathrm{d}x = 500 + [x^2/2 - 2x]_2^t = 502 + t^2/2 - 2t$$

Note that this gives $d = 500.5$ at $t = 3$, so for $3 \leqslant t \leqslant 5$ we have

$$d(t) = 500.5 + \int_3^t (1.9 - 0.3x)\mathrm{d}x = 500.5 + [1.9x - 0.15x^2]_3^t$$
$$= 496.15 + 1.9t - 0.15t^2$$

This gives $d = 501.9$ at $t = 5$, so for $5 \leqslant t \leqslant 9$ we have

$$d(t) = 501.9 + \int_5^t (0.9 - 0.1x)\mathrm{d}x = 501.9 + [0.9x - 0.05x^2]_5^t$$

$$= 498.65 + 0.9t - 0.05t^2$$

Collecting all our results together we have

$$d(t) = \begin{cases} 500 & 0 \leqslant t \leqslant 2 \\ 502 + t^2/2 - 2t & 2 \leqslant t \leqslant 3 \\ 496.15 + 1.9t - 0.15t^2 & 3 \leqslant t \leqslant 5 \\ 498.65 + 0.9t - 0.05t^2 & 5 \leqslant t \leqslant 9 \end{cases}$$

See Fig. 10.4.

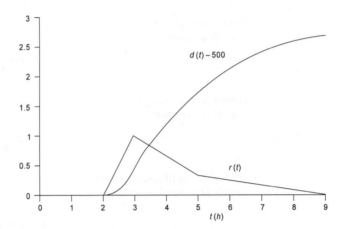

Figure 10.4

Note that these various expressions agree at the 'change-over' t values, so there are no sudden jumps in the graph of $d(t)$ against t. The depth at 9 a.m. is predicted to be $d(9) = 498.65 + 0.9(9) - 0.05(9)^2 = 502.7$ (cm).

10.9   A train leaves a platform at time $t = 0$ and accelerates steadily to a speed of 60 m.p.h. in 30 s. It then travels at a constant 60 m.p.h. for 5 minutes. It begins to slow down at time $t = 5.5$ min and by time $t = 6.5$ its speed is 40 m.p.h. It then steadily reduces speed so that it comes to a halt at $t = 7$. Write down equations representing its distance from the platform at time t (min).

Solution   The train's speed (m.p.h.) at time t (min) is given by

$$V = \begin{cases} 120t & 0 \leqslant t \leqslant 0.5 \\ 60 & 0.5 \leqslant t \leqslant 5.5 \\ 280 - 40t & 5.6 \leqslant t \leqslant 6.5 \\ 560 - 80t & 6.5 \leqslant t \leqslant 7 \end{cases}$$

(Check that these expressions match up at the change-over t values.) It will be more convenient if we convert to measuring time t in hours (since our speeds are in m.p.h.), so we rewrite these equations as

$$V = \begin{cases} 7200t & 0 \leqslant t \leqslant 0.5/60 \\ 60 & 0.5/60 \leqslant t \leqslant 5.5/60 \\ 280 - 2400t & 5.5/60 \leqslant t \leqslant 6.5/60 \\ 560 - 4800t & 6.5/60 \leqslant t \leqslant 7/60 \end{cases}$$

The distance of the train from the platform at time t (hours) is given by

$$s(t) = \int_0^t v(x)\mathrm{d}x$$

which leads to

$$S(t) = \begin{cases} 3600t^2 & 0 \leqslant t \leqslant 0.5/60 \\ 60t - 0.25 & 0.5/60 \leqslant t \leqslant 5.5/60 \\ 280t - 1200t^2 - 31/3 & 5.5/60 \leqslant t \leqslant 6.5/60 \\ 560t - 2400t^2 - 79.75/3 & 6.5/60 \leqslant t \leqslant 7/60 \end{cases}$$

(Note the constants of integration which take up the correct values to make $S(t)$ continuous.)

Since the question required t to be in minutes we convert our answers to:

$$S(t) = \begin{cases} t^2 & 0 \leqslant t \leqslant 0.5 \\ t - 0.25 & 0.5 \leqslant t \leqslant 5.5 \\ (14t - t^2 - 31)/3 & 5.5 \leqslant t \leqslant 6.5 \\ (28t - 2t^2 - 79.75)/3 & 6.5 \leqslant t \leqslant 7 \end{cases}$$

10.10   Suppose that the number of people (per km^2) living at a distance r (km) from a city centre can be modelled by $\rho(r) = 2000(ar - r^2)$, where a is a constant.

    (a) What is the total population of the city?
    (b) What percentage of the city's population live within a distance x (km) of the city centre?
    (c) Within what radius do the inner 50% of the city's population live?

Solution   The outer radius of the city is where the population falls to zero, i.e. where $r = a$ (it is also zero at the centre, $r = 0$).

    (a) The total population is given by

$$\int_0^a 2000(ar - r^2)2\pi r dr = 1000\pi a^4/3$$

    (b) The total population living within a distance x of the city centre is given by

$$\int_0^x 2000(ar - r^2)2\pi r dr = 4000\pi\{ax^3/3 - x^4/4\}$$

so the required percentage is

$$[4000\pi\{ax^3/3 - x^4/4\}/(1000\pi a^4/3)] \times 100 = 100\{4(x/a)^3 - 3(x/a)^4\}$$

    (c) Plotting the graph of (b) for $0 < (x/a) < 1$ we find the percentage is ≈ 50 when $x/a \approx 0.614$, so in this model 50% of the population live within 61.4% of the maximum radius.

10.3 Exercises

10.1   A balloon is blown up by pumping in 100 litres of gas per minute. Write down models for its volume $v(t)$ (m^3) and its radius $r(t)$ (m) at time t (min) if it contains v_0(m^3) of gas at time $t = 0$.

10.2   An aircraft is at an altitude of 10 000 ft and its vertical speed indicator is showing a rate of climb of $500\,ft\,min^{-1}$ which is decreasing at $5\,ft\,min^{-1}$ every second. At what altitude will the aircraft be 5 min from now?

10.3   At time $t = 0$ an ice cube of size one cubic centimetre starts to melt. If each edge decreases in length by 1 mm every minute, write down an expression for $v(t)$, its volume in cm^3 after t minutes.

10.4   The following data shows the number, N of people standing in a queue at various times during one morning.

Time	9 a.m.	10 a.m.	11:30 a.m.	12 noon
N	20	12	6	8

What was the average number in the queue over this period?

10.5   Sales of a new daily newspaper were 100 000 on the first day and reached 400 000 per day after 2 months. By 7 months however, sales were down to 275 000 per day. Use a simple quadratic model to represent the daily sales after t months and use it to find an expression for the total sales of the newspaper in the first t months.

10.6   Suppose the speed of flow in a deep canal with a rectangular cross-section depends only on the depth x below the surface and varies from V_{max} at the surface to zero at the bottom where $x = b$. Write down a simple linear model for the speed $V(x)$ at depth x and deduce the volume flow rate if the width of the canal is a.

10.7   A trench of width w and length L is to be dug. If the depth at the deepest point is to be d, use a simple quadratic model to estimate the volume of earth that has to be removed.

10.8   It begins to snow at 5 p.m., slowly at first but gradually increasing to $0.5\,cm\,h^{-1}$ at 5:45 p.m. It continues to snow steadily at this rate until 8 p.m. when it suddenly stops. Obtain equations defining a model for $d(t)$, the depth of snow on the ground at time t (hours) between 5 p.m. and 8 p.m. What is the final depth of the snow?

10.9   A new book sells 3000 copies in the first week of its publication but sales then dwindle to zero after 10 weeks. Write down a linear model for $S(t) =$ weekly sales, t weeks after publication and use it to calculate:

    (a) The total sales
    (b) The average number of copies sold per week over the 10 week period
    (c) The week when weekly sales drop below 1000
    (d) The week when total sales reach 10 000

10.10   A new computer game is proving very popular with young children. Ten weeks after first going on sale it is selling at the rate of 500 a day, rising to 1000 a day after 15 weeks. Write down a quadratic model for $S(t) =$ the daily sales t weeks after the launch and use it to obtain an expression for $T(t) =$ the total sales after t weeks.

10.11 A circular plate is made of a material whose density at distance r from the centre is modelled by $\rho(r) = k/r$, where k is a constant. If a is the radius of the plate, what is its mass?

10.12 A new toy sold 1000 on the first day and increased at a regular rate, reaching daily sales of 3000 after 2 months. Sales eventually peaked at 4 months and then declined to zero at 8 months. Using a linear model for the first 2 months and a quadratic from then on, write down expressions for the total sales $T(t)$ after t months.

10.13 The population density of a certain town (number of people per km^2) is modelled as inversely proportional to the distance r (km) from the centre for $1 \leqslant r \leqslant 10$.
 (a) What is the total population of the town according to this model, if the population density 1 km from the centre is 1000 people per km^2?
 (b) What is the answer if the *number* of people living at distance r is assumed to be inversely proportional to r?

10.14 A reservoir has radial symmetry and its depth at distance r from the centre is modelled by $d(r) = a - br^2$.

(a) What is the diameter of the reservoir?
(b) How much water does it hold?

10.15 Manufacturers of a certain type of garden furniture find that their sales reach a maximum of £5000 a day in June and fall to a minimum of £600 a day in December. Write down a model for $S(t)$, their daily sales in month t, where $t = 1$ is January. Use the model to calculate their total annual sales.

10.16 A town is modelled as a circle of radius R (km) and the population density, $\rho(r)$ at a distance r (km) from the centre can be modelled as

$$\text{(i) } \rho(r) = \rho_0(1 - r/R) \quad \text{or} \quad \text{(ii) } \rho(r) = \rho_0(1 - r^2/R^2)$$

For each model find (a) the total population and (b) the percentage of the town's population living within a distance $R/2$ of the centre.

10.17 Write down a simple quadratic model for the number of people per km^2 living at a distance r (km) from a city centre, given that this number is 4000 at the centre itself and rises to a peak of 20 000 km^{-2} at a distance of 3 km. Use your model to calculate:

(a) The total number of people living within a distance r (km) of the city centre
(b) The total number of people living at distances between 2 and 4 km from the city centre
(c) The number of people living further than 3 km from the city centre

10.18 Suppose that a seaside town can be modelled as a rectangle with one edge of length a (km) along the coast and an edge b (km) at right angles to the coast. Suppose also that the number of people per km^2 living at a perpendicular distance y (km) from the coast can be modelled by $\rho_0 e^{-ky}$, where ρ_0 and k are constants. Obtain an expression for the total population of the town.

10.19 Suppose that the number of people (per km^2) living at a distance r (km) from a city centre can be modelled by $\rho(r) = a \exp(-br^2)$, where a and b are constants.

(a) What is the total population of the city?
(b) What percentage of the city's population live within a distance x (km) of the city centre?
(c) Within what radius do the inner 50% of the city's population live?

10.20 The age distribution of a certain population can be modelled as

$$\text{(i) } N(t) = N_0(1 - t^2/a^2) \quad 0 \leqslant t \leqslant a$$

or

$$\text{(ii) } N(t) = N_0 e^{-bt} \quad 0 \leqslant t \leqslant \infty$$

where a and b are parameters. For each model find:

(a) The total size of the population
(b) The mean age of the population
(c) An equation satisfied by the median age (M) of the population
(d) The percentage of the population aged over 65

10.21 A rectangular plate is made of a material whose density varies from point to point. Suppose the bottom left corner has coordinates $(0, 0)$ and the other corners are $(2, 0)$, $(2, 1)$ and $(0, 1)$ (distances in m). What is the total mass of the plate if its density at the point (x, y) is modelled by $\rho(x, y) = 6x^2 y \,(\text{kg m}^{-2})$?

10.22 A train leaves a platform at time $t = 0$ and accelerates steadily to a speed of 40 m.p.h. in 45 s. It then travels at a constant 40 m.p.h. for 8 minutes. It then steadily reduces speed so that it comes to a halt at time $t = 10$ (min). Write down equations representing:

(a) Its speed in m.p.h. at time t (min)
(b) Its distance in miles from the platform at time t (min)

10.23 Suppose a channel has a rectangular cross-section of width a and carries a depth b of water. Suppose also that the speed of flow of the water depends on the distance x from the side, being zero at the sides and reaching a maximum $V_{\max}$ at the middle line of the channel. Write down (a) a piecewise linear model and (b) a quadratic model for $V(x)$. For each model find the volume flow rate through the channel. (Assume that the speed of flow does not depend on depth.)

10.24 Figure 10.5 represents the flow (m^3 s^{-1}) of water in a river following a storm which lasted 12 hours. Use a quadratic model to fit the data. If the storm covered the entire catchment area of 500 km^2 what was the average rainfall rate during the storm?

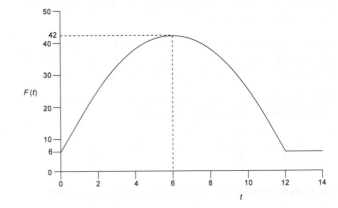

Figure 10.5

10.25 Suppose the thickness z (m) of a certain geological deposit at position (x, y) (km) can be modelled by

$$z = 10 + 4x + 2y - 3x^2 + 4xy + 3y^2$$

Find the total amount of material bounded by $0 < x < 1$ and $2 < y < 3$.

10.4 Answers to Exercises

10.1 $v(t) = v_0 + 0.1t$, $r(t) = \{(3/4\pi)(v_0 + 0.1t)\}^{1/3}$

10.2 8750 ft

10.3 $v(t) = (1 - 0.1t)^3$

10.4 $11\left(= \frac{1}{3}\int_9^{12} N(t)\mathrm{d}t\right)$

10.5 $100\,000(1 + t + t^2 - t^3/12)$

10.6 $abV_{\max}/2$

10.7 $2dwL/3$

10.8 $d(t) = \begin{cases} (t-5)^2/3 & 5 \leqslant t \leqslant 5.75 \\ (8t - 43)/16 & 5.75 \leqslant t \leqslant 8 \end{cases}$

1.31 cm

10.9 (a) 15 000, (b) 1500, (c) 5, (d) 4

10.10 $S(t) = 10t^2/3 + 50t/3$, $T(t) = 10t^3/9 + 25t^2/3$

10.11 $2\pi ka$

10.12 $\begin{array}{ll} 1000(t^2/2 + t + 1) & 0 \leqslant t \leqslant 2 \\ 1000(t^2 - t^3/12 + 5/3) & 2 \leqslant t \leqslant 8 \end{array}$

10.13 (a) 56 550, (b) 14 468

10.14 (a) $2\sqrt{(a/b)}$, (b) $\pi a^2/2b$

10.15 £33 600

10.16 (a) (i) $\pi\rho_0 R^2/3$ (ii) $\pi\rho_0 R^2/4$
(b) (i) 50%, (ii) 43.75%

10.17 (a) $8000\pi(8r^3 - r^4 + 9r)/9$, (b) 631 111, (c) 886 987

10.18 $[1 - \mathrm{e}^{-kb}]aN_0$

10.19 (a) $\pi a/b$, (b) $100\{1 - \exp(-bx^2)\}$, (c) $\sqrt{(\ln 2/b)}$

10.20 (a) (i) $2aN_0/3$, (ii) N_0/b
(b) (i) $3a/8$, (ii) $1/b$
(c) (i) $M - M^3/3a^2 = a/3$, (ii) $M = \ln 2/b$
(d) (i) $100\{1 - 97.5/a + 137\,312.5/a^3\}$, (ii) $100\mathrm{e}^{-65}a$

10.21 8 kg

10.22 $V(t) = \begin{cases} 160t/3 & 0 \leqslant t \leqslant 0.75 \\ 40 & 0.75 \leqslant t \leqslant 8.75 \\ 320 - 32t & 8.75 \leqslant t \leqslant 10 \end{cases}$

$S(t) = \begin{cases} 4t^2/9 & 0 \leqslant t \leqslant 0.75 \\ 2t/3 - 1/4 & 0.75 \leqslant t \leqslant 8.75 \\ 16t/3 - 4t^2/15 - 62/3 & 8.75 \leqslant t \leqslant 10 \end{cases}$

10.23 (a) $V(x) = V_{\max}\{1 - 2|x/a - 1/2|\}$, $abV_{\max}/2$
(b) $V(x) = V_{\max}\{1 - 4(x/a - 1/2)^2\}$, $2abV_{\max}/3$

10.24 $F(t) = 6 + 12t - t^2$, 0.288 mm h^{-1}

10.25 $4 \times 10^7 \text{ m}^3$

11 Modelling with Random Numbers

11.1 Background

Most of this book deals with deterministic models in which values of output variables are inevitable consequences of the input data. Real life, however, is full of uncertainty and this too can be modelled. Models which take uncertainty into account are called **stochastic models** and the output from them is in the form of a **pattern** of results. This pattern is usually summarised into a histogram or distribution or encapsulated into summary measures such as the mean and standard deviation.

In all our previous models, all the variables were **deterministic**. In stochastic models, some or all of the variables are **random**. Any **input** variables which are random must be described in terms of their statistical pattern, either by a histogram (usually based on data) or by a standard theoretical model. The purpose of the model is to derive the statistical pattern of the **output** variables. Only for very simple models can this be done mathematically. More usually, the output variables depend in a complicated way on the input variables and we use computer-generated pseudo-random numbers to **simulate** the random variables. The whole model is then 'run' on a computer and the pattern of results displayed. Most real problems are so complicated that simulation models are built with the aid of specially developed simulation software. In this chapter we are only concerned with developing the concepts and skills involved in simulation, and our simple examples could be regarded as 'submodels' which could form parts of a bigger and more realistic model.

If you are not sure about the precise meanings of terms such as **distribution**, **probability density function (pdf)**, **cumulative distribution function (cdf)**, please refer to any textbook in basic statistics or probability theory, for example those listed in the Bibliography.

11.2 Simulating Qualitative Random Variables

We have previously classified variables as discrete (Chapter 5) or continuous (Chapter 6). These were variables with *numerical* values. Other variables can be described as *qualitative*, meaning that their possible 'values' are not numbers but qualities expressed in words. Examples are a person's sex or colour of eyes.

We could 'predict' an unborn baby's sex by tossing a coin, taking 'heads' to mean 'male' and 'tails' to mean 'female'. Here sex is the variable, which is clearly qualitative, with two values, male and female, and the coin is a mechanism by which we produce a random result. What we are doing is using the random result to **simulate** the baby's sex. For more general cases a coin is obviously inadequate. Suppose, for example, that 30% of the population smoke cigarettes and 70% are non-smokers. To simulate the smoking status of a person we can no longer toss a coin, since we need an unequal division of the frequency of results, in the proportions 30% and 70%. We can achieve this by using a computer-generated pseudo-random number instead of tossing a coin. On many pocket calculators this is available using a button marked RND, RAND or RAN#. A number between 0 and 1 is produced, conforming to the *uniform* distribution $U[0, 1]$, usually taken to 3 decimal places. Most high-level programming languages also have a standard facility for producing these random numbers, which we shall denote by RND. Such numbers are also printed in statistical tables and can be produced on software spreadsheets. We can simulate the random variable 'smoking status' using the model

if $0 \leqslant$ RND < 0.3 you have a smoker
if $0.3 \leqslant$ RND $\leqslant 1$ you have a non-smoker

This procedure is easily extended to deal with qualitative variables with more than two categories. We just need to divide the range from 0 to 1 in the correct proportions. For example, suppose 55% of the vehicles travelling along a motorway are cars, 40% are heavy goods vehicles and 5% are motorcycles. In a simulation the next vehicle to come along will be

a car   if $0 \leqslant$ RND < 0.55
a HGV if $0.55 \leqslant$ RND < 0.95
a MC   if $0.95 \leqslant$ RND $\leqslant 1$

When more than one variable is involved we use appropriate tables like the above for each variable, but remember that each individual RND value must be used for one purpose only. For example, to simulate a card selected at random from a pack we could simulate its suit and rank separately using two random numbers RND_1 and RND_2. The card is

a ♠ if $0 \leqslant RND_1 < 1/4$
a ♡ if $1/4 \leqslant RND_1 < 1/2$
a ◇ if $1/2 \leqslant RND_1 < 3/4$
a ♣ if $3/4 \leqslant RND_1 \leqslant 1$

and an ACE if $0 \leqslant RND_2 < 1/13$, a TWO if $1/13 \leqslant RND_2 < 2/13, \ldots$, a KING if $12/13 \leqslant RND_2 \leqslant 1$.

An alternative method would be to number the cards from 1 to 52 and use a single RND number. If two or more cards are picked we must distinguish between selection with and without replacement. In most games, cards are dealt *without* replacement, so if our random numbers lead us to simulate the same card twice in one deal we just ignore that choice and go on to the next random number.

11.3 Simulating Discrete Random Variables

We proceed in the same way as for qualitative variables by first modelling the distribution or histogram. Suppose that the number X of accidents per day in a certain factory has the following distribution:

x	0	1	2	3 or more
prob$(X = x)$	0.6	0.2	0.1	0.1
prob$(X \leqslant x)$	0.6	0.8	0.9	1

Note that we use a capital letter for the random variable itself and a lower case letter for an actual value taken by the random variable (often called a 'realisation' of the random variable). It is the **cumulative** distribution shown on the bottom line of the above table which we need to carry out simulations. The model is

$$0 \leqslant \text{RND} < 0.6 \Rightarrow X = 0$$
$$0.6 \leqslant \text{RND} < 0.8 \Rightarrow X = 1$$
$$0.8 \leqslant \text{RND} < 0.9 \Rightarrow X = 2$$
$$0.9 \leqslant \text{RND} \leqslant 1 \Rightarrow X = 3$$

For example, the random numbers 0.571, 0.922, 0.346 lead to the simulated X values 0, 3, 0.

11.4 Simulating Continuous Random Variables

As for discrete random variables, the starting point for simulating continuous random variables is the histogram. The difference is that each class in the histogram includes a range of values of the variable. Suppose that the time T between the arrival of buses at a bus stop has the following distribution:

T (min)	0–5	5–10	10–15
Frequency (%)	20	50	30
Cumulative frequency (%)	20	70	100

Our model is

$$0 \leqslant \text{RND} < 0.2 \Rightarrow \ 0 \leqslant T < 5$$
$$0.2 \leqslant \text{RND} < 0.7 \Rightarrow \ 5 \leqslant T < 10$$
$$0.7 \leqslant \text{RND} \leqslant 1 \ \Rightarrow 10 \leqslant T \leqslant 15$$

Suppose our RND value is 0.36. Since this comes between 0.2 and 0.7 we translate into a value of T between 5 and 10. To write down a specific value of T we could either take the mid-point of the interval, $T = 7.5$, or use linear interpolation, i.e.

$$T = 5 + [(0.36 - 0.2)/(0.7 - 0.2)](10 - 5) = 6.6$$

This is equivalent to reading off the graph obtained by joining the cumulative frequency points by straight lines, as shown in Fig. 11.1.

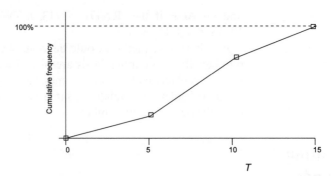

Figure 11.1

If the last class is open (of the form $T > 10$, for example) we need to close it by assuming a reasonable upper limit for the variable.

A distribution such as the one for T in the above example can either be derived from data or assumed. An alternative approach is to use a mathematical model for the pdf of the random variable. A function $f(x)$ can be used as a **probability density function** (pdf) for a random variable X over an interval $[a, b]$ if $f(x) \geqslant 0$ on $[a, b]$ and

$$\int_{-\infty}^{\infty} f(x) \mathrm{d}x = 1$$

which (because $f(x) = 0$ for x outside $[a, b]$) is equivalent to

$$\int_{a}^{b} f(x) \mathrm{d}x = 1$$

A common way of satisfying the second condition is to put a constant k in front of a positive valued function g and find k from

$$k \int_{a}^{b} g(x) \mathrm{d}x = 1$$

The pdf can be used to find the probability that the random variable takes a value between two values x_1 and x_2. This probability is given by

$$\int_{x_1}^{x_2} f(x)\mathrm{d}x$$

To use the pdf to **simulate** values of the random variable we first find the **cumulative distribution function** (cdf) which is given by

$$F(x) = \int_{-\infty}^{x} f(t)\mathrm{d}t$$

This varies from 0 to 1, and if we give it the value RND we then have a connection between x and RND expressed by $\mathrm{RND} = F(x)$. In principle we can turn this around to find $x = F^{-1}(\mathrm{RND})$. This corresponds to using the RND value to read off the corresponding x value from the graph of F in a similar manner to Fig. 11.1, shown here in Fig. 11.2.

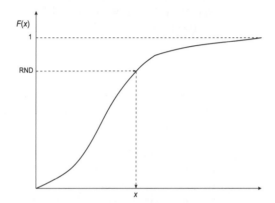

Figure 11.2

This method of simulating x is called the **inverse cdf method**. In practice the equation $\mathrm{RND} = F(x)$ is likely to be non-linear and therefore difficult to solve for x. In such cases a rearrangement of the equation into the form $x = $ function of x will give an iterative scheme in which an initial guess x_0 is substituted into the right-hand side to work out the next iteration x_1. By repeating the process we hope to find our sequence of iterations converging to the required value of x, the root of the non-linear equation. A particularly successful way of rearranging the equation for iteration is the Newton–Raphson method (see the Bibliography).

11.5 Using Standard Models

In situations where we do not have data from which to form a histogram we have to base the distributions of our random variables entirely on assumptions. There are standard models which can be used for convenience. The simplest is the **continuous uniform** distribution $U[a, b]$ defined by the pdf

$$f(x) = \begin{cases} 1/(b-a) & a \leqslant x \leqslant b \\ 0 & \text{otherwise} \end{cases}$$

The RND values mentioned earlier are assumed to come from the $U[0, 1]$ distribution and values from the $U[a, b]$ distribution can be created from the RND values by using the formula $X = a + (b-a)\mathrm{RND}$. For example, if we wanted to simulate the random angle θ at which a spinning pointer eventually comes to rest with respect to a fixed direction, we would take $a = 0$ and $b = 2\pi$ so $\theta = 2\pi\mathrm{RND}$. If we had a **discrete uniform distribution** with our random variable X taking any integer value between integers a and b we would use $X = a + \mathrm{INT}[(b - a + 1)\mathrm{RND}]$.

If we need a distribution which is spread non-uniformly around a central value a very common model to take is the **Normal** distribution $N(\mu, \sigma^2)$ which is characterised by the values of the mean μ and variance σ^2 (see the Bibliography). Two values for the standard Normal distribution $N(0, 1)$ can be produced by taking two RND values and using the formulae

$$z_1 = \sqrt{(-2\ln\text{RND}_1)}\cos(2\pi\text{RND}_2) \text{ and } z_2 = \sqrt{(-2\ln\text{RND}_1)}\sin(2\pi\text{RND}_2)$$

These can be converted into two values from the $N(\mu, \sigma^2)$ distribution by $X_1 = \sigma Z_1 + \mu$ and $X_2 = \sigma Z_2 + \mu$.

The time T between random events such as the arrival of customers at a shop can often be modelled to a good accuracy by the **exponential distribution** whose cdf is $F(t) = 1 - e^{-t/m}$, where m is the mean time between events. The decreasing exponential shape of the pdf, $f(t) = (1/m)e^{-t/m}$ indicates that small time intervals between events are the most common with increasingly longer time intervals being increasingly unlikely. Inverting the cdf in the usual way, we can simulate values of T by $T = -m\ln(1 - \text{RND})$ or, equivalently, $T = -m\ln\text{RND}$ (since if RND is uniformly distributed on [0, 1], so is $1 - \text{RND}$). If the distribution of T does conform to this exponential model then the random events form a **Poisson process** and the number N of events occurring in a time interval of given length L is a discrete random variable with the **Poisson distribution**, whose probability function is $p(n) = e^{-\lambda}\lambda^n/n!$. Here λ stands for L/m, which is the mean number of events per interval. Values of N can be simulated by finding the sum $\sum -m\ln\text{RND}_i$ and taking N to be the smallest n for which $\sum_{i=1}^{n} -m\ln\text{RND}_i > L$.

11.6 Worked Examples

11.1 You are standing at the side of a single carriageway watching the traffic go past. Classify the following random variables as qualitative, discrete or continuous and suggest possible models for the distributions.

(a) The type of vehicle
(b) The length of a vehicle
(c) The colour of a vehicle
(d) The number of persons in a vehicle
(e) The speed of a vehicle
(f) The time between vehicles passing your point
(g) The number of vehicles passing your point in one minute

Solution   (a) This is a qualitative variable. Possibilities could be listed as cars, vans, lorries, buses, motorcycles or bicycles, for example. The distribution could be something like:

Car	Van	Lorry	Bus	Motorcycle	Bike
0.6	0.1	0.15	0.05	0.05	0.05

(b) This is a continuous variable. Rather than have one distribution covering all types of vehicles it would be more sensible to have distinct models for each type. For example, bicycle lengths are almost constant and car lengths vary from say 3 m to 5 m. The simplest distribution of lengths to assume for cars would be a uniform distribution $U[3, 5]$.

(c) This is a qualitative variable. The precise answer depends how many shades of colour we want to consider. We could avoid the problem almost totally by taking:

White	Non-white
0.2	0.8

(d) This is a discrete variable. The distribution is easier to contemplate if we exclude buses, in which case we may have something like:

1	2	3	4 or more
0.6	0.2	0.1	0.1

(e) This is a continuous variable. Suppose the median speed is 35 m.p.h. and that there is a spread of speeds from 0 to 70 m.p.h. with just a few very slow and very fast vehicles. The simplest pdf for representing this would be a triangular distribution as shown in Fig. 11.3.

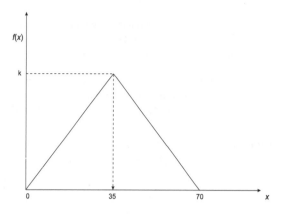

Figure 11.3

We find k from the fact that the total probability (represented by the area under the graph) = 1 so $35k$ = 1. Using the techniques of Chapter 6 we can write down expressions for the pdf:

$$f(x) = \begin{cases} x/35 & 0 < x < 35 \\ (70 - x)/35 & 35 < x < 70 \end{cases}$$

Other possibilities are $f(x) = kx(70 - x)$ with k calculated from

$$\int_{35}^{70} kx(70 - x)\mathrm{d}x = 1$$

or a normal distribution $N(35, \sigma^2)$ for some variance σ^2 (although this has an infinite range, allowing rare instances of negative speeds as well as speeds over 70!).

(f) This is a continuous variable. Small time gaps between vehicles will be common and large time gaps rare. A good model for this kind of distribution is the exponential $f(x) = (1/m)\mathrm{e}^{-x/m}$, where m is the mean time gap.

(g) This is a discrete variable and is obviously linked to (f). If the distribution of the time gaps between vehicles is exponential then the number N of vehicles passing a fixed point in a time interval of constant length L has the Poisson distribution. The probability function is $p(n) = \mathrm{e}^{-\lambda}\lambda^n/n!$ for $n = 0, 1, 2, \ldots$, where $\lambda = L/m$.

11.2   Use the answers to Example 11.1, together with the RND values given on p. 145, to simulate values of each of the variables for the next vehicle.

Solution   (a) RND $= 0.577$ comes between 0 and 0.6, so this is a car.

(b) Its length is $3 + 2\text{RND} = 3 + 2(0.976) \approx 4.95$ m.

(c) It is not a white car because RND $= 0.525 > 0.2$.

(d) The next RND value on our list is 0.128 which is < 0.6 so we conclude that there is only one person in the car.

(e) If we use the triangular distribution and the RND value 0.887, we find the speed x from $0.887 = (70 - x)/35$, which gives $x \approx 39$ m.p.h. Alternatively, from the normal distribution, using the two RND values 0.887 and 0.123 and taking $\sigma = 10$ (so that the total range is approximately from 5 to 65 m.p.h.) and with $\mu = 35$ we get $x = 35 + 10\sqrt{(-2\ln(0.887))}\cos(2\pi \times 0.123) \approx 38.5$ m.p.h.

(f) Suppose the mean time between vehicles is 10 s; then using the exponential model, the next vehicle comes along after $-10\,\ln\text{RND} = -10\ln(0.649) \approx 4.3$ s.

(g) Using the assumption of a mean time gap of 10 s we can calculate the next few time gaps and add them up until we reach a total exceeding one minute. The next RND values on our list are 0.229, 0.112, 0.375, 0.683 . . . The simulated time gaps given by $-10\ln(\text{RND})$ are (in seconds, to 2 decimal places):

	14.74	21.89	9.81	3.81	51.2 . . .
Cumulative time:	14.74	36.63	46.44	50.25	101.4 . . .

so in this minute we observe 4 vehicles passing.

11.3   A student recorded the arrival times of 20 customers at a newsagent's shop one morning, as follows (the timing started at 8 a.m. exactly and was recorded to the nearest second):

	8:00:27	8:00:59	8:01:01	8:01:56	8:03:00	8:05:32	8:05:37
	8:06:48	8:07:31	8:09:16	8:11:43	8:13:01	8:13:39	8:14:30
	8:15:54	8:16:05	8:16:28	8:17:53	8:20:17	8:22:59	

(a) Use the data to produce a frequency table for the distribution of the inter-arrival times of customers.

(b) Suppose a customer arrives at 8:00 a.m. tomorrow. Use your cdf and the RND values on p. 145 to simulate the arrival times of the next three customers.

Solution   (a) The intervals in seconds between the arrivals are 27, 32, 2, 55, 64, 152, 5, 71, 43, 105, 147, 78, 38, 51, 84, 11, 23, 85, 144, 162. We can organise these into a frequency table as follows:

	0–40	40–80	80–120	120–160	160–200
Frequency	7	6	3	3	1
Cumulative frequency (%)	35	65	80	95	100

The cumulative frequency diagram is shown in Fig. 11.4.

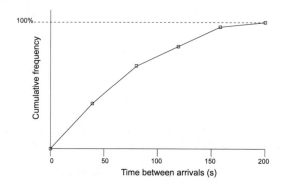

Figure 11.4

(b) From Fig. 11.4 we see that the first RND value, 0.577 (or 57.7%) translates into an inter-arrival time of between 40 and 80 seconds. To pin down the value we can use linear interpolation, which gives $(X - 40)/(80 - 40) = (57.7 - 35)/(65 - 35)$ or $X \approx 70$.

Similarly the RND values 0.976 and 0.525 lead to $X \approx 181$ and $X \approx 63$ respectively. Using these simulated inter-arrival times we have the first three customers arriving at 8:01:10, 8:04:11 and 8:05:04.

11.4   The duration of a certain journey by bus is a random variable whose pdf can be modelled as shown in Fig. 11.5.

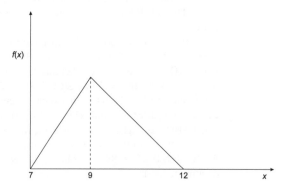

Figure 11.5

(a) What is $f(9)$?

(b) Write down expressions for $f(x)$ in terms of x.

(c) What is the probability that the journey takes 9 minutes?

(d) What is the probability that the journey takes less than 8 minutes?

(e) What is the probability that the journey takes between 8 and 11 minutes?

(f) Obtain a formula for simulating the journey time X from a random number RND.

(g) Simulate the journey time if (i) RND = 0.122 and (ii) RND = 0.853.

Solution (a) The total probability is

$$\int_7^{12} f(x)dx = \text{total area under graph} = 1$$

Adding the areas of the two triangles we get

$$(1/2) \times 2 \times f(9) + (1/2) \times 3 \times f(9) = 1$$

so $f(9) = 0.4$.
  (b) For $7 \leqslant x \leqslant 9$:

$$\frac{f - 0}{x - 7} = \frac{0.4 - 0}{9 - 7}$$

from which $f = (0.4/2)(x - 7) = 0.2x - 1.4$.
  For $9 \leqslant x \leqslant 12$:

$$\frac{f - 0.4}{x - 9} = \frac{0 - 0.4}{13 - 9}$$

from which $f = 0.4 - (0.4/4)(x - 9) = 1.6 - 0.4x/3$.
  (c) Zero: there has to be a *range* of values of x to give a non-zero probability.
  (d) This is given by

$$\int_7^8 f(x)dx = \int_7^8 (0.2x - 1.4)dx = [0.1x^2 - 1.4x]_7^8 = 0.1$$

  (e) This is given by

$$\int_8^{11} f(x)dx = \int_8^9 (0.2x - 1.4)dx + \int_9^{11} (1.6 - 0.4x/3)dx$$
$$= [0.1x^2 - 1.4x]_8^9 + [1.6x - 0.2x^2/3]_9^{11}$$
$$= 0.833.$$

  (f) The cdf is given by $F(x) = 0$ for $x < 7$ and

$$F(x) = \int_7^x (0.2t - 1.4)dt = [0.1t^2 - 1.4t]_7^x = 0.1x^2 - 1.4x + 4.9$$

for $7 \leqslant x \leqslant 9$. Note that this gives $F(9) = 0.4$, which is the area under the graph of f up to the point $x = 9$.
  For $9 \leqslant x \leqslant 12$, $F(x)$ is given by

$$F(x) = 0.4 + \int_9^x (1.6 - 0.4t/3)dt = 0.4 + [1.6t - 0.2t^2/3]_9^x$$
$$= 1.6x - 0.2x^2/3 - 8.6$$

and for $x > 12$, $F(x) = 1$.
  For simulating values of X we therefore use the following scheme:

$$\text{if RND} < 0.4 \text{ use } 0.1x^2 - 1.4x + 4.9 = \text{RND}$$
$$\text{if RND} > 0.4 \text{ use } 1.6x - 0.2x^2/3 - 8.6 = \text{RND}$$

  (g) From part (f), (i) RND = 0.122 gives $x \approx 8.10$ and (ii) RND = 0.853 gives $x \approx 10.52$.

11.5 In a certain city the daily consumption of water (X million litres) is a random variable, but it tends to be mainly around $x = 3$. Small and large values of X are very rare. A mathematical modeller decides that a suitable model for the pdf would be of the form

$$f(x) = \begin{cases} kxe^{-bx} & x \geqslant 0 \\ 0 & x < 0 \end{cases}$$

  (a) What would be suitable values for the parameters k and b?
  (b) Find the cdf $F(x)$ and use it to simulate a value of X from RND = 0.445.

Solution (a) We want f to peak around $x = 3$. Now

$$f' = ke^{-bx} - kbxe^{-bx} = (1 - bx)ke^{-bx}$$

So

$$f'(3) = (1 - 3b)ke^{-3b} = 0 \text{ if } b = 1/3$$

We find k from the condition

$$\int_{-\infty}^{\infty} f(x)\,dx = 1$$

which gives

$$\int_{0}^{\infty} kxe^{-x/3}\,dx = 1$$

(since f is 0 for $x < 0$).

The integration comes to $9k$, so k must be $1/9$ and our model is therefore $f(x) = xe^{-x/3}/9$.

(b) The cdf is

$$F(x) = \int_{-\infty}^{x} f(t)\,dt$$

which gives $F(x) = 1 - (x/3 + 1)e^{-x/3}$. Putting this equal to RND = 0.445, we have the following equation for x:

$$(x/3 + 1)e^{-x/3} = 0.555$$

Using the Newton–Raphson method to solve this we find $x \approx 4.525\,36$ so the simulated water consumption is 4 525 360 litres.

11.6 A train is due to arrive at London Bridge at 10 a.m. every day, but could be anything up to 10 minutes late. Which of the following is likely to be the most realistic model for the pdf of the random variable X, where the train arrives X minutes after 10 a.m.?

(a) $f(x) = k/10$ $0 \leqslant x \leqslant 10$
(b) $f(x) = k(100 - x^2)$ $-10 \leqslant x \leqslant 10$
(c) $f(x)\begin{cases} = kx & 0 \leqslant x \leqslant 5 \\ = k(10 - x) & 5 \leqslant x \leqslant 10 \end{cases}$
(d) $f(x) = k(10 - x)^2$ $0 \leqslant x \leqslant 10$

(In each case, $f(x) = 0$ outside the stipulated range.)

For each model, (i) find the appropriate value of k, (ii) find the probability that the train arrives between 10:02 and 10:05, and (iii) use RND = 0.137 to simulate the arrival time.

Solution   Model (a) is unlikely to fit the real facts because it implies that the train is as likely to be about 10 minutes late as it is to be on time.

The problem with model (b) is that it suggests that the train is equally likely to be X minutes early as X minutes late. In reality the train is far more likely to be late than early.

Model (c) could apply, but it assumes that the most likely arrival time for the train is 10:05 and this would be the long-term average.

Model (d) is probably the best because it assumes that the train is most likely to be almost on time, with increasing lateness being decreasingly probable.

(i) In each case the appropriate value of k is found from

$$k \int_{a}^{b} g(x)\,dx = 1$$

This gives (a) $k = 1$,   (b) $k = 3/4000$,   (c) $k = 1/25$,   (d) $k = 3/1000$.

(ii) The probability that the train arrives between 10:02 and 10:05 is given by

$$\int_{2}^{5} f(x)\,dx$$

which gives the answers (a) 0.3, (b) 0.195 75, (c) 0.42 and (d) 0.387.

(iii) In each case the cdf is given by

$$F(x) = \int_{-\infty}^{x} f(t)\,dt$$

Putting RND in place of F gives us the required formula.

For (a), $F(x) = x/10 = \text{RND}$ so $x = 10\text{RND} = 1.37$ when $\text{RND} = 0.137$, so the simulated arrival time is approximately 10:01.

For (b), $F(x) = (300x - x^3 + 2000)/4000 = \text{RND}$, but finding x from the RND value gives us a problem because we have to solve a cubic. Rewriting the equation as $x = (4000\text{RND} - 2000 + x^3)/300$ and using iteration starting with $x = 0$ we converge to $x \approx -5.35$, so this time the train comes about 5 min early.

For (c),

$$F(x) = \int_{-\infty}^{x} f(t)\mathrm{d}t = \int_{0}^{x} f(t)\mathrm{d}t$$
$$= \int_{0}^{x} kt\mathrm{d}t = x^2/50 \text{ if } x \leqslant 5 \tag{1}$$

$$F(x) = \int_{0}^{x} k(10 - t)\mathrm{d}t = 0.4x - 0.2x^2 - 1 \text{ if } 5 \leqslant x \leqslant 10 \tag{2}$$

Equation (1) gives $0 \leqslant F(x) \leqslant 0.5$ and (2) gives $0.5 \leqslant F(x) \leqslant 1$, so we can use (1) when $\text{RND} \leqslant 0.5$ and (2) when $\text{RND} > 0.5$. In this case $\text{RND} = 0.137$ so $x^2/50 = 0.137$, giving $x \approx 2.62$, so the train is about 3 min late.

(d) In this case we have

$$F(x) = \int_{0}^{x} 3(10 - t)^2 \mathrm{d}t/1000$$

which gives $1 - (10 - x)^3/1000 = \text{RND} = 0.137$, so $x \approx 0.48$, i.e. only about 29 s late.

(Note that there is no reason to expect the same x value for the same RND value from these different models.) Note also that the answers to part (ii) could be worked out from $F(5) - F(2)$ in each case.

11.7   You leave home at 8 a.m. and you have to catch a train which leaves at 8:30. To get to the station you first walk to the bus stop. This takes you 3 minutes if it is dry or 4 minutes if it is raining. The probability that it is wet is 0.4. Buses arrive with a mean time of 6 minutes between buses. The bus takes an average of 15 minutes to get to the station or 20 minutes if wet. Use as many as necessary of the random numbers given below to find out whether you catch the train.

0.495   0.325   0.658   0.729   0.091

State the assumptions you have made.

Solution   Let us assume:

1. That the day is either wet or dry and does not change
2. That the time between the arrival of buses at the stop follows the exponential model with mean = 6 minutes
3. That the travel time of the bus follows the exponential model with mean = 15 minutes if dry, or 20 minutes if wet
4. That all these random variables are independent

Taking $0 \leqslant \text{RND} \leqslant 0.4$ to mean the day is wet, we have $\text{RND} = 0.495$, so our day is dry and we arrive at the bus stop at 8:03. The next bus arrives after $-6\ln(0.325) \approx 7$ minutes at 8:10. Since it is dry the bus takes $-15\ln(0.658) \approx 6$ minutes to reach the station so we arrive at 8:16, well in time to catch the train.

11.8   A pedestrian is standing at the side of a road that carries a single stream of traffic moving in one direction. When he gets the chance he walks straight across to the other side, taking C seconds to do so. Model this situation by assuming that the time gaps between vehicles are independent exponentially distributed random variables with mean value T. Use the model to find the average time a pedestrian has to wait, for various values of C and T.

Solution   We model the time gaps between vehicles by $-T\ln(\text{RND})$.

On spreadsheet packages we can usually obtain RND values using a function such as @RAND. We can also use a function such as @IF(condition, this, else that) to output a conditional response.

Suppose we put values of T and C in cells A1 and B1 of the spreadsheet and type the following formulae in cells A2 and B2:

$$\text{A2: } - \$A\$1 * @LN(@RAND)$$
$$\text{B2: } + B2 + @IF(A2 > \$B\$1, 0, A2)$$

A2 gives the next time gap and B2 gives the accumulated waiting time. We start with 0 in B2 then keep pressing F9 (once for each passing car) to recalculate B2 until B2 does not change. If B2 does not change when we press F9, that indicates that the previous gap was long enough for the pedestrian to cross. The value in B2 then gives the total waiting time for that pedestrian. By repeating several times we can find a mean value for this waiting time. By changing the values of C and T and repeating the experiment, we can also find how this mean value depends on C and T.

11.9 A hospital wishes to study the utilisation of an emergency treatment facility. Casualties arrive at random with a mean time of $M_1 = 1$ hour between arrivals. The treatment times are also random with a mean of $M_2 = 1$ hour and standard deviation $\sigma = 0.2$ hours. If a patient arrives when the facility is already in use, he or she has to be transferred to another hospital.

Develop a simulation model and use it to answer the following questions:

(a) What percentage of patients have to be transferred? ($T\%$)
(b) What is the utilisation of this facility? ($U\%$)
(c) How do T and U vary when M_1, M_2 and σ are varied?

Solution We can simulate the time between arrivals by $-M_1 \ln(\text{RND})$ (this assumes the exponential model). For the treatment times, using the normal model we calculate $z = \sqrt{(-2 \ln\text{RND}_1)} \cos(2\pi\text{RND}_2)$, then take the treatment time to be $\sigma z + M_2$.

Let us take the case $M_1 = 1$, $M_2 = 1$ and $\sigma = 0.2$. Taking the RND values from p. 145 we simulate the times in hours between the arrivals of the next 10 patients (using the formula $-2 \ln(\text{RND})$) to be

$$0.550, \quad 0.024, \quad 0.644, \quad 2.056, \quad 0.120,$$
$$2.096, \quad 0.432, \quad 1.474, \quad 2.189, \quad 0.981$$

Their actual arrival times are therefore

$$0.550, \quad 0.574, \quad 1.218, \quad 3.274, \quad 3.394$$
$$5.490, \quad 5.922, \quad 7.396, \quad 9.585, \quad 10.566$$

Using the next 10 RND values we simulate the next 10 treatment times using the formulae $1 + 0.2\sqrt{\{-2 \ln(\text{RND}_1) \cos(2\pi\text{RND}_2)\}}$ and $1 + 0.2\sqrt{\{-2 \ln(\text{RND}_1) \sin(2\pi\text{RND}_2)\}}$ to be

$$1.175, \quad 1.007, \quad 0.892, \quad 1.236, \quad 1.028,$$
$$1.316, \quad 1.104, \quad 1.027, \quad 1.034, \quad 0.579$$

Arrivals 1, 4, 6, 8 and 9 are therefore treated immediately, with their treatments finishing at times 1.725, 4.281, 6.382, 8.632 and 10.613. The other five patients have to be transferred.

With this very small simulation we have obtained $T = 50\%$ and $U = 5.338/10.613 \approx 50\%$. This experiment can be repeated (using longer streams of RND values) with various values of M_1, M_2 and σ in order to answer the questions posed.

11.10 A reservoir is needed to provide a constant supply of $60\,000\,\text{m}^3$ of water every day. The monthly inflow rate ($10^6\,\text{m}^3$) is variable, but the following data are available:

Month	J	F	M	A	M	J	J	A	S	O	N	D
Mean	1.5	1.8	2.1	1.2	1.0	0.6	1.5	2.1	2.4	1.5	1.8	2.4
SD	0.5	0.6	0.8	1.0	0.8	0.4	0.5	0.6	0.8	1.0	0.6	0.5

Find the minimum size of reservoir needed to keep the probability of running dry to under 1%.

Solution Let us assume that each month's inflow is a random variable with a normal distribution. The mean μ and standard deviation σ are given in the data so we can simulate the flow from $\sigma z + \mu$, where

$z = \sqrt{(-2\ln\text{RND}_1)}\cos(2\pi\text{RND}_2)$, using the appropriate σ and μ values for each month. Taking the RND values from p. 145 we simulate the monthly flows ($10^6\,\text{m}^3$) for the next 12 months to be

J	F	M	A	M	J	J	A	S	O	N	D
2.918	2.272	2.380	1.287	0.163	0.847	1.310	2.159	2.670	1.622	2.076	2.232

Subtracting the demand, the net flows into the reservoir are

J	F	M	A	M	J	J	A	S	O	N	D
0.158	0.592	0.520	−0.513	−1.697	−0.953	−0.550	0.299	0.870	−0.238	0.276	0.372

The cumulative flows are

J	F	M	A	M	J	J	A	S	O	N	D
0.158	0.750	1.270	0.757	−0.940	−1.893	−2.443	−2.144	−1.274	−1.512	−1.236	−0.864

From our results, to avoid running dry we need a capacity of 2.443. This would make the maximum amount held over the year 3.713 in March. In order to avoid overflow we therefore require the reservoir to have a capacity of at least 3.713 ($10^6\,\text{m}^3$).

How do we take into account the 1% chance of running dry? We would need to simulate over a much longer period, say 1000 months and allow the reservoir to run dry no more than 10 times during that period.

11.7 Exercises

For each exercise requiring random numbers use as many as necessary of the RND values given on p. 145. Always take them in order, reading from left to right and starting with 0.577 for each separate exercise or part. Your answers should then agree with the answers given on p. 147, although in some questions the calculations can be done in different ways and if you have a different answer it need not be wrong.

11.1 Classify the following random variables as qualitative, continuous or discrete:

(a) A person's nationality
(b) A person's age
(c) A person's height
(d) A person's shoe size
(e) The species to which a plant belongs
(f) A vehicle's registration number
(g) The height of a tree

11.2 Suppose there is a 40% chance of rain on any day of next week.

(a) Simulate each day from Sunday to Saturday as wet or dry.
(b) More realistically, tomorrow's weather is often linked to today's. Suppose that if it is wet today, there is an 80% chance that it will be wet again tomorrow and that if it is dry today there is a 70% chance that it will also be dry tomorrow. Simulate the week's weather using this model, taking Sunday to be dry.

11.3 At a busy road junction 60% of vehicles go straight on, 30% turn left and 10% turn right. Simulate the next three vehicles.

11.4 Suggest distributions for the following random variables. (Sketch what you think are reasonable histograms.)

(a) The marks obtained by a student in an exam
(b) The number of cars owned by the members of one household
(c) The amount of rain falling on London in one day in September
(d) The cost of your next meal

(e) The height of a mountain
(f) The number of loose coins in your pocket
(g) The time a child spends watching television in one day

11.5 Six army officers A, B, C, D, E, F play Russian Roulette with 1 gun, 1 bullet and 5 empty chambers. If A goes first and each officer spins the barrel then pulls the trigger, who is the unlucky one?

11.6 A multiple choice exam paper consists of 10 questions each with 4 options and only one of them correct. A student goes through the paper guessing answers at random. If the examiner gives 2 marks for each correct answer and −1 for each wrong answer, simulate the student's total score for the test.

11.7 The number of accidents per day in a factory is distributed as follows:

Number of accidents	0	1	2	3	4 or more
% of days	63	18	10	6	3

Simulate the number of accidents for Monday to Friday of next week.

11.8 Suppose that at each stop the numbers of passengers getting on (X) and off (Y) a bus are random variables with the following distributions:

	0	1	2	3	4
prob(x)	0.15	0.15	0.2	*	0.2
prob(y)	*	0.3	0.2	0.1	0.1

(a) Find the missing values marked *.
(b) If the bus leaves stop number 1 with 20 passengers on board, simulate the number of passengers on the bus when it leaves stop number 5.

11.9 Customers arriving at a restaurant can choose to sit in the non-smoking area (60%) or smokers' area (40%). They want a table for 1, 2, 3 or 4 with frequencies 10%, 50%, 15%, 25%. Simulate the next three tables.

11.10 Mr and Mrs Jeans have just started life together and hope to have a family. Mr Jeans has brown eyes and Mrs Jeans has blue eyes and the rules of genetics predict that 25% of their children will have blue eyes. Assume that the distribution of the number of children per family is:

Children	0	1	2	3	4
Frequency (%)	20	20	30	20	10

and that the male:female ratio is 50:50. Use the random numbers to simulate the Jeans family by finding (a) the number of children, (b) the sex of each child, taking $RND < 0.5$ to mean male and (c) the eye colour of each child, taking $RND < 0.25$ to mean blue.

11.11 A and B are about to play a tennis match. When A serves she has a probability of 0.7 of winning the point while B's probability of winning a point on her own service is 0.6. Use the random numbers to find the score at the end of the first four games.

11.12 Suppose the length of consulting time between a doctor and his patients is distributed as follows:

Consultation time (min)	0–5	5–10	10–15	15–20	> 20
% of patients	19	26	33	15	7

Simulate the number of patients the doctor will see in the next hour.

11.13 Users of an automatic cash-dispensing machine either want to withdraw cash (80%) or make a deposit (20%). The distributions are:

Amount (£)		0–20	20–40	40–60	60–100
Frequency	(withdrawals)	10	20	30	40
	(deposits)	30	40	20	10

Simulate the net difference in the stock level after 10 people have used the machine. (Use class mid-points.)

11.14 Which of the following functions could be pdfs?

(a) $f(x) = 1 - x^2 \qquad 0 < x < 1$

(b) $f(x) = 4/3 - x^2 \qquad 0 < x < 1$

(c) $f(x) = 5/3 - 2x^2 \qquad 0 < x < 1$

(d) $f(x) = \begin{cases} 1 - x & 0 < x < 1 \\ x - 1 & 1 < x < 2 \end{cases}$

11.15 Sketch what you think is a reasonable pdf for the distance from the hole of the point where a golf ball comes to rest when the ball is hit from a point (a) 200 m from the hole and (b) 5 m from the hole.

11.16 Find the value of k for $f(x) = k\sqrt{x}$ to be a pdf on $[0, 4]$ for the random variable X.
   With this value of k:

(a) Find a formula for simulating X from RND

(b) Use the formula to simulate three values of X

11.17 Suppose that the amount of pay (£X000) received by graduates in the first year of their first employment can be modelled by a pdf of the form $f(x) = k/x^5$ for $x > 10$.

(a) What is the appropriate value of the constant k?
(b) Find a formula for simulating X from RND.
(c) Simulate the salaries of three graduates A, B and C.

11.18 The daily demand for pizzas at a take-away restaurant is a random variable Z. Suppose the pdf can be modelled by $f(z) = k \sin(\pi z/80)$ for $0 \leqslant z \leqslant 80$.

(a) Find the value of k.
(b) What is the most likely number of pizzas demanded in one day?
(c) Find the probability of selling more than 60 pizzas in one day.
(d) How many pizzas should be available daily to keep the probability of running out at 5% or less?
(e) Find a formula for simulating Z from RND.
(f) Use the formula to simulate the total number of pizzas sold from Monday to Friday of next week.

11.19 At a certain garage the weekly demand for petrol is never more than 3000 gallons. Let the weekly demand in thousands of gallons be denoted by the continuous random variable X.

(a) Select what you consider to be an appropriate model for the pdf of X from the following options, giving your reasons for accepting or rejecting each model.

(i) $f(x) = ke^{-3x} \qquad x \geqslant 0$
(ii) $f(x) = k(x - 3) \qquad 0 < x < 3$
(iii) $f(x) = kx^2(3 - x) \qquad 0 < x < 3$
(iv) $f(x) = k(3 - x) \qquad 0 < x < 3$

(b) Find the value of the constant k and use the inverse cdf method to simulate next week's demand.

11.20 Suppose that particles of a certain powder can be modelled as spheres and that the radius R of a particle can vary from 0.1 mm to 1.1 mm. If the pdf is fitted by a function of the form $f(r) = k(r - a)(b - r)$:

(a) Suggest suitable values of a, b and k.
(b) Find what percentage of particles will be trapped by a sieve where the holes are 2 mm across.
(c) Use the inverse cdf method to simulate the size of one particle selected at random.

11.21 The starship *Enterprise* is about to enter a belt of asteroids and Captain Kirk is worried that the ship may not survive if it is hit by a large asteroid. The asteroids are roughly spheres with diameters ranging from 0 to 2 m. Mr Spock thinks that the diameter D, of a random asteroid can be modelled by a pdf of the form $f(d) = ad^2 + bd + c$.

(a) Suggest suitable values for a, b and c.
(b) Simulate the diameter of the first asteroid to hit the *Enterprise*.

11.22 Incoming telephone calls arrive at an office at an average rate of 20 calls per hour. Assuming the time between calls is exponentially distributed, simulate the times of the first three calls after 9 a.m. tomorrow morning.

11.23 The average time between customers arriving at a counter is 2.5 minutes.

(a) Use the exponential model to simulate the number of customers arriving in the next half-hour.
(b) Suppose the customers are served immediately if the server is free but otherwise form a single queue. Suppose also that the service time is a random variable with a mean of 3 minutes. Simulate the size of the queue at $t = 20$ minutes if it is empty at $t = 0$.

11.24 Suppose that in a colony of bacteria, births occur at an average rate of two per minute and deaths occur at an average rate of one every two minutes. If the colony now contains 100 individuals, simulate its size 10 minutes from now.

11.25 A child has caught five butterflies. Suppose that in captivity they live an average of 5 days. Use the exponential model to simulate how long it will be before all five butterflies are dead.

11.26 Alf and Bert are both fishing from the same river, where 60% of the fish are trout. Alf catches fish at the average rate of 1 per hour and Bert's average rate is 2 per hour. Carry out a simulation of all the fish caught in three hours of fishing, giving the time of the catch, the name of the catcher and the type of fish caught in each case.
(Simulate A's catches first by calculating the time of catch and type for each fish, then similarly for B.)

11.27 If the average number of goals scored in a football match lasting 1.5 hours is 2 and when team A plays against team B, 40% of the goals are scored by team A, simulate the result of a match between A and B.

11.28 An office has 3 telephone lines for incoming calls which arrive with an average of 3 minutes between calls and last an average of 5 minutes. A call arriving when all 3 lines are engaged is lost. Simulate the number of lost calls in one hour.

11.29 You leave home at 8 a.m. and you have to catch a train which leaves at 8:25. To get to the station you first walk to the bus stop. This takes you 5 minutes if it is dry or 6 minutes if it is raining. The probability that it is wet is 0.6. Buses arrive with a mean time of 8 minutes between buses. The bus takes an average of 20 minutes to get to the station or 25 minutes if wet. Use as many as necessary of the random numbers given below to find out if you catch the train.

11.30 A shop sells an average of 25 packets of soap powder a day, with a standard deviation of 5 packets. When the stock falls to 50 packets the shopkeeper orders a further supply of 500 packets. This order takes an average of 4 days to be delivered. On Monday morning the shop has 80 packets. Assuming a normal distribution for the daily sales and an exponential distribution for the delivery time, simulate the number of packets in the shop on the following Saturday morning. (Use the first six RND values to simulate the sales from Monday to Friday.)

For any of the above exercises which require **random numbers**, use the following numbers. (They are taken from the $U[0, 1]$ distribution.)

0.577	0.976	0.525	0.128	0.887	0.123
0.649	0.229	0.112	0.375	0.683	0.006
0.431	0.318	0.285	0.236	0.865	0.041
0.108	0.763	0.537	0.849	0.448	0.311
0.442	0.565	0.917	0.799	0.266	0.271
0.537	0.356	0.536	0.006	0.573	0.108

The remaining exercises are longer investigations needing a large supply of random numbers and are best carried out by writing computer programs or using a spreadsheet. Answers are not provided.

11.31 Develop a simulation model to answer the following.
A cereal producer inserts into each packet of cereal a card showing a picture of one of 10 famous athletes. If these are produced in equal numbers and distributed evenly, how many packets will a customer need to buy (on average) before she collects the full set of 10 athletes?
If, instead of 10, there are N cards in the set, what should N be if customers are to be expected to complete their collections in an average of x purchases? Give a table showing values of N corresponding to $x = 20, 30, 40, 50, 60, \ldots$ etc.

11.32 A pedestrian is standing at the side of a road carrying a single stream of traffic moving in one direction, waiting for a chance to cross to the other side.
Given the traffic flow rate (number of vehicles per minute) develop a simulation model to find the average time the pedestrian has to wait. (Better still, can you produce a histogram to show the distribution of times a pedestrian has to wait?)
Make any necessary (and reasonable) assumptions about the behaviour and flow of traffic.
Extend the model to the case where there are two traffic streams travelling in opposite directions along the same road. How long does the pedestrian have to wait:
(a) If there is an island in the middle of the road?
(b) If there is no island?

11.33 The random walk problem in one dimension can be described in terms of a drunk who starts from a point exactly in the middle of a road and every second takes a step to the left or to the right (with equal probabilities).
If it takes 10 steps to go directly from the centre to the side of the road how long will the drunk take (on average) to get to the side?
Develop a simulation model and use it to answer the above question and also find how far from the centre he will be (on average) after taking N steps. Give answers for different values of N. How do the answers change if the drunk is more likely to stagger to the right than to the left?
Also develop a two-dimensional version of the model where the drunk is equally likely to take a step North, South, East or West. How far from the starting point will he be (on average) after taking N steps? Give answers for various values of N.

11.34 A simulation model is required to examine the following appointment system used by a dentist:
(a) Patients are scheduled to arrive every 10 minutes from 9 a.m. to 12 noon.
(b) 10% of patients fail to turn up.
(c) Some patients arrive early, some arrive late. The distribution is

	Early		On time	Late	
	10 min	5 min		5 min	10 min
Probability	0.1	0.2	0.4	0.2	0.1

(d) Consultation times have the following distribution:

Time spent with dentist (minutes)	5	10	15	20	25	30	35
Probability		0.1	0.15	0.2	0.25	0.15	0.1	0.05

(e) Patients are seen in the order in which they arrive.

Use the random numbers to run through the simulation of **one** morning.

Calculate

(a) The average time spent waiting by patients
(b) The percentage of time the dentist is busy
(c) The time when the dentist finishes with the last patient

11.35 A factory owns 12 machines which are used continuously, and owing to the enormous wear and tear they often break down. The average time between breakdowns for any particular machine is 10 days. While a machine is down it represents a loss of $L = £100$ per day. It takes between 2 and 3 days to repair a machine.

The manager is considering implementing a regular maintenance scheme. At a cost of $C = £50$ each the machines can be serviced, taking 6 hours per machine. After servicing a machine will run with 100% reliability for 8 days, after which it becomes liable to break down at the same rate as before.

You are asked to develop a simulation model which will enable you to advise the manager on how often the machines should be serviced to keep down overall costs to a minimum. You should give answers for various values of L and C.

11.36 The manager of a savings bank wants to find the optimum stock of cash (C) to hold on a daily basis. Carrying too much cash is unproductive and poses a security risk. By carrying too little cash he runs the risk of not being able to give his customers the service they expect, with consequent risk of loss of business. Customers may deposit or withdraw cash.

Develop a model which simulates customers arriving at the bank for service. Assume that $p\%$ of customers make a deposit and $(100 - p)\%$ make withdrawals.

Run the model for different values of C and p and find the daily closing stock and the minimum and maximum stock levels during the day. Advise the manager on the ideal opening stock.

Data
(a) The number of customers per day is a random number between 500 and 2000.
(b) Amount deposited/withdrawn by 10 000 customers:

£ up to	5	20	60	100	200	400	600	800	1000
No. of deposits	500	3000	6500	8000	9500	9750	9960	9975	9999
No. of withdrawals	150	300	1750	4500	7000	9500	9800	9970	9999

11.37 A raindrop forms at height H above the ground but does not fall directly to earth because of a swirling breeze. This can be modelled using the following probabilities. At any time:

probability raindrop moves one step down = 0.5
probability raindrop moves one step up   = 0.1
probability raindrop moves one step left = 0.2
probability raindrop moves one step right = 0.2

After a time T the raindrop touches down at a point a distance X horizontally from where it started.

Develop a model to simulate the path of the raindrop and use it to answer the following questions:

(a) How does the average value of T vary with H?
(b) How does the average value of X vary with H?
(c) What happens when the probabilities are changed slightly?

11.38 A software company is developing a microcomputer version of the children's game snakes and ladders and has asked your advice concerning the design of the board.

The specific question they want you to answer is, where is the best place to position a snake in front of a ladder in order to make it as difficult as possible for a player to land at the bottom of the ladder? Should it be one square before or two squares before the ladder, etc.?

Develop a simulation model and use it to give the required advice.

11.39 The Civil Aviation Authority is conducting a programme of research into passenger behaviour in aircraft emergencies. The main objective is to investigate the influence of changes to the cabin configuration on the rate at which passengers can evacuate an aircraft.

You are asked to help by constructing a mathematical model to simulate the process of evacuation. It is necessary to remember that passengers may be competing to evacuate the aircraft, as can happen in an accident when conditions in the cabin become life threatening.

Identify parameters which could influence the evacuation time (such as the number, position and size of the exits and the distances between seats) and use your model to predict how these parameters affect the evacuation time. Your model should be capable of calculating means and standard deviations for variables, such as the total time of evacuation when the aircraft contains N passengers, the time of evacuation from various starting positions inside the cabin and the graph of $n(t) = $ number of passengers evacuated by time t after start of evacuation. Your model may also be able to identify particular locations in the cabin where 'blockages' might occur.

11.40 A Health Authority is considering closing down a hospital in a small town. The decision will be based partly on the occupancy of beds in the hospital.

From records it is known that the number of patients admitted per day has the following distribution:

Number	0	1	2	3	4	5
% frequency	10	15	40	20	10	5

The length of stay of patients has the distribution:

Days	1	2	3	4	5	>5
% frequency	6	10	20	40	15	9

At present the hospital has 10 beds.

If all the beds are occupied, incoming patients have to travel a long distance to another hospital.

You are asked to develop a simulation model and use it to produce data which will help in making the decision about closing the hospital.

11.41 At the beginning of an accounting period of one year a small insurance company starts with a certain sum of capital resources. During the year it receives a flow of premiums in respect of policies exposed to risk of claims during the year. Also during the year claims will arise on the policies at random times and the size of any particular claim is also a random variable.

The company wishes to keep its premiums (P) as low as possible in order not to lose customers to competing insurance companies. It also wishes to minimise the amount of capital resources (R) tied up so that there is just sufficient to make the risk of insolvency small $(< 1\%)$.

Develop a simulation model and use it to advise the company on suitable values for P and R.

Data
Number of policy holders = 16 750
Average number of claims per month = 85

Size of claim (£)	% of claims
0–100	12
100–200	23
200–300	36
300–500	18
500–1000	7
> 1000	4

11.42 A newspaper seller buys newspapers every day for 25p each and sells them at 30p each. He gets back 10p for each unsold paper at the end of the day. Customers arrive at an average rate of one every C minutes.

Develop a simulation model and use it to decide how many copies the seller should buy every day to get maximum return. You should do this for different values of C and also investigate how sensitive your answers are to the values of 25, 30 and 10.

Can you obtain a realistic value of C from real data?

An alternative approach is to consider the number of papers sold per day as a random variable. What distribution would be appropriate for this?

Either use real data or make reasonable assumptions.

11.8 Answers to Exercises

11.1 (a) Q, (b) C (or D if age last birthday), (c) C, (d) D, (e) Q, (f) Q, (g) C

11.2 (a) DDDWDWD, (b) DDWWDDD

11.3 SRS

11.5 D

11.6 +2

11.7 0, 4, 0, 0, 2

11.8 (a) 0.3, 0.3, (b) 28

11.9 NS4, NS2, S2

11.10 (a) 2 children, (b) both girls, (c) one blue-eyed, one brown

11.11 2:2

11.12 Five altogether, the fifth still with the doctor.

11.13 −300

11.14 (b) and (d) are OK, (a) does not give total probability = 1, for (c), f is not > 0 for all $0 < x < 1$

11.16 $k = 3/16$, (a) $(8RND)^{2/3}$, (b) 2.772, 3.936, 2.603

11.17 (a) 10 000, (b) $(10\ 000/RND)^{1/4}$, (c) £11 474, £10 061, £11 748

11.18 (a) $\pi/160$ (b) 40, (c) 0.1464, (d) 69, (e) $(80/\pi)\cos^{-1}(1 - 2RND)$, (f) 239

11.19 (a) (i) has the wrong range, (ii) has $f < 0$ in the relevant range, (iii) is OK, (iv) has f highest at $x = 0$, which is unrealistic.
(b) $k = 4/27$, 1973 gal

11.20 (a) 0.1, 1.1, 6, (b) 2.8%, (c) 0.65 mm

11.21 (a) $-3/4$, 3/2, 0, (b) 1.103 m

11.22 9:01:39, 9:01:43, 9:03:39

11.23 (a) 11

11.24 110

11.25 10.28 days

11.26

Time (h)	Catcher	Fish
0.55	A	Other
0.98	B	Other
1.19	A	Trout
1.31	A	Trout
1.75	A	Trout

11.27 A wins 3–1 with goals at 25 min (B), 54 min (A), 59 min (A), 78 min (A)

11.28 1

11.29 Yes, arriving at 8:18

11.30 443

12 Fitting Models to Data

12.1 Background

Although modelling (involving as it does, ideas and imagination) can at times seem divorced from reality, the real world is the start and end of modelling. As was pointed out in Chapter 1, the interaction with the real world is through data. Two distinct situations commonly occur:

1. We have some data and we are looking for an appropriate *form* of model.
2. We have already decided on the form of the model but we want to find appropriate values for *parameters*.

Finding the Right Form of Model

In practice the form of model is usually decided upon by a combination of experience, common sense, intuition and by examining the data. The most helpful way to examine the data is usually to plot graphs, most conveniently using computer software such as a spreadsheet. A straight line (or nearly) is an obvious pointer to a model of the form $y = ax + b$. A non-linear relationship is more difficult to pin down, but we can often change curved graphs into straight lines by plotting the right combinations of variables. For example, if we think a relationship of the form $y = ax^2 + b$ is a suitable model we can test the assumption by plotting a graph of y against x^2 to see if this results in a straight line.

A quadratic model will give a good fit when the second finite differences are nearly constant for equally spaced x values.

For example, the Highway Code gives the following distances (in feet) as the overall stopping distances in good driving conditions for a car travelling at various speeds (m.p.h.).

Speed v (m.p.h.)	20	30	40	50	60	70
Distance s (ft)	40	75	120	175	240	315

The first finite differences obtained by subtracting adjacent values in the bottom row are

$$35 \quad 45 \quad 55 \quad 65 \quad 75$$

Taking the differences between these gives the *second* finite differences which are all $= 10$. This indicates that s must be a *quadratic* function of v; in fact the model is $s = v + v^2/20$. It can be seen that this fits the data. It can also be understood in terms of the sum of

1. A thinking distance resulting from a constant thinking time which leads to the first term v (distance $\propto$ speed)
2. A braking time proportional to the kinetic energy of the car which gives the second term $\propto$ (speed)^2.

When the values of the independent variable are *not* equally spaced we need to calculate the *divided differences* (see the Bibliography). Constant values for the second divided differences indicate a quadratic model.

Examples of other techniques which help in fitting models to data are (i) smoothing methods, (ii) splines and (iii) Fourier series. More information can be found in the Bibliography.

Finding the Right Values for the Model Parameters

Models are usually based on general assumptions which lead to equations in terms of variables, parameters and constants. When applied to a *particular* case there will be particular values of the parameters which are appropriate to that case. These values can usually be found only with reference to the real data. The concern of this chapter is how the relevant parameter values can be extracted from the data. When these values have been calculated we can (i) obtain an overall impression of how good the model is by comparing its predictions with the data values that we have (i.e. the 'goodness of fit'), and (ii) use the model to make a prediction concerning data values which we do *not* have.

Suppose, for example, that we have a model for the rate of growth of pumpkins. This model will probably contain a number of parameters. If we have a particular pumpkin, say for the first month of its growth, we may be able to use the data to calculate the values of the parameters relevant in this particular case. We could then use the model to make a prediction about our pumpkin's growth for the next month.

The problem of how to make best use of available data in estimating parameter values is a very important and general question which is properly the domain of statistics rather than modelling. Techniques of parameter estimation can be found described in almost any book on statistical methods (see the Bibliography), and in this chapter we limit our examples to simple cases. In principle we only need as many data points as the number of parameters, but in practice the data usually contains measurement errors. We cannot normally expect a perfect fit of the model to the data so we make do with the choice of parameters that gives the 'best' fit.

One of the most frequently used techniques for obtaining parameter estimates for the 'best' fit is based on the *least squares* principle. Suppose we have a model for predicting a variable y from another variable x which involves a parameter, a. Let us write this as $Y = f(x, a)$, where Y stands for the predicted y value. Suppose we have actual data values (x_1, y_1), (x_2, y_2), ..., (x_n, y_n). The errors in our predictions are $Y_i - y_i = f(x_i, a) - y_i$ for $i = 1$ to n and the sum of the squares of these errors is $S = \sum [f(x_i, a) - y_i]^2$. This can be regarded as a function of the parameter a and if it is to be minimised then the derivative $\partial S / \partial a$ will be zero. This gives an equation of the form $\sum (\partial f / \partial a)[f - y] = 0$, from which we should be able to find the value of a which gives the minimum value of S. There may be many parameters and many variables involved in our model. For each parameter we will get an equation of this form and the set of equations will have to be solved simultaneously to find all the parameter values.

Suppose for example that our model is $Y = a + b \sin x$. Then $S = \sum [a + b \sin x - y]^2$ will be minimised when

$$\partial S / \partial a = \sum 2[a + b \sin x - y] = 0$$

and

$$\partial S / \partial b = \sum 2 \sin x [a + b \sin x - y] = 0$$

We therefore find a and b by solving

$$na + b \sum \sin x = \sum y, \quad a \sum \sin x + b \sum \sin^2 x = \sum y \sin x$$

The quantities $\sum y$, $\sum \sin x$, $\sum \sin^2 x$ and $\sum y \sin x$ are first worked out from the data and then the simultaneous equations are solved. In this example the equations are linear (because the model was linear in the parameters), so the task is not difficult, but a model such as $Y = a e^{bx}$, for example, would give non-linear equations for a and b. When the model is not linear in all the parameters we have the following choices:

1. Make a transformation of the model resulting in an equation which *is* linear in all the parameters. In the case of $y = a e^{bx}$, if we take logs we get $\ln y = \ln a + bx$, which is linear in $\ln a$ and b and the application of least squares will give us linear equations to solve. The resulting estimates of a and b will *not*, however, be the same as the ones obtained by applying least squares directly to $y = a e^{bx}$, although they may be close. Another drawback is that the transformed data points may have a very uneven distribution. In some cases it

may not be possible to find a suitable transformation (e.g. $y = a(1 - e^{-bx})$), or there may be several alternatives (e.g. $y = a/(x + b)$ can be written $1/y = (1/a)x + (b/a)$ or $y = a - b(y/x)$ or $x/y = x/a + b/a$, all of which are linear in the various parameters).

2. Solve the non-linear least squares equations numerically by an iterative technique such as Newton's method.
3. Use a numerical search method to find the parameter values which minimise S.
4. Software packages such as MINITAB will provide least square estimates of parameters (including interval estimates which indicate the range of uncertainty).

Note: Many pocket calculators have facilities for obtaining least squares estimates for the parameters a and b in the simple linear model $Y = ax + b$. Very often however, the point $(0, 0)$ is a logical necessity and the appropriate model is $Y = ax$. For this, the least squares estimate of a is $\sum xy / \sum x^2$. (Putting the data into the calculator's built-in procedure would give an incorrect non-zero value for b.)

In many situations, especially in the life sciences, an initial period of rapid growth is followed by a gradual levelling off to a limiting value. The two simplest models for this kind of behaviour are the linear first-order and logistic models described in Chapter 9.

$$\text{Linear first-order: } Y = L + (y_0 - L)e^{-kt}$$

$$\text{Logistic: } Y = L/[1 + (L/y_0 - 1)e^{-kt}]$$

In both models, $Y \to L$ as $t \to \infty$, but the shapes of the two graphs are different as shown in Fig. 12.1. Both models have three parameters, L, k and y_0, but y_0 (the initial value) will usually be known.

The effect of the parameter k is to alter the shape of the curves. In all cases a larger k means that $Y \to L$ more quickly so the curve becomes steeper.

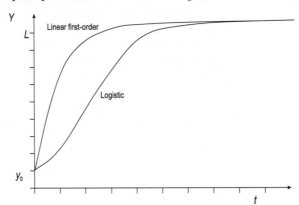

Figure 12.1

Fitting the Linear First-Order Model

The least squares principle leads to non-linear equations for k and L which are difficult to solve. Two simple alternative methods are available.

1. If the data shows y values that appear to have levelled off, then we are immediately provided with the value of L, or at least a good estimate of it. Taking this value we can then plot $\ln(L - y)$ against t, and if the model is a good fit the result should be nearly a straight line with gradient $-k$.
· 2. If our data consists of measurements made at equally spaced times, we can obtain estimates of both L and k as follows. Suppose our measurements are separated by a constant time difference d and let y_n be the y value after n time steps (i.e. $y_n = y(nd)$). From the model,

$$(L - y_n)/(L - y_0) = e^{-knd} \text{ and } (L - y_{n+1})/(L - y_0) = e^{-k(n+1)d}$$

By division, we get $(L - y_{n+1})/(L - y_n) = e^{-kd}$, which we can rearrange into $y_{n+1} = e^{-kd}y_n + L(1 - e^{-kd})$. A plot of y_{n+1} against y_n should therefore be a straight line with gradient e^{-kd} and intercept $L(1 - e^{-kd})$. By measuring these we can then derive estimates of L and k. Note that this scheme has 'removed' time from the analysis and the plot is between y_{n+1} and its adjacent neighbour y_n.

Fitting the Logistic Model As for the linear first-order model, application of the least squares principle leads to very difficult non-linear equations for the parameters k and L, and it is usually simpler in practice to apply one of the other methods. The equivalent of method 1 is derived by rewriting the logistic equation in the form $L/y - 1 = (L/y_0 - 1)e^{-kt}$, so $\ln(L/y - 1) = \ln(L/y_0 - 1) - kt$ and a plot of $\ln(L/y - 1)$ against t should be a straight line of gradient $-k$. The drawback of this method is that we have to guess the value of L from the data by taking a value a bit larger than the last y value we have. We can get a confirmation from the intercept of our line and repeat the plotting if necessary.

When the t values are equally spaced we can use the alternative method 2 based on the fact that

$$L/y_n - 1 = (L/y_0 - 1)e^{-knd} \text{ and } L/y_{n+1} - 1 = (L/y_0 - 1)e^{-k(n+1)d}$$

so by division

$$(L/y_{n+1} - 1)/(L/y_n - 1) = e^{-kd}$$

which rearranges to

$$1/y_{n+1} = e^{-kd}(1/y_n) + (1 - e^{-kd})/L$$

A plot of $1/y_{n+1}$ against $1/y_n$ should therefore give a straight line and from the gradient and intercept we can derive estimates of k and L.

Fitting Periodic Models The simplest case is where the period is known ($= 2L$ say), the angular frequency is then $\Omega = \pi/L$. For a simple model, fit $Y = a + b \sin \Omega t + c \cos \Omega t$ using the least squares principle to find estimates for the parameters a, b and c (see Example 12.5). A model which fits all the data points exactly can be found using a discrete Fourier series as follows.

Suppose the t values are $0, h, 2h, \ldots, Nh$ with N odd and that the corresponding y values are $y_0, y_1, \ldots, y_N$ with $y_{N+1} = y_0$. In other words, $(N+1)h =$ the period $= 2L$. Then the required model can be written as

$$y(t) = \frac{a_0}{2} + \sum_{k=1}^{M}\left[a_k \cos\left(\frac{\pi k t}{L}\right) + b_k \sin\left(\frac{\pi k t}{L}\right)\right] + \frac{a_{M+1}}{2}\cos\left(\frac{(M+1)\pi t}{L}\right)$$

where $N = 2M + 1$. The a and b coefficients are found from

$$a_k = \frac{h}{L}\sum_{i=0}^{2M+1} y_i \cos\left(\frac{\pi k t_i}{L}\right), \quad k = 0, 1, \ldots, M + 1$$

and

$$b_k = \frac{h}{L}\sum_{i=0}^{2M+1} y_i \sin\left(\frac{\pi k t_i}{L}\right), \quad k = 1, 2, \ldots, M$$

A simpler model, not passing through all the data points, can be obtained by taking only the terms with the largest coefficients.

12.2 Worked Examples

12.1 The table below shows the number y of bacteria on a plate in a laboratory at various times t.

t (hours)	1	2	3	4	5	6	7
Y	80	140	210	320	450	570	679

Fit models of the form (a) $Y = at$, (b) $Y = at^2$ and (c) $Y = Y_0 e^{at}$ to the data. Which model appears to give the best fit?

Solution (a) The quickest way to check whether $Y = at$ might be a good model for the data is to work out the values y/t and see if they are roughly constant. We find $y/t = 80, 70, 70, 80, 90, 95, 97$, which is encouraging. We could estimate the value of a by taking the average of these, which comes to ≈ 83.

Alternatively, using the least squares principle, the best estimator of a is $\sum yt / \sum t^2$, which gives $a \approx 90.66$.

(b) In the same way as for (a) we check the suitability of the model $Y = at^2$ by calculating y/t^2 which gives the values 80, 35, 23.3, 20, 18, 15.83, 13.86, which are not remarkably constant. The least squares estimator of a is $\sum yt^2 / \sum t^4$ which gives $a \approx 15.54$.

(c) The plot of $\ln y$ against t should be a straight line if this model is valid. The least squares line fitted to the data gives $a \approx 0.357$ and $\ln Y_0 \approx 4.20$, giving the model $Y = 66.69 e^{0.375t}$.

The values of S, the sum of the squared errors are (a) 10 139, (b) 30 919 and (c) 22 598, so on this criterion model (a) gives the best fit.

Figure 12.2 shows all three models compared with the original data. We conclude that the simple linear model $Y = at$ seems best over the range of data supplied.

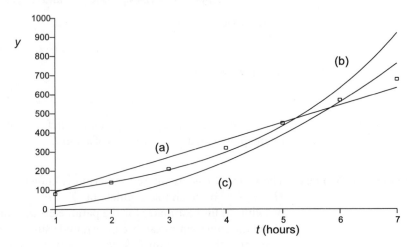

Figure 12.2

12.2 The following data shows the amount of a chemical dissolved in a solvent (mg l^{-1}) at various times. Fit an appropriate model.

$t\,(s)$	0	5	10	15	20	25	30
$y\,(\text{mg l}^{-1})$	0	3.3	5.4	6.6	7.4	7.8	8.1

Solution A plot of the raw data is shown in Fig. 12.3, indicating a levelling off in the amount of chemical dissolved as time elapses. This is to be expected in practice, with a maximum limit for the amount dissolved. Since no chemical is initially dissolved, the model $Y = L(1 - e^{-kt})$ seems appropriate. This is the linear first-order model with $y_0 = 0$. We shall apply both of the methods discussed above for finding values for k and L.

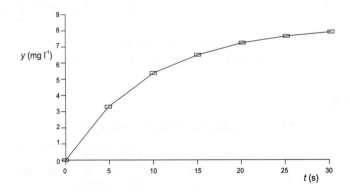

Figure 12.3

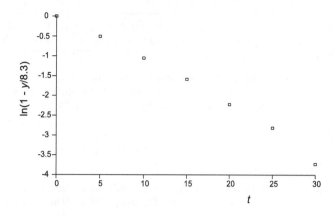

Figure 12.4

(a) The graph of y against t (Fig. 12.3) shows that the concentration has almost levelled off. Let us guess $L \approx 8.3$. The method requires a plot of $\ln[(L - y)/(L - y_0)]$ against t, which in this case means $\ln[(L - y)/L] = \ln(1 - y/8.3)$ against t, using the fact that $y_0 = 0$ and taking $L = 8.3$. This plot is given in Fig. 12.4 and shows an almost straight line with gradient -0.12, so $k \approx 0.12$. The fitted values of the model $Y = 8.3(1 - e^{-0.12t})$ rounded to the same accuracy as the original data, are

$$Y(\mathrm{mg\,l}^{-1}) \quad 0 \quad 3.7 \quad 5.8 \quad 6.9 \quad 7.6 \quad 7.9 \quad 8.1$$

(b) Since the t values are equally spaced we can also use the second method here. Plotting y_{n+1} against y_n gives a good straight line and linear regression yields $Y_{n+1} = 3.41 + 0.598\,Y_n$ so $e^{-kd} = 0.598$ and $L(1 - e^{-kd}) = 3.41$. Substituting for e^{-kd} in the second equation we get $L = 8.5$ and since $d = 5$ we get $k = -\ln(0.598)/5 \approx 0.103$. The fitted values of the model $Y = 8.5(1 - e^{-0.103t})$ are

$$Y(\mathrm{mg\,l}^{-1}) \quad 0 \quad 3.4 \quad 5.5 \quad 6.7 \quad 7.4 \quad 7.9 \quad 8.1$$

12.3   The following table gives the estimated number of fish y in a lake over a number of years:

Time (years)	0	1	2	3	4	5	6
$y\,(\times 10^3)$	500	700	820	890	930	960	980

(a) Show that y can be reasonably represented by a logistic model and obtain estimates for the parameters L and k.

(b) Compare the model's predictions with the actual data.

Solution   (a) From the data we can guess that the population is approaching the limiting value $L \approx 1000$. A plot of $\ln(1000/y - 1)$ against t gives a good straight line with gradient ≈ -0.62. This leads us to the model $Y = 1000/[1 + e^{-0.62t}]$.

Since the t values are equally spaced we can also test whether a logistic model is a good fit by plotting $1/y_{n+1}$ against $1/y_n$. This also gives a good straight line with gradient 0.42 and intercept 0.0006. The gradient is e^{-kd}, and since the spacing between the t values is $d = 1$ this gives $k \approx 0.87$. The intercept is $0.0006 = (1 - e^{-kd})/L$ which gives $L \approx 967$. Note that the last data point actually has a y value, which is larger than this, although in the model Y cannot exceed L. Since the fit is not perfect we must regard the imperfections as 'errors' in the data. The model we are led to is therefore

$$Y = 967/[1 + (967/500 - 1)e^{-0.87t}] = 967/[1 + 0.934e^{-0.87t}]$$

(b) The model $Y = 1000/[1 + e^{-0.62t}]$ gives the predicted values

$$500 \quad 650 \quad 772 \quad 865 \quad 912 \quad 956 \quad 976$$

with sum of squared errors $= 5246$.

The model $Y = 967/[1 + 0.934e^{-0.87t}]$ gives the predicted values

$$500 \quad 695 \quad 831 \quad 905 \quad 940 \quad 955 \quad 962$$

which represents a better fit, with error sum of squares $= 820$.

12.4   (a) In an experiment to investigate how the weight of a tomato crop can be increased by applying fertiliser, the yield $y\,(\mathrm{kg\,m}^{-2})$ for various amounts $x\,(\mathrm{kg\,m}^{-2})$ of fertiliser was found to be as follows.

Fertiliser, $x\,(\mathrm{kg\,m^{-2}})$	0	0.2	0.5	0.8	1.0	1.5
Yield, $y\,(\mathrm{kg\,m^{-2}})$		1.00	1.20	1.40	1.50	1.55	1.65

Fit a model of the form $Y = L + (y_0 - L)\mathrm{e}^{-kt}$.

(b) To investigate the effect of temperature on the yield, a number of plots were maintained at different temperatures and gave the following results:

Temperature, $T\,(°C)$	10	15	20	25	30
Yield, $y\,(\mathrm{kg\,m^{-2}})$	1.0	2.5	4.0	4.5	4.8

Fit a similar model to that of part (a), relating Y and T.

(c) The total costs of heating, $C\,(\mathrm{£\,m^{-2}})$ at constant temperature T were found to be as follows:

T	10	15	20	25	30
C	10	25	45	70	100

Fit the simplest model for C as a function of T.

(d) If the cost of fertiliser is £10 per kg and each kg of tomatoes is worth £5, write down a model for the net value of the crop obtained from one m^2 of compost in terms of x and T.

Solution (a) From the data we can guess that L is about 1.7. A plot of $\ln(1.7 - y)$ against x gives a good straight line with gradient -1.71, so $k \approx 1.71$ and the model is $Y = 1.70 - 0.70\mathrm{e}^{-1.71x}$. The fitted values from this model are

Fertiliser, $x\,(\mathrm{kg\,m^{-2}})$	0	0.2	0.5	0.8	1.0	1.5
Yield, $Y\,(\mathrm{kg\,m^{-2}})$		1.00	1.20	1.40	1.52	1.57	1.65

(b) We could not use the second method for (a) because the x values were not equally spaced, but here the T values *are* equally spaced and plotting y_{n+1} against y_n gives a reasonable straight line with gradient 0.627 and intercept 2.07.

These give $\mathrm{e}^{-5k} = 0.627$, so $k \approx 0.09$ and $L(1 - \mathrm{e}^{-5k}) = 2.07$. It follows that $L \approx 5.55$ and the model is therefore

$$Y = 5.55 + (1.0 - 5.55)\mathrm{e}^{-0.09(T-10)} \approx 5.55 - 11.19\mathrm{e}^{-0.09T}$$

(c) Checking the ratio C/T^2 we find 0.1, 0.111, 0.112, 0.112, 0.111. Since these are nearly constant the model $C = 0.11T^2$ should be a good fit.

(d) Putting the models (a) and (b) together, the yield at temperature T using $x\,(\mathrm{kg\,m^{-2}})$ of fertiliser is predicted to be

$$Y = (1.70 - 0.70\mathrm{e}^{-1.71x})(5.55 - 11.19\mathrm{e}^{-0.09T})$$

The total cost is $10x + 0.11T^2$ and the net value is therefore

$$Y = (1.70 - 0.70\mathrm{e}^{-1.71x})(5.55 - 11.19\mathrm{e}^{-0.09T}) - 10x - 0.11T^2$$

12.5 The data below gives the apparent diameter of the Sun's disc (in minutes of arc) as seen from Earth at various times during a year. The variation is due to the fact that Earth's orbit around the Sun is elliptical and we are closest to the Sun at the end of the year. Fit a mathematical model to the data and use it to predict the apparent diameter of the Sun on 20 October.

Date	1 Jan	1 Feb	1 Mar	1 Apr	1 May	1 Jun	1 Jul	1 Aug	1 Sep	1 Oct	1 Nov	1 Dec
y	32.6	32.5	32.3	32.0	31.8	31.6	31.5	31.6	31.7	32.0	32.3	32.5

Solution Since this is clearly a periodic situation with known period of one year ≈ 365.24 days, we should be able to fit a model of the form $Y = a + b\sin(\Omega t) + c\cos(\Omega t)$, where $\Omega = 2\pi/365.24$.

We can use the data to obtain estimates of the parameters a, b and c by the least squares principle.

To minimise $\sum[a + b \sin \Omega t + c \cos \Omega t - y]^2$ we differentiate with respect to each of a, b and c and set the derivatives equal to zero. This leads to the set of equations

$$\sum[a + b \sin \Omega t + c \cos \Omega t - y] = 0$$
$$\sum \sin \Omega t[a + b \sin \Omega t + c \cos \Omega t - y] = 0$$
$$\sum \cos \Omega t[a + b \sin \Omega t + c \cos \Omega t - y] = 0$$

In matrix form,

$$\begin{bmatrix} 12 & \sum \sin \Omega t & \sum \cos \Omega t \\ \sum \sin \Omega t & \sum \sin^2 \Omega t & \sum \sin \Omega t \cos \Omega t \\ \sum \cos \Omega t & \sum \sin \Omega t \cos \Omega t & \sum \cos^2 \Omega t \end{bmatrix} \begin{bmatrix} a \\ b \\ c \end{bmatrix} = \begin{bmatrix} \sum y \\ \sum y \sin \Omega t \\ \sum y \cos \Omega t \end{bmatrix}$$

If we measure t in days with $t = 0$ being 1 January, then we can quantify the data as follows:

t	0	31	59	90	121	152	182	212	243	273	304	334
y	32.6	32.5	32.3	32.0	31.8	31.6	31.5	31.6	31.7	32.0	32.3	32.5

From the data we calculate $\sum y = 384.4$, $\sum y \sin \Omega t = 0.590\,651\,2$, $\sum y \cos \Omega t = 3.639\,825$, $\sum \sin \Omega t = 0.016\,47$, $\sum \cos \Omega t = 0.013\,355\,7$, $\sum \sin^2 \Omega t = 5.987\,702$, $\sum \sin \Omega t \cos \Omega t = 0.044\,079$, $\sum \cos^2 \Omega t = 6.012\,298$. Putting these values into the matrix and solving, we get $a = 32.0327$, $b = 0.0066$, $c = 0.5342$ and so our model is $Y = 32.0327 + 0.0066 \sin \Omega t + 0.5342 \cos \Omega t$. Figure 12.5 compares the model with the original data. 20 October corresponds to $t = 292$ and our model predicts $Y \approx 32.2$.

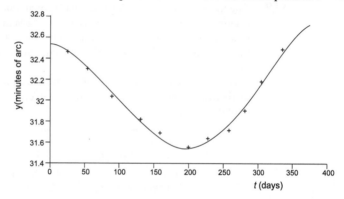

Figure 12.5

12.6 Table 12.1 gives the weekly gas consumption (m^3) and average outside temperature (°C) for a particular house before the installation of cavity wall insulation. Table 12.2 gives similar data for the same house after insulation.

Table 12.1

Temperature	−1	0	2	4	5	7	10
Gas	206.6	195.6	173.2	149.4	115.7	116.0	82.4

Table 12.2

Temperature	−1	0	1	3	6	8	10
Gas	134.4	127.6	120.6	110.1	89.4	72.7	59.4

Table 12.3 gives monthly averages of the outside temperature at the location of this house from October to May.

Table 12.3

	O	N	D	J	F	M	A	M
°C	10.3	6.7	4.4	3.4	3.8	5.7	8.7	11.5

(a) Fit the simplest possible model to Table 12.1.
(b) Fit the simplest possible model to Table 12.2.
(c) Fit an appropriate model to Table 12.3.

(d) Write down an expression for the amount of gas saved in one year by having insulation.

(e) Calculate a numerical answer for (d).

Solution   Let y_1 = gas used (m³) without insulation, and y_2 = gas used (m³) with insulation, and x = the outside temperature (°C).

(a) Linear regression gives the model $Y_1 = 193 - 11.6x$.

(b) Linear regression gives the model $Y_2 = 128 - 6.8x$.

(c) If we measure t in months from October, a periodic model with period 12 months seems appropriate.

Let $x = a + b\sin(\pi t/6) + c\cos(\pi t/6)$; then, using the least squares method as in Example 12.5, we find that $x = 9.31 + 0.73\cos(\pi t/6) - 5.99\sin(\pi t/6)$ gives the best fit.

(d) Assuming the heating is used only from October to May, the total amount of gas used is

$$\int_0^7 (Y_1 - Y_2)\,\mathrm{d}t = \int_0^7 (65 - 4.8x)\,\mathrm{d}t$$

$$= \int_0^7 (65 - 4.8[9.31 + 0.73\cos(\pi t/6) - 5.99\sin(\pi t/6)])\,\mathrm{d}t$$

$$= \int_0^7 (20.3 - 3.5\cos(\pi t/6) + 28.8\sin(\pi t/6))\,\mathrm{d}t$$

(e) The integral gives $[20.3t - 55\sin(\pi t/6) - 6.7\cos(\pi t/6)]_0^7$, which comes to 127.1 m³.

12.7   One technique for estimating the capacity of an internal organ is known as dye dilution. At time $t = 0$ a known amount of a dye is injected into a vein carrying blood into the organ. The dyed blood flows through the organ and appears in the vein carrying blood from the organ. The concentration of the dye is monitored at regular time intervals at a convenient point in the blood vessel coming from the organ.

For a particular patient 5 mg of dye was injected and data were collected as follows. Fit a mathematical model to the data and use it to estimate (i) the blood flow rate ($1\,\mathrm{s}^{-1}$) and (ii) the capacity (l) of the organ.

Time (s)	0	1	2	3	4	5	6	7	8
Concentration (mg l⁻¹)	0	0	0	0.1	1.8	3.0	3.8	4.4	4.9

Time (s)	9	10	11	12	13	14	15	16	17
Concentration (mg l⁻¹)	5.2	5.4	5.6	5.7	5.8	4.2	3.0	2.1	1.5

Time (s)	18	19	20	21	22	23	24
Concentration (mg l⁻¹)	1.1	0.8	0.6	0.4	0.6	0.7	0.6

Solution   See Fig. 12.6.

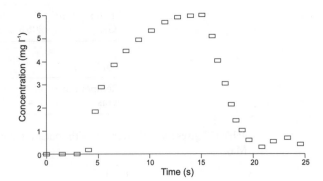

Figure 12.6

From the data we note the following facts:

(a) There is a delay of 3 seconds before any dye appears in the blood at the sampling point.

(b) The concentration continues to rise for 10 seconds and then falls.

(c) After 21 seconds the fall in the concentration level is checked.

Let V = volume of organ (l)

F = blood flow rate $(1\,s^{-1})$

$c(t)$ = concentration of dye in the blood $(mg\,l^{-1})$ at time t (s).

Taking note of observation (a) above, we will assume that at any time t the concentration $c(t)$ at the measuring point will be the same as it was in the organ, *3 seconds earlier*. In other words we will use $c(t)$ to denote the concentration in the organ and start from $c(0) = 0.1$ at time $t = 0$. There must clearly be a finite period of time during which dye is still entering the organ from the syringe while clean blood is also flowing into the organ and blood carrying dye is flowing out. During this time the rate of change of the mass of dye in the organ is $d(Vc)/dt = Vc'$, assuming V is constant. This must equal the mass flow rate in minus the mass flow rate out. The total mass of drug injected was 5 mg and taking note of observation (b) we will assume that this is received over a 10 s period, giving a mass flow rate of $0.5\,(mg\,s^{-1})$ into the organ. The mass flow rate out of the organ is Fc so we have the differential equation model

$$Vc' = \begin{cases} 0.5 - Fc & 0 \leqslant t \leqslant 10 \\ 0 & t > 10 \end{cases}$$

For $t < 10$ this is a linear first-order differential equation with solution $c(t) = 0.5/F + [c(0) - 0.5/F]e^{-Ft/V}$. In terms of our previous notation, this is $c(t) = L + [c(0) - L]e^{-kt}$ and plotting c_{n+1} against c_n from $t = 0$ to $t = 10$ with $c(0) = 0.1$ we get a straight line with equation $c_{n+1} = 0.715c_n + 1.708$.

Therefore $e^{-k} = 0.715$ and $L(1 - e^{-k}) = 1.708$, giving $k \approx 0.335$ and $L \approx 5.99$. It follows that $F/V \approx 0.355$ and $0.5/F \approx 5.99$. The second of these gives $F \approx 0.083\,(1\,s^{-1})$ and substituting in the first then gives $V \approx 0.25$ (l).

We have not yet used the data for $t > 10$. From that point on there is no input of dye and the differential equation is $c' = -Fc/V$ with solution $c = 5.8e^{-Ft/V}$ (if we measure t from that point). A plot of $\ln(c)$ against t has gradient ≈ -0.331, so this part of the data gives $F/V \approx 0.331$, which agrees well with the previous estimate.

Observation (c) can be explained by the fact that blood circulates around the body in about 20 seconds, so instead of dropping to zero for $t > 21$ the concentration level is reinforced by dye arriving for the second time.

12.8 It is necessary for a body to achieve a minimum speed before it can escape from the gravitational influence of a planet. Otherwise it will eventually fall back to the surface of the planet. The following table gives the escape speed for some of the planets in the Solar System.

Planet	Average radius (km)	Mass ($10^{24}kg$)	Escape speed (km s^{-1})
Mercury	2 439	0.33	4.3
Venus	6 052	4.87	10.4
Earth	6 378	5.98	11.2
Mars	3 397	0.642	5.0
Jupiter	71 500	1900	59.6
Saturn	60 300	569	35.6
Uranus	25 600	86.9	21.3
Neptune	25 300	103	23.8

Is it possible to find a simple model which expresses the connection between the escape speed U and the mass M and radius R of the planet?

Solution Here there are two independent variables (R and M) and we are looking for a model $U = U(R, M)$. One possible line of investigation is to see whether the dependent variable (U) could depend simply on the *ratio* of the other two variables. We then reduce the problem to a function of one dependent variable, i.e. $U = U(R/M)$. Figure 12.7 shows the graph of U plotted against R/M, revealing a non-linear relationship. A plot of $\ln U$ against $\ln(R/M)$ shown in Figure 12.8 gives a good straight line with gradient -0.5 and intercept 5.91. We therefore fit the model $\ln U = 5.91 - 0.5 \ln(R/M)$ or $U = 369\sqrt{(M/R)}$. This predicts the following escape speeds for the above planets:

Planet	M	V	E	M	J	S	U	N
Speed (km s^{-1})	4.3	10.5	11.3	5.1	60.2	35.8	21.5	23.5

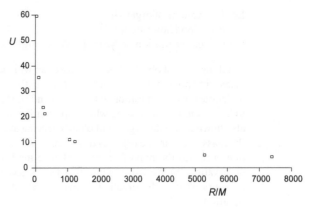

Figure 12.7

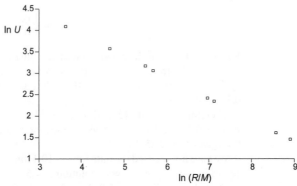

Figure 12.8

12.9   Road traffic continues to increase and it is important to be able to plan ahead by predicting future trends. A sensible measure of traffic is to combine the number of vehicles with the annual distance they cover to give annual vehicle km. A model for making predictions can be based on relating next year's traffic to (a) this year's traffic or (b) other variables which might be relevant. The table below gives estimates of the traffic on UK roads from 1982 to 1991 and also the population and average annual income for those years.

Year	Traffic ($\times 10^9$ vehicle km)	Population ($\times 10^6$)	Average income ($£10^3$)
1982	284.5	56.31	0.713
1983	288.1	56.35	0.755
1984	303.1	56.46	0.773
1985	309.7	56.62	0.834
1986	325.3	56.76	0.889
1987	350.5	56.93	0.957
1988	375.7	57.07	1.033
1989	406.9	57.24	1.115
1990	410.8	57.41	1.206
1991	411.6	57.80	1.270

Fit simple models to these data.

Solution   Let us use symbols Y for the traffic, X_1 for the population and X_2 for the average income. Using statistical software we can investigate linear models for Y in terms of each of X_1 and X_2, separately and together. The results, based on the above data, obtained by least squares fitting are

$$Y = -5404 + 101X_1, \text{correlation coefficient} \approx 0.96$$

$$Y = 100 + 258X_2, \text{correlation coefficient} \approx 0.98$$

$$Y = 4555 - 81.7X_1 + 461X_2, \text{correlation coefficient} \approx 0.99$$

Although the third of these is seen to provide the best fit, it does carry the (illogical) implication that an increase in X_1 (population) results in a decrease in Y (because of the negative coefficient). Relating the current Y to the previous Y we obtain the model $Y_{n+1} = 19.3 + 0.985Y_n$, with correlation coefficient

≈ 0.97. Note that none of these models can be *reliably* used for predicting *future* values of Y (extrapolation).

12.10 In order to simulate human movement on a computer a model is to be developed by starting with a simple stick figure, as shown in Fig. 12.9. During walking the angle ϕ at the knee varies as shown and approximate values were obtained from photographs. A continuous periodic model for ϕ in terms of t is required.

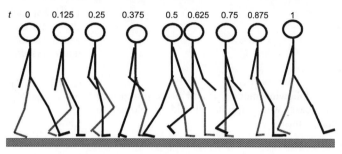

Figure 12.9

Solution The data is given at nine points covering one stride, i.e. one period. Let t be the fraction of a period between two snapshots. Then t goes from 0 to 1 in steps of $1/8$ in our data and corresponding values of ϕ were measured from photographs. Using the notation given in the background to this chapter we have $N = 7$ and $2L = 1$ so $M = 3$ and our data values are:

t_i	0	0.125	0.25	0.375	0.5	0.625	0.75	0.875
ϕ_i	180	160	165	175	170	130	110	150

Using the given formulae we calculate

$$a_0 = \frac{2}{8}\sum_{i=0}^{7} \phi_i = 310, \quad a_1 = \frac{2}{8}\sum_{i=0}^{7} \phi_i \cos(2\pi t_i) = 3.384,$$

$$a_2 = \frac{2}{8}\sum_{i=0}^{7} \phi_i \cos(4\pi t_i) = 18.75, \quad a_3 = \frac{2}{8}\sum_{i=0}^{7} \phi_i \cos(6\pi t_i) = 1.616,$$

$$a_4 = \frac{2}{8}\sum_{i=0}^{7} \phi_i \cos(8\pi t_i) = 2.5, \quad b_1 = \frac{2}{8}\sum_{i=0}^{7} \phi_i \sin(2\pi t_i) = 23.473,$$

$$b_2 = \frac{2}{8}\sum_{i=0}^{7} \phi_i \sin(4\pi t_i) = -8.75, \quad b_3 = \frac{2}{8}\sum_{i=0}^{7} \phi_i \sin(6\pi t_i) = -4.027$$

Our continuous periodic model for ϕ is therefore

$$\phi(t) = 155 + 3.384\cos(2\pi t) + 18.75\cos(4\pi t) + 1.616\cos(6\pi t) + 1.25\cos(8\pi t)$$
$$+ 23.473\sin(2\pi t) - 8.75\sin(4\pi t) - 4.027\sin(6\pi t)$$

Note that we can substitute any value of t into this. The graph from $t = 0$ to $t = 1$ is shown in Fig. 12.10, together with the original data points.

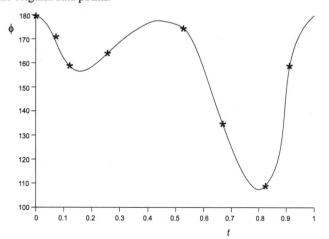

Figure 12.10

12.3 Exercises

12.1 For each of the following models, x and y are the variables and a is a parameter. In each case suggest a plot which should produce a straight line.

(a) $Y = x^a$

(b) $Y = a^x$

(c) $Y = \sqrt{(a + x)}$

(d) $Y = \sin ax$

(e) $Y = \ln(a + x)$

12.2 In each of the following models, a and b are (unknown) parameters. In each case, what variables should be plotted to produce straight line graphs?

(a) $y = a\sqrt{x} + b$

(b) $w = a/(x + b)$

(c) $s = a/(b + \sqrt{t})$

(d) $q = \sqrt{\{a/(b + t)\}}$

12.3 The table below shows the synodic period P_1 (the number of days to return to the same point as viewed from Earth) and the sidereal period, P_2 (the number of days to return to the same point as viewed from the Sun) for some of the planets in the Solar System. Find a simple model connecting P_1 and P_2.

Planet	P_1	P_2
Mercury	116	88
Venus	584	225
Mars	780	687
Jupiter	399	4 330
Saturn	378	10 800

12.4 Derive a formula for the least squares estimator of the parameter a for each of the following models.

(a) $Y = a/t$

(b) $Y = ae^t$

(c) $Y = e^{(a+t)}$

12.5 For the following data:

t	0	1	2	3
y	0	1.1	3.7	8.8

(a) Find the best fitting model of the form $Y = at$

(b) Find the best fitting model of the form $Y = at^2$

(c) Find the best fitting model of the form $Y = ae^t$

Which model gives the best fit to the data?

12.6 Obtain equations for the least squares estimators of the parameters a and b for the following models.

(a) $Y = a + b/t$

(b) $Y = at + bt^2$

(c) $Y = a \sin bt$

12.7 For each of the following, rewrite the model in a form which makes it linear in the parameter a and derive a formula for the least squares estimator of a.

(a) $Y = \sqrt{(a + t)}$

(b) $Y = t^a$

(c) $Y = a^t$

(d) $Y = (t - a)^3$

(e) $Y = \sin at$

12.8 For each of the data sets (a), (b), (c), (d) and (e) in Fig. 12.11, choose the most appropriate *form* of model (from the options given) which you think would give a good fit to the data illustrated in the figure. (Assume a, b and k are positive parameters.)

(i) $a(1 - e^{-kt})$ (ii) $a + be^{-kt}$ (iii) $a - be^{-kt}$ (iv) $1/(a + be^{-kt})$
(v) $(1 - ae^{-kt})/(1 + be^{-kt})$ (vi) $(1 + ae^{-kt})/(1 + be^{-kt})$

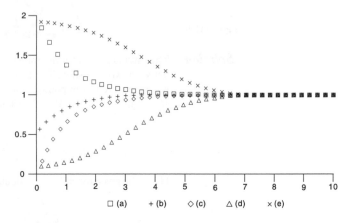

Figure 12.11

12.9 The following data shows the estimated size of a colony of birds on an island over the past 6 years.

Time t (years)	0	1	2	3	4	5	6
Population y	350	480	670	940	1300	1820	2540

(a) Fit an exponential model of the form $Y = y_0 e^{kt}$

(b) Use the model to:

(i) predict the number of birds next year

(ii) estimate the number of birds on the island 8 years ago

12.10 The following data gives the cooking time t (min) for a turkey of weight w (lb) to be cooked at $160°C$.

w	2	4	6	8	10	12	14
t	75	120	155	190	220	250	275

Fit a model of the form $T = aw^b$ and use it to estimate the cooking time of a turkey weighing 8.5 lb.

12.11 The following table shows the numbers of different species of reptiles and amphibians living on a number of neighbouring islands of various sizes. Fit a model of the form $N = kA^b$, where N is the number of species on an island of area A.

A (km^2)	3	21	234	2600	240 000
N	3	5	10	20	78

12.12 The following table shows the daily growth rate r $(\text{g m}^{-2}\,\text{day}^{-1})$ in a grass pasture for various values of grass biodensity $x\,(\text{g m}^{-2})$.

x	200	400	600	800	1000
r	7	15	18	17	13

(a) Which one of the following model types seems to be the most appropriate? (Assume a and b are positive parameters.)

(i) $r = ax + b$ (ii) $r = b - ax$

(iii) $r = ax^2 + b$ (iv) $r = ax^2 + bx$

(v) $r = ax^2 - bx$ (vi) $r = ax - bx^2$

(b) For your choice of model, find values of a and b to fit the data as closely as possible.

12.13 The sales of a new weekly magazine during the first few weeks of its publication were as follows

Time t (weeks)	0	1	2	3	4	5
Sales $y\,(\times 10^3)$	18.0	20.3	21.9	22.9	23.6	24.1

(a) Fit a model of the form $Y = L + (y_0 - L)e^{-kt}$ using two different methods.
(b) Use the models to predict the sales in week 8.

12.14 The data below shows the height (cm) of a plant measured at 2-monthly intervals.

t	0	2	4	6	8	10	12
$h(t)$	3.9	26.3	114.3	208.9	235.3	239.3	240.1

(a) Obtain a logistic model for $h(t)$ in terms of t.
(b) Compare the fitted values with the data.
(c) Use the model to estimate the height of the plant (i) after 3 months and (ii) after 15 months.

12.15 An experimenter found that when asked to memorise a collection of objects his subject had the following percentage recall after x hours.

x hours	1	2	3	4	5	6	7	8	9	10
Percentage recall	89	75	67	61	57	53	50	47	45	43

Find a simple model for the percentage recall as a function of x.

12.16 A manufacturer finds that when the price of her product is fixed at £10, the level of sales $S(\times 10^4)$ depends on the amount spent on advertising $A(\times £10^3)$ as follows:

A	1.0	2.2	2.4	3.0
S	1.5	2.2	2.3	2.6

(a) Show that this can be fitted by a model of the form $S = k\sqrt{A}$. What is the appropriate value of the constant A?
(b) Sales also depend on the selling price P (£) as follows:

P	10	15	
S	1.5	1.0	(when $A = 1$)

Fit a linear model for S in terms of P.
(c) Use your models from (a) and (b) to write down an expression for S in terms of P and A.
(d) If costs consist of fixed overheads C, plus £1 per item production cost plus the advertising cost, write down an expression for the net revenue R when the selling price is P.
(e) Use your answer to (d) to find (i) the optimum price P^* and (ii) the optimum amount A^* to spend on advertising in order to maximise the revenue.

12.17 On a production line, as operators become skilled in a particular task the speed at which they can work increases. Suppose that it is found that the average number of units per hour that can be completed by trainee operators depends on their number of hours (x) experience as follows:

x	0	10	20	30	40	50	60	70	80	90
Units h^{-1}	48	61	72	79	84	88	91	94	95	96

Fit a simple model for the number of units h^{-1} as a function of x.

12.18 Table 12.4 gives the weekly electricity consumption (MW h) and average outside temperature (°C) for a particular house before the installation of double glazing. Table 12.5 gives similar data for the same house after double glazing had been installed.

Table 12.4

Temperature	−1	0	1	2	5	8	10
Electricity used	15.9	15.0	14.1	13.2	10.5	7.8	6.0

Table 12.5

Temperature	−1	0	2	4	7	8	10
Electricity used	14.4	13.6	12.0	10.4	8.0	7.2	5.6

Table 12.6 gives monthly averages of the outside temperature at the location of this house from October to May.

Table 12.6

	O	N	D	J	F	M	A	M
°C	10.0	7.2	5.2	4.5	5.2	7.2	10.0	12.7

(a) Fit the simplest possible model to Table 12.4.
(b) Fit the simplest possible model to Table 12.5.
(c) Fit an appropriate model to Table 12.6.
(d) Write down an expression for the amount of electricity saved in one year by having double glazing.
(e) Calculate a numerical answer for (d).

12.19 For a particular patient 8 mg of dye was injected into a vein carrying blood into an organ. The concentration of the dye in the blood was monitored at regular time intervals at a convenient point in a blood vessel coming from the organ and data were collected as follows.

Time (s)	0	1	2	3	4	5	6	7	8
Concentration (mg l^{-1})	0	0	0	0.2	5.0	8.0	9.8	10.8	11.5

Time (s)	9	10	11	12	13	14	15	16	17
Concentration (mg l^{-1})	11.9	12.1	12.3	7.5	4.5	2.7	1.7	1.0	0.6

Time (s)	18	19	20	21	22	23	24
Concentration (mg l^{-1})	0.4	0.2	0.1	0.3	0.4	0.4	0.3

Fit a mathematical model to the data and use it to estimate (a) the blood flow rate $(1\,s^{-1})$ and (b) the capacity (l) of the organ.

12.20 Show that the model $Y = (ky_0 + tL)/(k + t)$ has a similar property to the logistic and linear first-order models in that $Y \to L$ as $t \to \infty$. Show also that the value of k can be estimated by plotting $(L - y)^{-1}$ against t.

12.4 Answers to Exercises

12.1 (a) $\ln y \sim \ln x$, (b) $\ln y \sim x$, (c) $y^2 \sim x$, (d) $\sin^{-1} y \sim x$, (e) $e^y \sim x$

12.2 (a) $y \sim \sqrt{x}$, (b) $1/w \sim x$, (c) $1/s \sim \sqrt{t}$, (d) $1/q^2 \sim t$

12.3 $1/P_1 = 1/P_2 - 1$

12.4 (a) $\sum(y/t)/\sum(1/t^2)$, (b) $\sum(e^t y)/\sum(e^{2t})$, (c) $\ln[\sum(e^t y)/\sum(e^{2t})]$

12.5 (a) $Y = 2.49t$, $S \approx 5.34$
(b) $Y = 0.97t^2$, $S \approx 0.05$
(c) $Y = 0.44e^t$, $S \approx 0.41$
Model (b) has the smallest sum of squared errors, S.

12.6 (a) $na + b\sum(1/t) = \sum y$,
$a\sum(1/t) + b\sum(1/t^2) = \sum(y/t)$
(b) $a\sum t^2 + b\sum t^3 = \sum ty$, $a\sum t^3 + b\sum t^4 = \sum t^2 y$
(c) $a\sum \sin^2 bt = \sum y \sin bt$, $a\sum \sin bt \cos bt = \sum y \cos bt$

12.7 (a) $Y^2 = a + t$, $a = \sum(y^2 - t)/n$
(b) $\ln Y = a \ln t$, $a = \sum(\ln t \ln y)/\sum(\ln t)^2$
(c) $Y^{1/t} = a$, $a = \sum y^{1/t}/n$
(d) $Y^{1/3} = t - a$, $a = \sum(t - y^{1/3})/n$
(e) $\sin^{-1} Y = at$, $a = \sum(t \sin^{-1} y)/\sum t^2$

12.8 (a) (ii), (b) (iii), (c) (i), (d) (iv), (e) (vi)
(Note that (e) $= 2 - $ (d)).

12.9 (a) $347e^{0.331t}$, (b) (i) 3520, (ii) 179

12.10 $T = 47.07w^{0.671}$, 198 min

12.11 $N = 1.9A^{0.3}$

12.12 (a) (vi), (b) 0.0519, 0.000 039

12.13 (a) $25.0 - 7.0e^{-0.408t}$, $23.2 - 5.2e^{-0.435t}$
(b) 24 732, 23 040

12.14 (a) $H = 239/[1 + 60.3e^{-t}]$
(b)

t	0	2	4	6	8	10	12
$H(t)$	3.9	26.1	113.6	207.9	234.3	238.9	239.0

(c) (i) 59.7, (ii) 239.0

12.15 $89 - 20 \ln x$

12.16 (a) $k \approx 1.5$, (b) $S = 2.5 - 0.1P$,
(c) $S = \sqrt{A}(2.5 - 0.1P)$,
(d) $R = \sqrt{A}(2.5 - 0.1P)(P - 1) - A - C$,
(e) (i) $P^* = 13$, (ii) $A^* = £51\,840$

12.17 $100 - 52e^{-0.03x}$

12.18 (a) $15.0 - 0.9x$, (b) $13.6 - 0.8x$,
(c) $x = 10.0 - 5.5 \sin(\pi t/6)$,
(d) $\int_0^7 [0.4 + 0.55 \sin(\pi t/6)]dt$
(e) 2.24 MW h

12.19 $V \approx 0.16$ (l), $F \approx 0.08$ $(1\,s^{-1})$

Bibliography

The following list gives a selection of books currently available which contain material relevant to the topics covered in this book. Most of them deal with the general topic of mathematical modelling at an introductory level. Those with particular relevance to certain chapters are indicated.

Beltrami, E., *Maths for Dynamic Modelling*, Academic Press, New York, 1987.

Berry, J., Norcliffe, A. and Humble, S., *Introductory Mathematics Through Science Applications*, Cambridge University Press, Cambridge, 1989.

Borreli, A. and Coleman, C., *Differential Equations, a Modelling Approach*, Prentice-Hall, Englewood Cliffs NJ, 1987. [8 and 9]

Braun, M., *Differential Equations and their Applications*, Springer, Berlin, 1975. [9]

Burghes, D. N. and Borrie, M. S., *Modelling with Differential Equations*, Ellis Horwood, Chichester, 1981. [9]

Cullen, M. R., *Linear Models in Biology*, Ellis Horwood, Chichester, 1985. [8 and 9]

Dancel, W. W. and Terrell, J. C., *Business Statistics*, Houghton Mifflin, Boston, 1995.

Doucet, P. and Sloep, P. B., *Mathematical Modelling in the Life Sciences*, Ellis Horwood, Chichester, 1992.

Edwards, D. and Hamson, M., *Guide to Mathematical Modelling*, Macmillan, Basingstoke, 1989.

Fowles, N. D. and Mahoney, J. J., *An Introduction to Mathematical Modelling*, Wiley, New York, 1994.

Giordano, F. R. and Weir, M. D., *A First Course in Mathematical Modelling*, Wadsworth, California, 1985.

Huntley, I. D. and James, D. J. G., *Mathematical Modelling – a Source Book of Case Studies*, Oxford University Press, Oxford, 1990.

Mesterton-Gibbons, M., *A Concrete Approach to Mathematical Modelling*, Addison-Wesley, Wokingham, 1989.

Murphy, D. N. P., Page, N. W. and Rodin, E. Y., *Mathematical Modelling*, Pergamon, Oxford, 1990.

Neelamkavil, M., *Computer Simulation and Modelling*, Wiley, New York, 1987. [11]

Sandefur, J. T., *Discrete Dynamic Systems*, Clarendon Press, Oxford, 1990. [5]

Strang, G., *Introduction to Applied Mathematics*, Wellesley-Cambridge, 1986.

Townend, M. S. and Pountney, D. C., *Learning Modelling with DERIVE*, Prentice-Hall, Englewood Cliffs NJ, 1995.

Tuckwell, H. C., *Elementary Applications of Probability Theory*, Chapman and Hall, London, 1988.

Zill, D. G., *A First Course in Differential Equations with Applications*, PWS-KENT, 1989. [8 and 9]

Index

Learning Resources
Centre